THE NEW NATURALIST
A SURVEY OF BRITISH NATURAL HISTORY

BRITISH TITS

The aim of this series is to interest the general reader in the wild life of Britain by recapturing the enquiring spirit of the old naturalists. The Editors believe that the natural pride of the British public in the native fauna and flora, to which must be added concern for their conservation, is best fostered by maintaining a high standard of accuracy combined with clarity of exposition in presenting the results of modern scientific research.

THE NEW NATURALIST

BRITISH TITS

C. M. PERRINS

COLLINS
ST JAMES'S PLACE, LONDON

William Collins Sons & Co Ltd
London · Glasgow · Sydney · Auckland
Toronto · Johannesburg

First published 1979
Reprinted 1980

© C. M. Perrins, 1979

ISBN 0 00 219537 2

Made and printed in Great Britain by
William Collins Sons & Co Ltd Glasgow

CONTENTS

LIST OF PHOTOGRAPHS

EDITORS' PREFACE

AFTER the Robin, the Blue Tit is probably the best-loved British bird. It is so small, so beautiful and so easy to observe. In the suburbs and even in many urban areas tits will appear, often in only a few minutes, if half a coconut, a bag of peanuts or a lump of suet is hung near a window. While it feeds, the bird's acrobatics are a delight to watch, and have often cheered bedridden patients or elderly people unable to leave their homes. If a sparrow learns how to share the tit's food, it is looked upon as an unwelcome intruder: we resent it consuming expensive items willingly provided for what we consider to be more attractive species.

A suitable nesting box erected in almost any suburban garden is likely to be occupied during the first spring that it is available by a Great Tit. When the eggs hatch the adults will be seen making repeated visits to the box, many times in an hour, to bring food to the young. They will often be observed to be carrying caterpillars, and this soon convinces the gardener that they are his allies, consuming the pests which would otherwise destroy his vegetables or defoliate his trees and shrubs.

The tit's habit of pecking the top of milk bottles and drinking the cream may annoy the housewife, but it also convinces her of the bird's cleverness. If she will not tolerate this minor inconvenience, she may persuade the milkman to put covers over the bottles he delivers.

Thus tits are birds which are particularly easy to observe at close quarters, when they are guests in our gardens. Nevertheless most of us know very little about their lives and habits, particularly about the majority of the birds which generally remain within their natural habitat – deciduous woodland in the case of the Blue and Great Tits we so commonly entertain.

Dr Christopher Perrins, the author of this book, has studied tits for many years, particularly in Wytham Wood near Oxford. He has himself made many interesting and important discoveries about their behaviour and biology. His ability to communicate this information to specialist and non-specialist readers alike make him an ideal choice as a writer in the New Naturalist series. As well as incorporating his own work, he also gives full recognition to the work of many other ornithologists, in Britain and in other parts of Europe, and in Asia, where the species found in Britain also occur. He has thus produced a factual and authoritative account which should be of value and interest both to serious ornithologists and to those who wish to know something more about the charming birds they see so often in their gardens.

Seven different birds are here described in detail. These include six (Coal

Tit, Great Tit, Blue Tit, Crested Tit, Marsh Tit, Willow Tit) which all authorities recognize as members of this group. Dr Perrins has also included the Long-tailed Tit, which purists consider only a distant relation. We believe that this inclusion is justified, particularly by the way in which comparisons between the true tits and the Long-tailed Tit are developed.

Dr Perrins shows us what is known about tits, and he also draws attention to many gaps in our knowledge. We hope that this will stimulate readers to make their own observations so as to increase further our understanding of some of the most attractive members of our natural wildlife.

AUTHOR'S PREFACE

PERHAPS this book should have been written many years ago; so much has been published on the European tits that it is difficult to synthesize it now. These small birds are so amenable to study that the journals are full of observations on them. Curiously, apart from a small work in 1846,[405] no one until recently has tried to write a book covering all the British species.

It has been, therefore, quite impossible to try to include all that has been published about these birds. I have tried to cover the main topics, though doubtless others would have selected differently. Further, I have tried to keep the references from filling all the pages. The system of numbers should enable the reader to find the references that he wants to follow up, but at times he may have to look at the references in the paper to which I refer.

Most of the topics covered are inter-related and it is not always easy to decide where to put certain pieces of information. As a result I have allowed myself a certain amount of repetition in order that each chapter may be taken more or less on its own without the cross-referencing that would otherwise be required.

In particular, I have given a broad outline of the behaviour and life cycles of the tits in chapter 1. Although much of this material is presented in greater detail later, it seemed important to put the outline here, before chapters 2-8 on the individual species. In these I have concentrated on features peculiar to the separate species. The reader who is more interested in the general biology of the birds than the detailed differences between the species might like to pass over these chapters, though he might still find chapter 8, on the Long-tailed Tit, worthy of examination.

So many people have contributed to the vast array of literature that this book could best perhaps be regarded as the outcome of an enormous piece of teamwork; the only advantage that the others have had is that they cannot be held responsible for the end product! One of the most pleasing aspects of working on tit populations has been the contact with other ornithologists, both in Britain and abroad. While we have disagreed (and still do!) about some of the basic factors which affect the birds at different stages of their lives, it has been a great pleasure to me to meet other workers in this field and discuss our work. In addition I owe a great amount to some of them for generously supplying me with their data for certain analyses.

Some of these debts cannot pass unnoted. My greatest debt is to the late Director of the Edward Grey Institute, Dr David Lack, F.R.S. David Lack was responsible for starting the study in Wytham Woods near Oxford and always took a keen interest in the studies of those who kept it going; his encouragement and friendly, helpful criticism are sorely missed. Outside Oxford, our closest contacts have been with the Dutch workers, especially the late Dr H. N. Kluijver, father of all current population studies of tits, having published a major work on them a quarter of a century ago[190] and Dr J. H. van Balen. In Germany Dr H. Löhrl's studies have been of great value to us.

Many others have kindly read and criticized earlier drafts of this book. Since some of these have done the key work in certain parts of the field they have in that sense provided the data also. I am particularly indebted to Dr D. Chitty, Dr E. K. Dunn, Dr M. C. Garnett, Dr A. J. Gaston, Dr J. A. Gibb, Dr. J. R. Krebs, Dr T. Royama, Dr D. W. Snow, Miss V. A. Wood and the late Dr M. I. Webber for their comments. Our main study area in Wytham Woods near Oxford has also been used by other ecologists. In particular a group of entomologists from the Hope Department, led by Prof. G. C. Varley and the late Dr G. R. Gradwell have studied the insects of the oak trees, a major food supply for the tits.

To my wife, Mary, I owe a great deal for her help and tolerance. Not only has she done some of the field work for me, but she has put up with irregular and unpredictable (though usually late!) re-appearances from field work. She has also been of inestimable help in putting this book together, typing drafts, drawing diagrams and sorting references.

It is also a pleasure to be able to thank Miss Dorothy Vincent and Mr A. S. Cheke for help with checking the references and Miss Margaret Norris for assistance in typing the final versions.

This book was largely incubated while I was on sabbatical leave in Darwin, Australia – a country free from tits where, consequently, I did not feel compelled to rush out and carry on with field work instead of writing. Though there were many other ornithological delights, the air-conditioned laboratory of the Wildlife Division of the CSIRO proved attractive enough in the middle of the day to get the bulk of the writing done. I owe a great debt for the hospitality given by my hosts Dr H. J. Frith, Dr M. G. Ridpath and all the many Australians who helped us during our stay.

Lastly, but by no means least, all those who have studied the tits owe a great debt of gratitude to the birds themselves for the determined and imperturbable way in which they accept our presence and get on with their daily lives despite our interference.

CHAPTER I

INTRODUCTION

'Nor will it easier be – nay, not a whit –
To keep from your domain the greedy Tit.
Small is the naughty Fowl, yet it can wreak
No small Destruction with its claws and beak.
For, when Paper from afar it spies,
Straightway through open Window in it flies,
Its frequent blows the sheet do quickly tear
Still sodden, and make Havoc everywhere . . .
To Gin and Snare it grows too soon inured,
And Carelessness is by Experience cured.
The Lime untouched, always the naughty Tit,
So keen its zest, to Paper straight will flit.'

The above is a translation, by Professor Eric Laughton, of a poem by Father Jean Imberdis, S.J. entitled 'Papyrus'; it was written in 1693 – almost three hundred years ago.

These lines perhaps epitomize the first of the two main reasons for this book: the close association of the tits with man. In most parts of Britain they occur commonly around houses and the ease with which some species have adapted to garden life, in spite of their forest origins, together with their general tameness and approachability have made them familiar to us all. They provide considerable enjoyment – and education – to adults as well as children. In winter they visit bird tables in large numbers (often such tables are erected specifically for the tits) and in summer they freely accept the nesting-boxes man puts up for them.

In this sense they may be regarded as 'popular' birds; in addition they cause no real nuisance. Perhaps neither Father Imberdis nor the harassed milkman – trying to prevent tits opening bottles on his float the moment that his back is turned – would share this view, but nevertheless the damage they do is usually minor, of relatively infrequent occurrence and far outweighed by the enjoyment and interest that they bring – to say nothing of the possible good arising from their insectivorous habits.

The second main reason for this book is that the abundance and approachability of the tits has made them ideal subjects for detailed scientific study. As a result, the biology of some of the tits must be better known than that of almost any other species of wild animal. In addition to the intensive – and often long-term – studies, much has been learned about these birds by more casual observation; the general public, as well as bird-watchers, have often provided useful information in response to appeals for records about certain aspects of these familiar birds.

The more we know, the more intricate the adaptations of these birds are found to be. The scientist is trained to be wary of using the word 'intelligence' in relation to the behaviour of wild animals but, notwithstanding this, one sometimes wonders at the 'comprehension' of these small birds; some birds are able to solve complicated puzzles in order to get food. If they are not intelligent, then they have been well equipped by Nature – through evolution – to respond correctly to a wide variety of situations, some of which they are not likely to meet, even in a similar form, in the wild.

In an imaginative vein, we may perhaps even regard Father Imberdis as one of the first observers of tit behaviour, for we now know that there is a biological basis underlying his seemingly casual complaint (p. 139). As we shall see, the habit of paper-tearing is not a random one. It occurs most frequently in the late autumn of years when the numbers of tits are high and natural foods are short; often at such times there are wide-scale movements of Continental tits, some of which enter Britain for the winter; most frequently the offender is a Blue Tit. It could be, therefore, that Father Imberdis's poem provides us with evidence that these conditions held in the autumn of 1692 or 1693.

RELATIONSHIPS AND RANGES

It is, perhaps, necessary to put this small group of birds in perspective in relation to other birds. Here, and throughout this book, I use the classification adopted by Snow[346] for the Family Paridae in Volume 12 of *Check-List of Birds of the World*. The Paridae are a family of Passerine birds of the sub-order Oscines or song-birds. The passerines are usually held to be, from an evolutionary viewpoint, a relatively recent order of birds. Within this huge order (over half the living birds) and within the sub-order Oscines, the relationships of the families are not always clear. The Paridae have sometimes been held to be closely related to the Crows (Corvidae), a group held to be among the most 'advanced' birds of all. Currently they have been moved closer to the Old World Flycatchers (Muscicapidae), a very large family of mostly smallish birds with largely insectivorous diets.

The prefix or suffix 'tit' has been applied to several groups of birds, for example shrike-tit, tit-lark and wren-tit. Many of these groups are not at all closely related and, according to the *Shorter Oxford English Dictionary*[274], the word seems to have been used originally merely to denote something small. The birds to be discussed in this book were originally called 'titmice', a name that subsequently became shortened to 'tit'. Even within Europe four groups of birds, not all of which are closely related, are still known as tits. These are:

1. The true tits (Family Paridae, sub-family Parinae)
2. Long-tailed Tit (Family Paridae, sub-family Aegithalinae)
3. Penduline Tit (Family Paridae, sub-family Remizinae)
4. Bearded Tit (*Panurus biarmicus*)

As can be seen from this list the true tits, the Long-tailed Tit and the Penduline Tit are considered to belong to separate sub-families though they all belong to the same Family.

The Bearded Tit, however, is now considered to belong to the sub-family Paradoxornithinae of the huge family Muscicapidae – the Old World Fly-catchers. If so, it lives in an area well beyond that inhabited by most of its relatives, namely the Oriental region. Whatever the case, it is unlikely that it is closely related to the true tits and there has been an attempt in recent years to recognize this by changing its English name from Bearded Tit to Reedling – a name that aptly describes its almost total restriction to reed-beds. It will not be considered in this book.

The Bearded Tit is not alone in being well beyond the range of its closest relatives. Both the Long-tailed and Penduline Tits are represented in Europe by a single species only; the other members of their sub-families occur some distance away in Asia or Africa respectively. Possibly even Long-tailed and Penduline Tits are no more closely related to the true tits than are some other birds. For example some taxonomists have put the Tree-creepers (Certhiidae) and the Nuthatches (Sittidae) between the true tits and these other tits[389]. Others[242] have suggested that the Aegithalidae are an offshoot of the Babblers (Timaliidae) and that the Remizidae may have evolved from the Flowerpeckers (Dicaeidae). If this is so, then neither group should be considered with the Paridae; however the Long-tailed Tit would be more closely related to the Bearded Tit under this classification than is the case with the one used here. The exact taxonomic positions of these families have not yet been settled and it is not my purpose here to try to do so, even were a final decision possible at the present time – which it is not.

The tits are found in most wooded areas of the northern hemisphere and of Africa, but not in South America, Madagascar or Australia (fig. 1). While they are generally confined to well-wooded areas, they will at times be found in quite sparsely shrubby habitats.

Fifty-eight species are currently recognized and of these about three-quarters (42) are true tits (Parinae). The true tits occur throughout the range listed above for the whole family. Some have a very extensive distri-bution; for example the Great Tit occurs from Ireland to Japan and from the northern Siberian forests to Iran and south-east Asia. Three other British species (Coal, Marsh and Willow Tits) also reach Japan, though their ranges are more restricted in Asia.

The Aegithalinae are represented by only eight species. Six of these occur in the Palaearctic and two in the United States and Central America. Amongst these the European Long-tailed Tit *Aegithalos caudatus*, besides

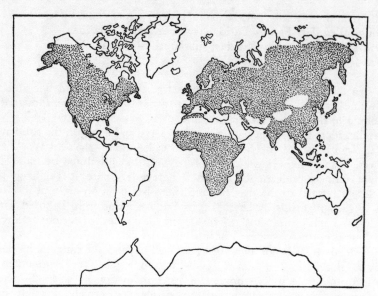

FIG. 1.   An approximate world distribution of the tits, family Paridae.

being the only one of its sub-family in Europe, has the widest distribution elsewhere, being found over a large area of Asia; as with some of the true tits it breeds from the British Isles to Japan. Four other species of *Aegithalos* – with more restricted ranges – are found in the Himalayas and China. The sixth Old World species, *Psaltria exilis*, is confined to Java. The two New World species are the bush-tits of the Genus *Psaltiparus*. Again taxonomic difficulties arise since not all taxonomists agree that these are closely related to *Aegithalos*. All that need be said here is that if the two groups are not closely related, they show remarkable convergences since the two genera have many characteristics of behaviour (including nesting habits) in common.

Another small group of eight species form the Remizinae. Again the only European species, the Penduline Tit *Remiz pendulinus*, has a wide range in the Palaearctic while the remaining six Old World species all occur in Africa south of the Sahara. The eighth species, the Verdin *Auriparus flaviceps*, occurs in open rather scrubby country on the edge of deserts southwards from south-western United States into Mexico. Once again there has been some doubt as to its relationship with other members of this family. It is also an exception in that its eggs are greenish, not white with reddish spots as in all the other tits[132].

EUROPEAN SPECIES

Ten or eleven species of Paridae occur in Europe (depending on where one draws the eastern boundary), of which I shall discuss the seven British ones in detail. These are:

English Name	Latin Name
Coal Tit	*Parus ater*
Great Tit	*Parus major*
Blue Tit	*Parus caeruleus*
Crested Tit	*Parus cristatus*
Marsh Tit	*Parus palustris*
Willow Tit	*Parus montanus*
Long-tailed Tit	*Aegithalos caudatus*

The Willow Tit is not now considered to be conspecific with the American Black-capped Chickadee *Parus atricapillus*, as was once thought[346]. Since this Latin name was first applied to the American species, by the laws of nomenclature it must remain applied to that species and so the Willow Tit must take the more recent name of *P. montanus*. Nevertheless many older works refer to the Willow Tit as *P. atricapillus*.

In addition to these seven species, three or four others occur in Europe:

Azure Tit	*Parus cyanus*
Siberian Tit	*Parus cinctus*
Sombre Tit	*Parus lugubris*
Penduline Tit	*Remiz pendulinus*

The first of these is an eastern species whose range extends westwards as far as eastern Poland, hence just getting into Europe. The Siberian Tit is a bird of the northern spruce forests and the Sombre Tit occurs in Europe only in the Balkans Peninsula. The Penduline Tit is more widespread through central and southern Europe and appears to be spreading northwards; again, as in the previous list, the last species is not so closely related as the others. These species have been less well studied than the others and I shall only refer to them on occasions.

APPEARANCE AND BEHAVIOUR

A few tits are drab, but many are strongly coloured or patterned. The true tits in particular tend to have striking head patterns, often with dark caps; these head patterns may be exaggerated by the presence of a crest. In colour the tits tend to be predominantly browns, greys or blacks above with yellow, white, buff or brown underparts, though there are exceptions to this – the Blue and Azure Tits, for example, are a striking blue on the upper surfaces.

In size most of the tits are small and, although weights of birds vary markedly around the year (chapter 11), few weigh more than about 20 grams – the weight of a Great Tit; for comparison a House Sparrow, *Passer domesticus*, weighs about 30. A notable exception is the relatively very large Sultan Tit, *Melanochlora sultanea*, from eastern Asia. This striking bird is a glossy blue-black above, bright yellow below and has a large yellow crest; it must be more than twice the weight of a Great Tit. The majority of birds in the tit family, however, weigh in the range of 8 to 15 grams. The Long-tailed Tit and some of the bush-tits may weigh as little as 5 or 6 grams – a factor which can cause problems for them during cold weather (chapter 8).

As a group tits are extremely agile, most of them being able to hang on to the slender outer twigs of trees in their search for food. A combination of light weight, shortish legs and a strong grip enables them to do this. Obviously the heavier the bird the harder it is for it to hang from a twig without causing the branch to bend and sway too much for ease of feeding; shortish legs prevent the birds from having too much movement and swinging out too far. Even the Great Tit is really too heavy and long-legged to be able to search for food effectively on the smaller branches; consequently it feeds on the ground a great deal. It is of interest to compare the tits with the finches. Here again the smaller, shorter-legged birds such as the Redpoll are much better than the larger long-legged ones at grasping the small twigs in their search for seeds. Most of the tits, though not the Great Tit, are smaller than the Redpoll and even more agile under such circumstances. Associated with the strong legs are feet with a powerful grip. These are used a great deal during feeding; all but the Long-tailed Tit frequently hold seeds or insects under their feet while hammering at them with the beak. Several species have also been shown to have considerable dexterity with their feet; when set 'intelligence' tests (which many tits are good at) they use their feet, in combination with their beaks, to pull up lengths of string in order to reach food (p. 131).

The British tits do not migrate in the strict sense in order to avoid harsh conditions in winter, though some of those that live in the high latitudes of Russia are known to move considerable distances in winter. Great Tits ringed in northern areas of Russia have been recovered as far south as the Crimea and Portugal – distances of up to 2000 kilometres. It is not known whether northern Russian birds migrate regularly every year or whether they move only under conditions of particular hardship. Birds from populations in north-western Europe may show such 'irruptive' movements and at times of food shortage the birds may cover long distances in search of food. However, at least some of the Great Tits that breed north of the Arctic Circle remain there during the winter and in Scandinavia several species are known to store food for the winter (chapter 12).

In winter the birds may cease to defend territories and wander over larger areas in search of food. When food is scarce, tits may leave the woods during the day and visit nearby urban areas, joining resident garden birds and taking food from bird tables. It is at this time that they most commonly come into contact with man. The food put out for them helps maintain their numbers during particularly hard weather. Some of the birds that come into urban areas from woodland may spend the winter there, but at least some are 'commuters' in that they come from woodland as much as two or three miles away, but return there in the evening to roost.

When not defending territories, tits are gregarious, spending much of their day foraging in flocks. Often these flocks seem to form round a party of Long-tailed Tits (which almost always occur in small parties of six to eight or more outside the breeding season). Other species of small birds may join the flocks, amongst the most common additions being Goldcrest, *Regulus regulus*. The flocks are formed in late summer and maintained throughout the winter, breaking up each evening and reforming each morning. As warmer weather comes in early spring the birds tend to leave the flocks and set up their breeding territories. In some cases, at least, the birds seem to pair up while in the flock and so the pair take up the territory together.

BREEDING BIOLOGY AND LIFE HISTORY

The breeding biology of the tits has been intensively studied; this is, of course, especially true for the Great and Blue Tits but a number of studies, albeit with smaller samples, have been made of the other *Parus* species and of the Long-tailed Tit. Later I devote a full chapter to a detailed description of the nesting cycle (chapter 13). However, since within the genus *Parus* the nesting behaviour of the different species is often closely similar, I have included this brief description here as a prelude to the series of chapters on the individual species. If the reader bears this general outline in mind, it will save continual repetition of the basic details. This description applies basically to the *Parus* species and much less to the Long-tailed Tit whose nesting behaviour receives fuller attention in the species chapter than that of the other tits.

One of the most characteristic features of the tit family is their nesting habit. All species nest in holes (the Long-tailed and Penduline Tits are a partial exception to this in that they make a purse-like nest, with a small side entrance, in a tree or shrub; however, living inside the nest bears close similarity to living in a hole in a tree). The holes chosen are often in a hollow tree or stump, but may be in the ground; they may be enlarged or accepted as they are. In two species – the Crested and Willow Tits – the birds excavate the complete nest-hole in a rotten stump. Man's familiarity with the tits comes partly as a result of the nesting habits since several species not only nest close to man, in the walls of his house or in his garden, but also nowadays in nest-boxes specially provided for them.

The nest itself is usually built of moss and lined with hair or feathers. It can be quite a large structure if the interior of the nest-site happens to be large. Usually the female alone builds the nest. She may well also choose the site since she often roosts in it for some weeks prior to nesting.

The eggs of all species are white covered with a variable amount of light pink or reddish spots. This is a common colour for eggs in nests in dark places such as holes, other colours in such sites being usually pure white or pale blue. The reason for this is not fully understood, but is probably connected with the need for the bird itself to be able to see the eggs in order to look after them; eggs of darker colour would be difficult to see in such a site.[211]

The tits are noted for the large numbers of eggs that they lay. In temperate areas of the world some species lay very large clutches. Blue Tits, for example, commonly lay 12 eggs in woodland in Britain. This species has the largest clutches but all the other European tits have 6–10 eggs in their clutch. Probably no other nidicolous species (those which bring all the food to the young in the nest) lay so many eggs as the Blue Tit; most lay in the region of 3–6 eggs. Clutches of all species of birds in the tropics tend to be smaller than those of closely related species in temperate areas[213] but there too the clutches of tropical tits are large when compared with those of most other species.

In all species so far studied the eggs are incubated by the female alone, the male only visiting the box occasionally, usually to bring the female food while she is sitting. The incubation period is about 12–13 days – on the long side for such small birds, but typical for hole-nesting species.[215] Tits are monogamous and both parents feed the young; the male usually brings most of the food during the first few days as the female has to brood the tiny young in order to keep them warm and hence is not free to collect food for them; this is particularly noticeable when the weather is cold. Later, when the young are larger, the female may bring most of the food.

With such a large brood the parents have to bring food very frequently and some species may make feeding visits at rates as fast as one per minute over considerable periods. The young are in the nest for at least fifteen days in some of the smaller species, longer in the larger ones. As with the incubation period, this is a slightly longer period than that recorded for many small birds; again long nestling periods are often associated with the habit of nesting in holes.[215] Thus Blackbirds which have more exposed nests than tits, have fewer young, raise them faster and have a larger number of broods.

Most of the tits (few of those outside Europe and North America have been studied) have only a single brood during a season. The nestling period is timed to coincide with a good food supply for the young which may be very abundant but present for only a very short time. When food is plentiful some species may have a second brood.

The young are looked after by the parents for a few days after leaving the nest. Within a week of fledging, many of the family parties have broken up and, soon after, the juveniles are to be found wandering around in small parties. At this time the adults have started to moult and do not seem to associate with the young. The young themselves commence their moult a little later than the adults and in the true tits, at least, do not have a complete moult at this time, retaining the juvenile wing feathers and sometimes most of the tail feathers. These are not shed until the next moult when the birds are just a little over one year old and have survived their first breeding season.

LONGEVITY

Like many small birds, the tits are short-lived. In Britain one can say that roughly half of the adults die per year. Therefore, as can be readily calculated, in order that the population remains stable, approximately one young bird per brood must survive to breed. Ringing studies have shown that this is indeed what happens; only one out of every ten eggs laid produces a bird that lives long enough to breed. Obviously there are many differences between different years but this gives an indication of the average situation (p. 220).

ABUNDANCE

Most people regard the tits as extremely numerous. However to some extent this is misleading and is, in part, a result of seeing so many at well-stocked bird tables. In Europe the Blue and Great Tits are abundant birds, often reaching breeding densities as high as one pair to every one or two acres of woodland (0·4–0·8 pairs per hectare). None the less this is not the situation for other species nor is it the case in other parts of the world. Coal Tits and Marsh Tits may breed at densities of one pair per eight or ten acres but many other species are even less common than this. The abundance of tits in western Europe is therefore largely a result of the commonness of just two species.

Moreover more species of tits occur together in any one place in western Europe than in almost any other part of the world. In many areas of woodland in southern Britain and in western Europe one may find five, or occasionally six, species of *Parus* breeding, together with the Long-tailed Tit; in many other areas normally only two or three species are found breeding together. In North America and Africa there are often only two common species in any one area. Further, since these are not so abundant as the Great and Blue Tits, tits in these countries form a much less significant part of the total avifauna than is the case in Britain.

MOULT

Moult involves the bird in replacing its old feathers with new ones. It is discussed in greater detail later (p. 189), but is mentioned here because of one feature that is important to those who make studies of the birds.

All European tits undergo an extensive moult just after the end of the breeding season. However, with the exception of the juvenile Long-tailed

Tits which replace all their feathers, the juveniles only replace their body feathers, retaining most of the wing feathers and, often, many of their tail feathers.

The importance of this seemingly trivial difference to the biologist lies in the fact that in the three species, Coal, Great and Blue Tit, some of the covert feathers of the juveniles are different from those of the adult. Hence birds in their first year (strictly speaking their first 13–14 months) of life retain a small number of juvenile feathers. These birds are easily recognized throughout this period which includes their first breeding season and this has made it possible for the biologist to know the age of many of the birds in his study population. Unfortunately, the plumage of both young and old Marsh, Willow and Crested Tits are too similar for such a technique to be used with them.

STUDIES OF TITS

Tits have been, perhaps, more intensively studied than any other group of wild birds. The reasons for this lie in a combination of the characteristics mentioned in this chapter. Many of these birds are relatively common, resident and nest willingly in nesting-boxes. Hence the biologist can obtain a larger series of data for these birds than for almost any other species. It is hardly surprising therefore that many people have made studies of them or that several long-term population studies now exist.

The first person to collect comprehensive long-term records for the tits was H. Wolda, a Dutch ornithologist who started a study in 1912. While he did not himself publish many of his findings, he maintained a valuable set of records from that year and these have been of considerable value to other workers.

Tollenaar[382] produced the first important paper on the breeding biology of tits, using Wolda's information. Subsequently a major series of studies have sprung up. These have been carried out from the Dutch Institute for Ecological Research, initially under the direction of Dr H. Kluijver and latterly by Dr J. H. van Balen. Records now exist in Holland from Wolda's initial study in 1912 up to the present day, almost without a break. Although at one point the study area had to be changed, these data are among the longest series existing for any bird anywhere in the world. Currently the main study area is at the Hoge Veluwe, an extensive area of pinewoods on sandy soil; other smaller but parallel censuses are made in a series of other forest habitats, including both pinewoods and broad-leaved woods.

After the second world war, Dr David Lack visited Dr Kluijver in Holland and discussed his classic studies with him. While there, Lack realized the enormous potential of the tits for some of the studies that he was trying to carry out in England. As a result a second group of people started working on the tits at the Edward Grey Institute of Field Ornithology, in Oxford.

This study started in 1947 and has continued ever since. Some interesting differences between the Dutch and British populations have emerged from these parallel studies (the populations in the two countries are from different subspecies and the local ecology of the woodlands is also subtly different). The workers in Oxford have benefited considerably from the generous co-operation of Dr Kluijver and his colleagues.

The studies at Oxford have included a series of years of observations in many different woodland types, undertaken with the help of amateurs. In addition, members of the Institute have carried out studies in the oak-woods of the Forest of Dean (Gloucestershire), in the pinewoods of the Norfolk Brecklands and in garden habitats around Oxford.

The main areas of study for members of the Institute, however, have been in Wytham Woods. These woods lie only some three miles to the west of Oxford and are owned by the University so that work can be carried out there fairly conveniently and largely free from disturbance. Wytham Woods are about 800 acres (320 ha.) in extent. They are mainly of mixed deciduous woodland, though there are some plantations of conifers. Within the Wytham estate lies a small area of woodland called Marley. This is relatively isolated from the other woodland areas, being surrounded on about three-quarters of its edge by farmland. Because of its relatively isolated nature, Marley Wood was chosen as the basic census area for the Oxford tit studies. Although there are now nest-boxes over most of the estate, Marley remains the area with the longest series of records. The reader will meet frequent mention of both Marley and Wytham in this book. We have been fortunate to be able to work in an ecological reserve where many other people were studying other aspects of the environment. In particular, Prof. G. C. Varley and the late Dr G. R. Gradwell and their team have made a long-term study of the caterpillars on the oaks. As we shall see these are a very important part of the tits' spring food and we have been exceedingly lucky to have access to Varley and Gradwell's help and information.

While the studies mentioned above are the two longest intensive ones, they are by no means the only studies of tits and workers in many European countries have provided much valuable information. Mention must be made of German studies, many of them by Dr Lörhl and his co-workers, and of other European studies by Prof. J. Hublé and Dr A. A. Dhondt in Belgium and by Dr S. Haftorn and Dr L. von Haartman in Scandinavia. In Britain there is also another series of long-term records. In 1945, two years before the Oxford study commenced, Dr Bruce Campbell started a recording system for the birds breeding in nest-boxes in an oakwood called Nagshead in the Forest of Dean, Gloucestershire. While not such an intensive study, weekly visits have been made to the nest-boxes and records of breeding numbers and breeding success have been kept for almost thirty years. This study was started in an attempt to study the effects on the caterpillar populations of encouraging insectivorous birds to nest. It has been continued largely because of the interest aroused by the large numbers of Pied Flycatchers, *Ficedula hypoleuca*, that breed in the boxes there. Much of the recording work has been done by students and staff from the near-by Forestry School and the area has recently become a reserve of the Royal Society for the Protection of Birds.[51]

Taken together, these studies have revealed a great deal of information about several of the species of tits. However, the biologists who have studied these birds hope that the information that they have gathered and analysed provides something more than this. From these studies general biological principles emerge which we hope apply not only to other birds but also to other groups of animals as well. If the reader feels that this is the case, our studies will have been the more worthwhile.

CHAPTER 2

THE COAL TIT – *Parus ater*

THE Coal Tit is the only European tit with a black cap and a large white patch on the nape. The glossy black of the top of the head extends backwards to the sides of the nape and down the sides of the face to the level of the eye, below which is a striking white cheek. The chin, throat and upper breast are also black and are joined to the back of the cap by a black collar.

The rest of the underparts are buff, paler towards the centre and without a black line down the middle of the belly. The upperparts, wings and tail are olive grey though the rump is more rufous. The greater, lesser and median wing coverts have large white tips giving the closed wing two white bars; at very close quarters these may be seen as two rows of large white spots. It is not possible to distinguish the sexes in the field or in the hand. Occasionally, the underparts appear greyish or blackish apparently as a result of the buff tips of these feathers having been abraded away, leaving the greyish-black bases visible[4, 32].

The juveniles are generally duller than the adults with a sooty grey, instead of a glossy black, head and yellow, instead of white, cheeks; the tips to the coverts are also yellow instead of white. The young tits undergo their first moult in late summer when they acquire a plumage similar to that of adults, but they retain most of the main wing coverts and the feathers of the bastard wing (p. 189); also they may retain most of their juvenile tail feathers. Hence they can be distinguished from the adults and, although this is not so easy as in the case of Blue and Great Tits, it is usually possible to see a break between the faded yellow tips of the juvenile primary coverts and the whiter ones of the first year plumage.[366]

Many of the calls of the Coal Tit are rather similar to those of the Great Tit in form, though higher and thinner. The normal 'tsee-tsee-tsee' call of these tits is thin and can sound rather more like a Goldcrest than is the case with the other species. The song is also like that of the Great Tit in form though again much higher and thinner; it is a double note, repeated several times: 'teachoo-teachoo-teachoo'. There are a number of different song types and individual males may have as many as six of these. The repertoire of an individual is, in part, acquired as a result of learning from its neighbours; local groups tend to have similar songs[369].

Five of the seven species discussed in this book have very extensive ranges; the Coal Tit is one of these, its range extending over most of the Palaearctic (fig. 2). In Europe, the range of the Coal Tit extends from Scandinavia southwards through southern Europe into North Africa and south-eastwards through the Balkans as far as Iran.

25

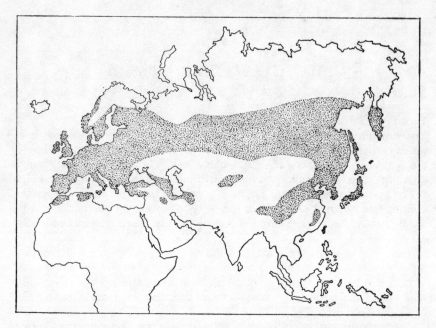

FIG. 2. The world distribution of the Coal Tit, *Parus ater*. Although this species is most widespread in coniferous forests many, especially of the more southerly populations, live in broad-leaved woodland.

Several subspecies are recognized throughout this range. In the western part *P. a. atlas* and *P. a. ledouci* occur in north-west Africa while *P. a. ater* is found throughout western Europe except the British Isles. This bird is greyer on the back than the British Coal Tit which is recognized as a separate race *P. a. britannicus*; the British bird tends to be browner on the back, with a hint of green in the mantle. The Coal Tits in Ireland often have a tinge of yellow in their cheeks and in the nape patch; there has been much discussion as to their status, and some authors have considered them to be a separate race *P. a. hibernicus*. However, the differences are small and not always present[411]. The situation is further complicated by there being some variation within Ireland itself. The birds of the north and east tend to resemble the British form more closely than do those of the south and west. In the latter areas the beak tends to be stouter than in the British form, a character associated with living in the broad-leaved woods that it frequents there.

The Continental race is frequently recorded in Britain, especially in the south-eastern corner[155, 312]. It comes particularly in years when the beech crops fail and is usually the first tit species to arrive in these irruptions[68, 408]. Movements on the Continent may be extensive and are discussed further in chapter 12.

Within Britain, the Coal Tit is widespread though not quite so widespread as the Great Tit and Blue Tit. It does not occur as a breeding species in many of the outer islands, including Orkney, Shetland and the Outer Hebrides. The same is true for Stornoway, except that it may have bred in 1965 (fig. 3). Elsewhere it is widespread and numerous, though it is seldom as abundant as the Great and Blue Tits.

The Coal Tit is widely, and correctly, held to be a bird of conifers, but this is by no means an adequate description of its habitat either within Britain or elsewhere. It is true that the Coal Tit often nests at higher densities in

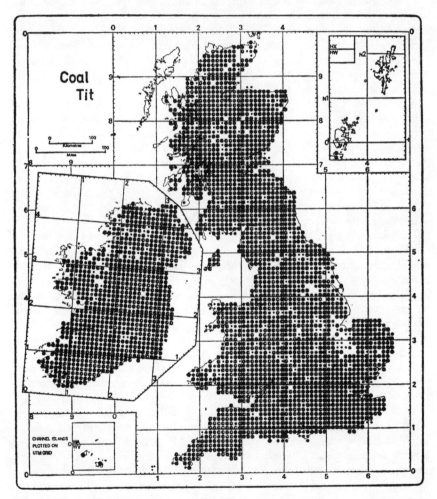

FIG. 3. The British distribution of the Coal Tit. The map shows the breeding distribution of the birds plotted on a 10 km grid, the largest dots denoting proved breeding (from Sharrock 1976).

conifer than in broad-leaved deciduous woods, but it is very definitely present, often in some numbers, in most types of woodland habitats.

It is the commonest species of breeding tit in southern conifer plantations and must have benefited considerably from the recent forestry practice of planting conifers. In the rich, older pinewoods of the Spey Valley only the Coal and Crested Tits occur in any numbers. In winter also the Coal Tit is the most abundant species in conifer, though some Great and Blue Tits move into these woods for the winter.

Although the Coal Tit is much scarcer as a breeding bird than either Great or Blue Tits in most deciduous woodland in southern Britain, it is relatively more abundant in such woods farther north. It is as common as or commoner than either of these other two species in the sessile oakwoods of the north and west and in the birchwoods of Ross and Sutherland. In the hill woods of these northern areas it is even commoner than in the lowlands and may out-number both Great and Blue Tits together[205, 410].

The British Coal Tit is generally believed to be largely sedentary but there must be a certain amount of local movement. For example, it seems even more abundant in the northern hill woods in winter than in summer and is said to be commoner in Herefordshire in winter than in summer, so inferring some level of movement[131]. In Westmorland many are reported to leave the spruce and pinewoods in the spring and go to hardwoods where there are better nesting sites[406]. This is likely to happen particularly where the plantations are young and clean (i.e. without holes) and the ground too waterlogged for nesting.

Detailed information on breeding densities are difficult to obtain because the birds do not always use nest-boxes. However, they tend to confirm this species' preference for conifer. In Marley Wood, an area of about twenty-seven hectares, there are usually only either one or two pairs of Coal Tits giving a breeding density of about one pair to every fifteen hectares or less, no more than one-fifth of the density found in the Breckland pines where they nest at densities of about 0·1–0·5 pairs (average 0·3 pairs) per hectare in Scots Pine, *Pinus sylvestris*,[77, 376]. Figure 4 shows the fluctuations in breeding density in pinewoods in East Anglia. Densities are slightly lower in Corsican Pine *P. nigra* than in Scots; the latter has a slightly richer insect fauna. Densities as high as a pair per hectare have been recorded in certain areas of conifer.

Looking beyond Britain, we again find that the Coal Tit is by no means wholly a bird of coniferous woodlands. It is relatively common in oakwoods in North Africa and Iran, though it may once have preferred the now largely extinct cedar forests. In Czechoslovakia it occurs in the beechwoods, but not the spruce at 1300 m and it is also found in the Italian beechwoods at Latium[2, 384]. Several workers have noted that the Coal Tit occupies a wider range of habitats in the south than in the north of its range[23, 94] (chapter 9).

However, in other parts of Europe the Coal Tits seem to be more closely

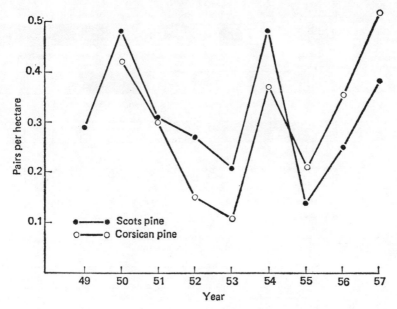

FIG. 4. Annual fluctuations in breeding density of Coal Tit, *Parus ater*, in Breckland pine plantations (from Lack 1966).

confined to conifer than is the case with the British birds. Not only this, but they seem to show stronger preferences for sprucewoods than for pine. This is true both in the summer and in winter. Indeed some breeding densities in spruce are much higher than those in pines. One report gives a breeding density of on average about a pair per hectare, roughly three times the normal level reached in pines in Britain[230].

Studies that have been made of the feeding of Coal Tits tend to confirm that it is better adapted to feed in conifers than many of the other species. It has a narrower, more slender bill, like that of other coniferous birds, and takes smaller food[28, 341]. In addition, in mixed woodland containing both conifer and broad-leaved trees, it spends far more of its time in the conifers than any of the other tits[119, 158]. Figure 5 shows the range of places where Coal Tits were recorded feeding in Wytham.

Within its range, the bill shape varies quite markedly, being relatively thinner in those areas where it frequents conifers, stouter where it occurs in broad-leaved woods. The bill shape is believed to be associated with the leaf structure in these different areas, a finer beak being required for probing into clusters of pine needles. The British Coal Tits possess a slightly stouter beak than those on the Continent and it seems likely that they are, or were, evolving a bill more suitable for broad-leaved woods. After Britain was isolated from the Continent and after the last glaciation when it became

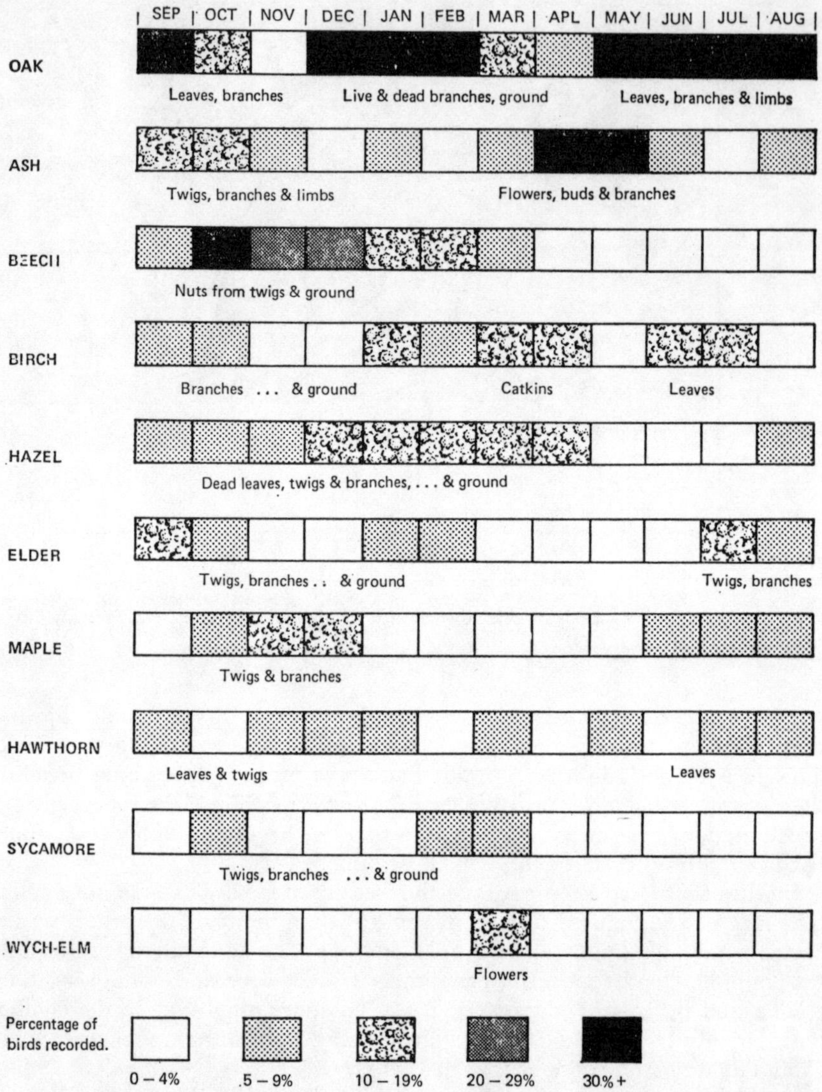

| | SEP | OCT | NOV | DEC | JAN | FEB | MAR | APL | MAY | JUN | JUL | AUG |

OAK
Leaves, branches   Live & dead branches, ground   Leaves, branches & limbs

ASH
Twigs, branches & limbs   Flowers, buds & branches

BEECH
Nuts from twigs & ground

BIRCH
Branches ... & ground   Catkins   Leaves

HAZEL
Dead leaves, twigs & branches, ... & ground

ELDER
Twigs, branches . ; & ground   Twigs, branches

MAPLE
Twigs & branches

HAWTHORN
Leaves & twigs   Leaves

SYCAMORE
Twigs, branches ... & ground

WYCH-ELM
Flowers

Percentage of birds recorded.

0 – 4%   .5 – 9%   10 – 19%   20 – 29%   30% +

FIG. 5. The main feeding sites of Coal Tits in Marley Wood, Oxford, showing the proportion of time spent in each tree species in each month. In winter Coal Tits fed primarily in oaks (conifers, to which they are primarily adapted, are absent from Marley Wood). Early in the winter they fed from the leaves, then later mostly from live and dead branches and limbs. The proportion which fed on beechmast from October to February was higher than in Great or Blue Tits. When beechmast was over, Coal Tits fed mainly in ash. They fed in ash more often than the other tits all winter, but especially in April and May. The main sources of food were the flowers, buds and branches. Other food-sources included: (a) twigs and branches generally, September–January; (b) the ground, January–March; (c) elm flowers in March; and (d) birch catkins in March–April (from Gibb 1954a).

habitable for woodland birds once more, conifers disappeared from most of the country, especially the south, and were replaced by broad-leaved woodlands. Hence, if Coal Tits were to continue to exist in Britain, they had to live in the latter habitat. The slightly stouter beak and their greater readiness (compared with their Continental cousins) to live in hardwood forests may be indications that they were slowly evolving the characteristics of a broad-leaved forest species. The recent spread of coniferous woodlands, as a result of forestry, has enabled them to re-occupy their 'primaeval' habitat.

The planting of conifers seems to have had a considerable effect on the Coal Tit. As mentioned, it breeds there in higher densities than in broad-leaved woodland and appears to have expanded its range in Britain as a result of such forestry; in particular its range has spread northwards in Scotland as a result of re-afforestation, though here presumably it was common before the forests were removed[3, 205, 278]. On the Continent also the planting of conifers must have benefited the Coal Tits, though there were always extensive areas of conifer there at higher altitudes; hence the birds there had less need to become adapted to hardwoods than was the case with those in Britain. The new plantations have merely enabled them to spread in the lowlands.

Unlike the British Coal Tits, the Continental Coal Tits may show considerable movements in autumn, especially when some of the seed crops, on which they are dependent in winter, fail. In such cases, as with the Great and Blue Tits, the Continental Coal Tits move widely and may enter Britain[67, 284]. Many of the birds moving in such irruptions come from eastern Europe[325]. However, if the food supply is plentiful they will remain in very cold areas for the winter.

Like the other tits, the breeding season varies in relation to the earliness or lateness of the spring, but laying normally commences in early to mid-April in southern Britain. Of the three common species (Coal, Blue and Great Tits) the Coal Tit is the earliest to lay, usually starting a few days ahead of the Blue Tit. Breeding starts, on average, about five days earlier in Scots Pine than in adjacent Corsican Pine; the food supply is lower in the latter habitat, but it is not known whether this is the cause of the difference[129]. At high altitudes laying may start before the snow has gone.

The nest-site is variable. While the Coal Tit will readily accept nesting boxes, it tends to prefer those with a very small entrance; it may even select boxes with a narrow vertical slit as an entrance in preference to those with a normal circular hole. When there is competition for a site, the Coal Tit is easily defeated by both Great and Blue Tits and, perhaps for this reason, selects sites with entrances too small or too difficult for these species. In the absence of nesting boxes, the Coal Tit may nest in the ground, often using a mouse-hole for this purpose. Where there is a choice, the Coal Tit usually seems to prefer a nest-box situated on a conifer to one on a deciduous tree. In Wytham, it may quite often nest in the only box on a conifer in an area of broad-leaved trees.

The nest itself is built largely of moss. The cup is lined with fur or hair which it may take from a dead animal such as the Field Vole *Microtus agrestis*[36]. The Coal Tit only rarely uses feathers in the lining and this, together with the very small size of the cup, helps to identify the species; it resembles a tiny Great Tit nest.

The Coal Tit lays a clutch of about ten eggs in Britain and seems less variable in this than several of the other species. There is little seasonal decline in clutch-size during the early part of the season, though those started in the second half of May tend to be a little smaller (by about one egg[214]). Genuine second broods are fairly regular in this species; particularly in conifer (where about 11% have second broods): they have also been recorded in deciduous woodland though they are much less common there. Based on the very small sample in Wytham, second broods are much smaller, averaging about seven eggs. At high altitudes on the Continent, where breeding starts late, there may be no second broods.

The food of the Coal Tit varies like that of the other tits, being primarily insects in the summer and a mixture of seeds and insects in the winter. Those in oakwoods take more insects in their winter diets than either Blue or Great Tits[28].

In Scandinavia it is well known that these birds store the seeds of spruce and other trees for use later in the winter[145]. The Coal Tit stores food more regularly than the other tits in southern Britain; apart from this species, only the Marsh Tit is known to store food so regularly. Birds may be watched removing large quantities of peanuts from bird tables and flying off to hide them. In the wild, they also store large quantities of insects.

The Coal Tits seem to survive quite well in snow-covered areas of conifer, especially if it is not too cold. At such times, although the branches are covered with snow, it seems to be relatively easy for this small bird to feed from the under surfaces of the branches which are free from snow. In addition, they may roost among the needles, often using the same site for long periods. They also roost in old nests of other birds and in hollows made by Treecreepers.

CHAPTER 3

THE GREAT TIT – *Parus major*

NEXT to the Blue Tit this species must be the best known of all the British tits. It is easily recognized by its large size – it is almost twice the size of any other British Tit – and by its yellow underparts with a black line running down the centre.

The Great Tit has a black cap which comes to just below the eye; a black collar runs round the back of the head and joins the cap to a black throat and bib; enclosed within these black areas are strikingly white cheeks. The black from the throat runs down the centre of the yellow underparts to the lower belly. The upperparts are greenish, the wing feathers dark brown with an edge of grey, the coverts light, bluish-grey. The tail feathers are grey, the outermost ones tipped and edged with white which shows clearly in flight.

Males are usually markedly brighter than females, with richer yellow underparts and glossy (as opposed to dull) black crown and throat. In addition the black stripe down the underparts is wider and more intense in males than in females; in the hand (and sometimes in the field) one can see that in the male the black extends across the belly to the base of both legs whereas in the female it is not so broad and does not reach the legs (plate 2). The yellow tips of the feathers of the underparts may occasionally become abraded away, showing their greyish-black bases[13].

The juvenile's plumage is similar to that of the adult in general pattern, but much duller. The black markings are less intense and lack the gloss of the adults, giving a rather sooty appearance, and the cheeks are pale yellow. The body plumage is moulted into one similar to that of the adults shortly after the young leave the nest, except that birds in their first year can usually be distinguished from older birds because they retain juvenile feathers in the bastard wing and primary coverts, these having bright blue-grey edges in adult males, as opposed to dull grey edges in young males, and dull grey edges in older females, as opposed to greenish or brownish edges in young females. These differences are apparent until the end of the complete moult after the bird's first breeding season. However, the same may not be true for all European populations since some appear to have different moult regimes (p. 189). The differences between young males and older females are not always very marked so that at times it is easiest to determine a bird's sex before trying to determine its age. From this it can be seen that there are slight differences between the covert feathers of the sexes even in juvenile plumage and it is possible, with practice, to distinguish the sexes of the young when they are fully grown; this can even be done with some young before they leave the nest[80]. However, the differences are far from clear at this stage and it is easier to sex the young when they are a week or two older.

The wing length of the Great Tit grows slightly larger with each successive moult until the bird reaches the age of three or four[16, 188]. An increase in the general brightness of the plumage probably accompanies this growth in size since males of three and four years old often seem much brighter than younger ones, but any such differences have not been quantified.

The calls of this species have been much studied and many different ones have been recognized. Nicholson and Koch[267] said that 'proper description of the Great Tit's language would almost require a book by itself, for no other British bird uses such a wide variety of different notes.' Major behavioural studies have been made of this bird by Hinde[165], Blurton Jones[34] and Gompertz[135], the latter concentrating in particular on the vocabulary.

The basic song is usually described as 'teacher-teacher', but to my ears the description of its sounding like a squeaky bicycle pump fits perfectly. Many variants have been described but the song usually sounds to be disyllabic, repeated many times; however detailed analysis shows that there are usually more than two notes. Gompertz points out that each male has a number of variations to its song. These have to be acquired; the whole range is not given by a one-year-old bird. Normally each individual has from two to six major variants of the song and Gompertz records one bird with as many as seven. Usually within each bird's repertoire there will be three songs of different tempo. The individual songster gives one song for only one to five minutes and then changes to another, usually of a different tempo. Gompertz suggested this was to avoid monotony; she was unable to find any correlation between the type of song given and the circumstances under which it was given. Howard[173] found it easy to distinguish, with practice, between the songs of several male Great Tits that nested near her house.

The female also sings, but rarely. Again according to Gompertz she only does so when she is more or less forced to in defence of her nest or territory if the male is weak or absent.

One of the best-known other notes of the Great Tit is the 'chink' or 'tink' call. This can be very reminiscent of the call given by the Chaffinch but Gompertz describes it as being clearly distinguishable by the rather echoing quality which the call of the Chaffinch lacks. Although this call is one of the best known, it is not given by all birds. Gompertz has shown that it is given almost solely by adult males and is associated with aggression. It is normally given most at times when the birds are not singing much; in a way it seems to replace song. It is of interest in this context to note that Morley[250] describes the familiar 'pitchou' call of the Marsh Tit as being given by territory holders only (p. 55). The main difference between the two species is that in the Marsh Tit the female gives the 'pitchou' call frequently, whereas in the Great Tit the 'chink' is given by the female only when for some reason she has to take part in the defence of the territory.

Other common calls of the Great Tit are described by Gompertz as 'tsee' or 'pee', both often repeated a series of times. These calls are most frequently given by birds moving round in parties or pairs and appear to be mainly contact notes.

When disturbed, the birds have a scolding 'cha-cha-cha', with a rather nasal quality. Gompertz described many varieties of this churring call, together with the different circumstances under which they were given.

The familiar begging call of the fledged young (also given by the female when begging for food from her mate) is well known to anyone who has been in woodland in June. Soon after the young have left the nest the woods are full of the 'tsee-tsee-tsee' calls of the young tits. These calls are easily recognized as belonging to tits but less easily identified as to species. Gompertz points out that the begging notes of the Great and Blue Tits – which tend to sound similar to the untutored ear – are quite different in that the 'pitch variation of the Blue Tit is nearly always such as to end in one or more falling notes whereas the Great Tit almost invariably rises.'

In all, Gompertz recognized up to 40 different utterances from a single individual and it is likely that there are regional differences in some of the calls as well. Certainly in Finland the basic song is different, being a tri-syllabic 'ti-ti-tu'[219].

Fig. 6 (on the following page) gives the range of the Great Tit. As might be expected, a large number of subspecies have been named over this extensive range. Basically, these fall into four main types. Great Tits seem to have spread into eastern China from two sources. Birds similar to ours have spread across the wooded areas of central Asia and have met birds that have reached the area from the south, spreading up from south-east Asia. There is some doubt as to the situation where they meet. It is possible that the two forms live together in this area without interbreeding, in which case an interesting 'ring-species' situation exists, where a perfectly good single species diverges into two distinct forms which do not interbreed when they meet again some-where else. Equally, the taxonomy of the *Parus major bokharensis* group – which link the Indian populations with those to the north – is somewhat unclear in that these have been said to overlap with the *P. m. cinereus* group in the south and the *P. m. major* group in the north, and again may not interbreed. Little work has been done on the birds in these regions for political reasons. If *P. m. bokharensis* does not interbreed with either of the other forms with which it overlaps then it should be considered a separate species, not a race of the Great Tit.

The form found throughout Continental Europe is *P. m. major*, while the British birds are recognized as a separate subspecies, *P. m. newtoni*. This bird is markedly larger than the Continental race and typical individuals can readily be distinguished from it[154]. However, as with the Blue Tit (p. 42), there is evidence that some of the birds breeding near the eastern coasts of Britain are intermediate between the typical British form and the Con-tinental one so that the situation may not be as clear cut as it first appears.

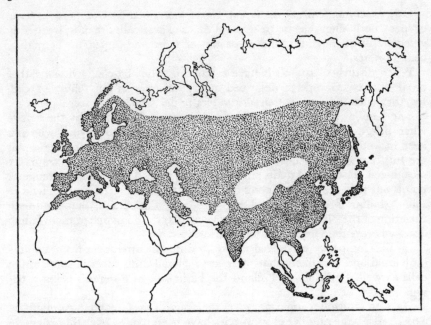

FIG. 6.   The world distribution of the Great Tit, *Parus major*. While, as with the Coal Tit, this species occurs in extensive areas of conifer forest, it is also found in a wide range of tropical vegetation.

It is of interest to note that the Continental race of the Great Tit is smaller than the British one, whereas the reverse is the case with the Blue Tit. The Continental race undertakes long distance movements in some years (p. 136) and has frequently been recorded in Britain[154, 155, 312]. In the autumn of 1959 two birds even reached Iceland, the first records for that country[68].

Within Britain, the Great Tit is very widespread, though it does not breed in all the outer islands (fig. 7). In general it has become more common in most of Scotland since about 1840, following re-afforestation[3, 283]. Although not abundant in the far north of Scotland, it has increased there also as a result of re-afforestation during the last 50 years[410]. The Great Tit was for some time the only breeding tit in the Scillies, arriving there sometime between 1906 and 1923[324, 398].

The Great Tit is one of the commonest British birds, breeding in a wide range of wooded habitats. Basically the British Great Tits are birds of open, broad-leaved, deciduous woodland. In suitable habitats, such as woodland or even wooded gardens, it frequently nests at densities of about one pair per two acres (0·8 pairs per hectare) and densities in excess of this are occasionally recorded. Exceptionally, different pairs may nest very close together, even in different nest-boxes on the same tree. Although they nest in coniferous woods, they are usually found there at much lower densities,

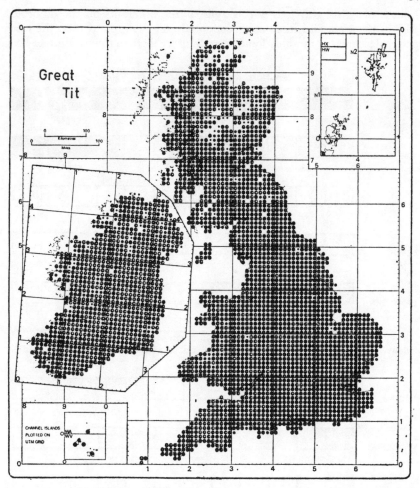

FIG. 7. The British distribution of the Great Tit. The map shows the breeding distribution of the birds plotted on a 10 km grid, the largest dots denoting proved breeding (from Sharrock 1976).

often at about 0·2 pairs per hectare[214]. According to Yapp[410], they are found in all the main forest types – oak, ash, beech, birch and yew (though rarely in other conifers). He suggests that their preference for feeding low down possibly results in their being more affected by the presence and type of shrub layer than by the composition of the main tree species. They are common in orchards and gardens, especially those of outer suburbs. In Poland they are regarded as a bird of the edges of the major forests or the edges of clearings rather than as a bird of dense forest.

The main feeding sites of the Great Tit in woodland are low down.

Because of its weight, it is not as agile as the other tits on the outermost twigs of the trees and feeds more commonly on the ground than the other species. It is most commonly found searching for food on the medium to large

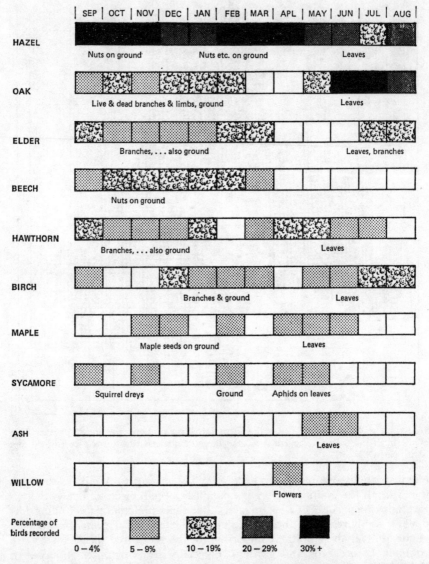

FIG. 8. The main feeding sites of the Great Tit in Marley Wood, Oxford, showing the proportion of time spent in each tree species. In winter Great Tits spend a high proportion of their time feeding on the ground (from Gibb 1954a).

branches and the trunks or boles of the tree. It often searches the lower trunk from the ground, flying up to catch whatever it may see; exceptionally it may climb up and down the trunk in a manner similar to the Nuthatch[323]. Figure 8 shows the main feeding sites of the Great Tit in Wytham.

The start of breeding is markedly affected by the spring weather, but usually occurs a little later than in the Coal and Blue Tits. The Great Tit tends to have more second broods than most of the other tits though they are still not common in Britain; second broods occur most frequently in pinewoods (p. 183).

The nest-site itself is very varied. Since this species is much larger than the other tits, it needs a larger hole. As with the Blue Tit a wide variety of nesting sites have been described. I have seen a nest about two foot down a vertical pipe, some four inches in diameter, and another occupying almost the whole of a floor in an empty beehive – an enormous amount of material had been brought in to fill the space, which was some twenty inches square. In addition to these, holes in walls, letter boxes etc., have been recorded and Campbell gives other sites such as rock crevices, the bases of large birds' nests, and even a nest in a Sand-Martin, *Riparia riparia*, burrow[50].

This species is the one which, of all the tits, most readily accepts nesting boxes, possibly because it requires a slightly larger hole than the others and this may be harder to find. Whatever the reason, it is relatively easy to induce virtually all the pairs of Great Tits in a given area to accept nesting boxes. It is as a result of this that so many studies have been concentrated on this species.

The nest itself is made mainly with moss with an inner lining of hair or fur; feathers are very rarely used by Great Tits. The fur may be collected from a variety of places including large mammals in moult[73]. The nest cup is considerably larger than in the other species in order to accommodate the larger bird.

The eggs also are larger than those of the other tits. Usually, fresh eggs weigh about 1·6–1·8 grams, though both heavier and lighter eggs are frequently recorded (p. 216). However, fresh Great Tit eggs are rarely less than 1·4 grams, which is still heavier than most eggs of the other British species. The size of the clutch is very variable, but usually falls within the range 5–12. Variations in clutch-size are discussed in detail in chapter 15.

The diet of the Great Tit is similar in type to that of the other tits. The birds are primarily insectivorous in summer but take large numbers of seeds in winter; at times the seed of Beech *Fagus sylvaticus* forms an important part of their diet (p. 142). This species differs from the other tits in that its large size and more powerful beak enables it to take larger food items. In particular, it can hold nuts such as those of Hazel *Corylus avellana* under one foot and hammer them open with its beak. It has also been reported to take bees from hives though if it took as many as has sometimes been claimed, it would certainly burst! The damage done seems to have been greatly exaggerated. Like the more regular bee-eating species the Great Tit apparently removes the sting before eating the bee. One observer describes a Great Tit as taking only the dead bees outside the hive and leaving the live ones untouched; this individual was eventually stung to death by the bees, suggesting one good reason why the habit of eating bees is not more widespread.[5] Records of other prey in the *Handbook of British Birds* make it clear that the Great Tit may take a number of large insects[409]. There is one record of a Great Tit killing a Goldcrest, *Regulus regulus*, and carrying it off, hawk-like, in its feet[53].

CHAPTER 4

THE BLUE TIT – *Parus caeruleus*

THE Blue Tit is one of our most distinctive tits; the blue plumage and lack of black cap are diagnostic. Only three of those species found in western Europe (four if one includes the Azure Tit whose range in eastern Europe almost extends this far) do not have a black cap. These are the Blue Tit, Crested Tit and Long-tailed Tit. Of these the latter is easily distinguished by its totally different appearance and long tail and the Crested Tit has a distinct crest. Apart again from the eastern Azure Tit, the Blue Tit is the only species which has any blue.

The wing coverts and the crown are the most striking blue, but the wings and tail are also blue as is an area running from the back of the head, round below the face and joining the blue-black throat; this band of dark blue frames the white sides to the head. A blackish line crosses the white face at eye-level giving the bird a white stripe above the eye and a white cheek. The back is green, becoming yellower on the rump. There is a small white patch on the nape and the wing coverts are tipped with white, giving a white wing bar.

The yellow underparts may or may not show a thin black line down the centre – usually a diagnostic feature of the Great Tit. This line varies in part in relation to how fluffed out the bird's plumage is. Only the tips of the feathers of the underparts are yellow, the bases are blackish-grey; hence when the bird fluffs out its feathers in cold weather, more of the lower parts of the feathers are visible and these produce the black streak down the centre of the underparts. In addition some of the yellow tips may be abraded if the plumage becomes very worn; in these circumstances varying amounts of the underparts appear greyish-black[13, 70].

Males are considerably brighter than the females especially in the blue on the head and inner wing coverts. The difference is easily noticeable with birds in the hand and is usually a reliable means of distinguishing pairs at a nest. However, the differences are not so clear that all birds can be easily and reliably sexed in the field. As with the Great Tit the birds probably get brighter with each moult for the first three or four years of life. Certainly the older birds have longer wings[358].

The underparts of juveniles are a duller yellow than those of adults, and the younger birds lack the bright blue of the adult in both wing coverts and head. These areas are a dull greenish colour and the cheeks are yellow; otherwise the pattern of the plumage is the same as in the adults. During the late summer the young birds moult into the adult plumage, but both unmoulted bastard wing and the primary coverts retain the green colour of the juvenile and, in the hand, the young birds can be distinguished from older ones[88] (p. 189). The easiest way to do this is to compare the primary coverts with those of the inner wing; if all are of the same colour, the bird is more than one year old; if there is a clear break in the colour, with outer feathers greener, then the bird was hatched the previous summer.

The call is not dissimilar to that of the Great Tit, a thin 'tsee-tsee' often finished with a 'tsit'. The song however is quite different from that of the Great Tit, being a slow phrase of two or three separate notes which build up into a more rapid trill; a good description being 'tsee-tsee-tsu-tsuhuhuhu-huhu'[170]. The alarm calls include a harsher 'tsee' often repeated several times, or a rapid scolding churr; the calls of young Great and Blue Tits are described in the previous chapter.

The Blue Tit has a more restricted range than most of the British tits; although it is found over much of Europe and western Russia, it does not extend farther east into Siberia (fig. 26). This latter area is occupied by the closely similar Azure Tit whose range is also shown in figure 26. The Blue Tit only occurs in the southern third of Scandinavia, becoming scarce at about the northern limit of the deciduous forests; it has however expanded its range in Finland since the early part of this century[37]. Its range of habitats becomes progressively narrower as one goes north until it is found almost exclusively in broad-leaved, deciduous woodland. Eastwards it extends to about the longitude of Moscow and from there south-eastwards to the Caspian Sea and thence as far south as the edge of the Persian Gulf, the most southerly point in its range. Its southern boundary is approximately Lebanon, Turkey, the Mediterranean islands, coastal areas of north-west Africa, and the Canary Islands. *P. c. caeruleus* extends from Scandinavia to central Spain and eastwards to the Balkans and Asia. *P. c. ogliastrae* is the main subspecies in and around the Mediterranean and *P. c. ultramarinus* is the subspecies in north-western Africa; other more local populations (e.g. Balearics, Canaries) have also been given subspecific rank.

The Blue Tit in Britain has been recognized as a distinct subspecies *Parus caeruleus obscurus* in contrast to *P. c. caeruleus* on the continental mainland. The latter is a larger, and a brighter blue bird than the British race. However, some of the birds breeding in the Brecklands of East Anglia and in east Kent have longer wings than the Blue Tits in other parts of Britain and are similar to those of the Continental race or at least intermediate between these and the British race. Others of Continental origin are sometimes caught in winter, especially in irruption years[62, 155, 312]. Possibly some of the birds that arrive in Britain remain to breed in the south and east resulting in a mixture of Continental and British forms in this area.

Within Britain, the Blue Tit is widespread and often very common. It occurs throughout most of the British Isles, except the outer islands and Orkney, Shetland and the Outer Hebrides where it is rare (fig. 9). Even on the mainland it becomes scarce as one goes into north-west Scotland and on to high land, though in general it has increased in Scotland since

1840 as a result of re-afforestation[3]. It is often the commonest species of tit except in conifer. In broad-leaved deciduous woodland breeding densities may be as high as, or higher than, one pair per acre (2.5 per ha.). In many areas where nest-box studies have been made, a number of pairs have been found to nest outside the boxes so that such censuses tend to underestimate the numbers present. In Marley, Gibb[118] estimated that only about 70% of the Blue Tits used the nest-boxes there, even though boxes were available at high densities.

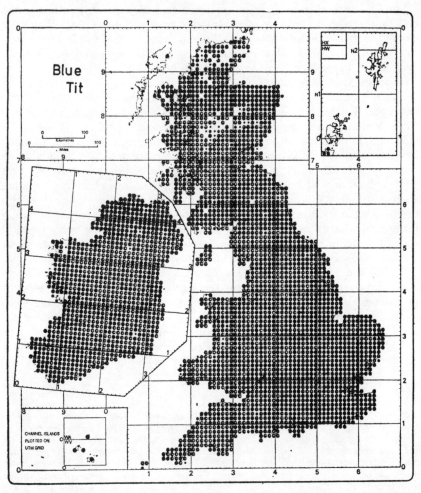

FIG. 9. The British distribution of the Blue Tit. The map shows the breeding distribution of the birds plotted on a 10 km grid, the largest dots denoting proved breeding (from Sharrock 1976).

The British Blue Tit is largely resident and recoveries of ringed birds show that in most years only about 5% of the birds move more than about ten miles. However, it may be a slightly more mobile species than the Great Tit. In Wytham a higher proportion of the ringing recoveries of Blue Tits are at relatively greater distances from the place of ringing than is the case with the Great Tit. It may be because of this tendency to move slightly longer distances that the Blue Tits are seen in such large numbers in gardens compared with other species; in winter they may make daily visits from woodland into towns for food.

The Continental birds wander more widely and, especially in winters of food shortage, may move considerable distances. At these times they may come to Britain in large numbers and reach many of the islands where they do not normally breed. The evidence suggests that at least some of these birds return to the Continent in the spring.

Although it is commonly found in such a wide variety of habitats, the Blue Tit is basically a bird of broad-leaved deciduous woodland, especially oakwoods. In the breeding season it tends to be more confined to broad-leaved woods than in winter when it may wander elsewhere. It breeds in conifer plantations at only relatively low densities and even then its nests are often close to small clumps of deciduous trees where the birds will be found to feed. As a result, this species is rare as a breeding bird in the pure conifer plantations of England and Wales and absent from both the Speyside firwoods (though it occurs in fir in Ross) and the Sussex yewwoods[410]. Yapp also notes that the Blue Tit is usually found in similar places to the Great Tit but he regards it as slightly less common than the latter species except in the pedunculate oakwoods and birchwoods of England and Wales, where it is far commoner than any other tit.

Within the mixed deciduous woodlands of Britain, this species definitely shows a preference for feeding on the oak and even frequently selects a nesting box on an oak tree in preference to boxes on other trees[158]. Blue Tits concentrate their foraging efforts in the outer twigs and branches of the trees[119]. Figure 10 shows the main feeding sites in Wytham.

The Blue Tit is the commonest species in gardens and hedgerows and is usually by far the commonest species to visit bird tables in winter in England

---

FIG. 10. The main feeding sites of the Blue Tit in Marley Wood, Oxford. Blue tits fed primarily in oaks throughout the winter. The main source of food from September to December was dead branches. From November to January the birds gradually shifted from dead branches to leaf-buds, which then became the most important source of food in oaks. Blue Tits ate elderberries in September, and when these were over switched to beechmast; beech was the second most favoured tree from October to February. As beechmast dwindled in February, Blue Tits increased their feeding at birch catkins, and attacked elm flowers for the first time. In March about half the Blue Tits recorded were feeding at the elm flowers; these were over by the end of March. Secondary foods and sources included (a) leaves, especially of oaks, in September; (b) dead branches and twigs September–February; (c) aphids from twigs and withering leaves of Sycamore, September–November; (d) berries o᭙ Hawthorn, October–November; (e) birch catkins, November onwards; (f) Willow flowers, early April; and (g) buds, flowers and branches of ash in late April (from Gibb 1954a).

and Wales. It also appears to spread inwards towards the centre of large cities farther than most other species, though many probably go there for the winter only, returning to the woods in the summer to breed. Its small size correlated with the ability to nest in tiny spaces may be a factor helping it to establish itself in hedges and gardens. One urban habitat that the Blue Tit has acquired is to roost in the street lamps[98]. Birds may commonly use lamps where they can get into a sheltered space above the bulb; the old-style glazed boxes around the bulb were ideal for them. These sites are well sheltered and give considerable warmth; not surprisingly they are used particularly in winter. I have seen birds using the street lamps in summer when they extended their feeding hours by catching moths attracted to the lights.

The breeding season varies with locality and year, but in southern and central Britain it usually starts about 20 April, though in early years it may start at the beginning of the month or in late ones not until early May. Late March nests occur exceptionally, though these are mainly in gardens where nesting starts slightly earlier than in woodland. Repeat clutches (usually resulting from loss of first clutch through predation) are frequent in the early part of the season. Genuine second broods (laid after the successful raising of the first broods) seem very rare, at least in Britain. I have never seen one in Wytham, even in those years when a proportion of the Great Tits have second broods, although Nethersole-Thompson[263] records a pair of Blue Tits rearing two broods in the same nest. On the Continent, second broods are more frequent[407].

The typical nest-site is probably a hole – often a narrow crack – in a tree, several feet above ground level or even higher. However, it often uses other sites such as holes in walls (where its small size enables it to squeeze between bricks) and nest-boxes. In addition to these, an almost endless variety of other sites have been recorded, such as letter-boxes, flower pots, street lamps etc. I have seen one in an old, lidless nest-box lying on its back on the woodland floor – very much the sort of nest-site that one would expect for a Robin. Another was in a three-foot length of iron pipe leaning against a shed; the pipe had an internal diameter of less than two inches and the nest was so cramped that the female had to incubate with her tail pushed over her head! There are a number of references to Blue Tits nesting in forks of trees. The nests are deep cups, rather similar to a Long-tailed Tit's nest without a roof, though made, of course, of different materials[55, 72, 176]. The owners of these nests have not always been positively identified, so this type of nest may be built by other species of tit as well. A further cup-shaped nest has been built by Blue Tits inside an old nest of a Blackbird[357].

The Blue Tit is an aggressive little bird and will contest a site with other species of small birds, often winning except against the larger Great Tit, though it may do so even with this species at times[303]. For example, there are a number of records of Blue Tits which have evicted Willow Tits from the holes that the latter had excavated for themselves and I have found a

Blue Tit nesting behind a piece of bark in a nest apparently built by a Tree-creeper.

The Blue Tit does not normally excavate a hole itself, though it may peck away at the entrance or enlarge the interior of an existing hole to some extent. Occasionally the birds excavate a large amount of the chamber[307]. As in the Great Tit, the nest foundation is primarily of moss, although the Blue Tit's nest can usually be distinguished by the small twigs, grass and bast (the long thin strips of the inner bark off dead trees) which are built into the moss. The completed nest is almost always lined with feathers. Neither the Great Tit nor any of the other British species make their nest in this way, but unfortunately not all Blue Tits use these materials; some build of moss alone. Blue Tits have also been recorded stealing fur for their nest from the nest of a Willow Tit[304].

The eggs are similar to those described in chapter 1 for all tits and the species can be more easily determined from the type of nest. Clutch-size is very variable, but is usually within the range of 7–13, the larger clutches are usually found in oak woodland early in the season (chapter 15). In Wytham the average size of first clutches is about 11 eggs, but clutches of 15 or 16 are recorded in most years and as many as 19 have been laid by the same female. Clutches tend to be smaller in gardens. Within Europe there is a gradation in clutch-size; the clutches in the southern parts of the bird's range being smaller than those in the north[159, 343].

The diet of the Blue Tit is similar to that of several of the other tits; it takes mainly insects in summer, but a mixture of seeds and insects in the winter. Some individuals, such as those in pine plantations, may continue to take a diet primarily of insects in winter while others may spend almost their whole time taking seeds. Beechmast, when present, is an important food for Blue Tits in winter (p. 142). Some Blue Tits take a considerable amount of their food from bird tables and the species is well known for its ability to remove the tops of milk bottles and drink the cream. Sap from trees, honey and pollen have all been recorded in their diet, but it is not known whether any of these are of importance.

CHAPTER 5

THE CRESTED TIT – *Parus cristatus*

ALTHOUGH there are many species of tits in other parts of the world with crests, this is the only European species with a crest; indeed no other small British bird has a crest. Hence it is unmistakable. The young have a smaller, less striking, crest but the absence of either a black crown or any blue in the plumage distinguishes Crested Tits from all the other European tits.

The crown feathers get progressively longer towards the back of the head and hence a crest is formed; the feathers of the crest are dull black, edged with creamy white. Behind the crest feathers, the black colouring runs round the sides of the neck so as to form a collar and joins the small black bib. The sides of the face are dull white but they do not form as striking a facial pattern as in some of the other species. On the pale facial patch there is a black C-shaped line which runs backwards from the eye, round the ear coverts and ends beneath the eye.

The rest of the upperparts are a medium shade of brown, the flight feathers being somewhat darker. The underparts are dirty white becoming a warmer buff colour on the flanks.

The female tends to have a slightly shorter crest than the male, but the sexes are not easily separable in the field or in the hand. The juveniles have still shorter crests but are otherwise similar to the adult birds. There are no known ways of distinguishing birds in their first year from older ones. Although the primary coverts are not moulted by the juvenile in its first autumn of life[409], those of the juvenile and the adult are so similar that they cannot be distinguished.

The Crested Tit is sometimes said to have no song, but this is only because it is so rarely heard; being thinly spread, the pairs seldom come into contact and so singing is uncommon. One version of the song is similar to that of some of the other species of tits in form; another, more distinctive, is described as being a high-pitched double note[185]. The most commonly heard call is a distinctive, fairly high-pitched churr or trill. The birds are said to have a special call used only when they are prospecting for nest-sites[261, 263].

In company with the Blue Tit, the Crested Tit has a more restricted range than any of the other British tits, extending eastwards only as far as the Balkans and western Russia (fig. 11). As with all the other species, the British birds *P. c. scoticus* are recognized as being subspecifically distinct from those in western Europe; the two subspecies that occur nearest to Britain are *P. c. cristatus* from Scandinavia and *P. c. mitratus* from Holland, Belgium and northern France; both races have been recorded in Britain.

The Crested Tit is highly resident, with very few records far outside the

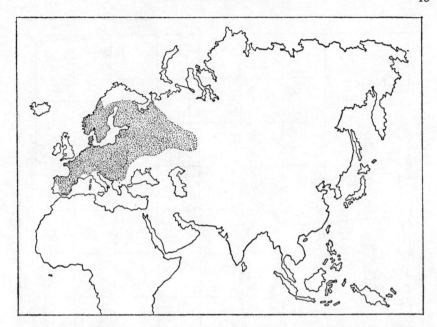

FIG. 11. The world distribution of the Crested Tit, *Parus cristatus*. This species has a relatively restricted range. Although found in Britain in mature pine forest, the species is not confined to this habitat in other areas of Europe.

known breeding range in Scotland. A small number of Crested Tits have been recorded in England but these seem as likely to be members of the Continental races as of the Scottish one; indeed some of them have been identified as such[409]. The British race is confined to the pine forests of Speyside and the adjacent counties of Nairn, Moray, Banff, Ross and Inverness-shire (fig. 12). There is some evidence that the species was once more widespread than at present, and then became even more restricted than it is today, and confined to the Spey Valley; since then it has spread out a little and now occupies some of the Moray Basin. These changes of range are believed to be as a result of de-afforestation followed by re-afforestation[3]. If so, the species may spread still farther as the younger pine plantations mature, though the presence of dead wood for nest-sites is usually necessary.

In Europe the Crested Tit is usually thought of as being a bird of conifers, but some of those in southern Europe occupy mixed woodland, or even pure deciduous woods on occasion.

In Britain also, Crested Tits are usually thought of as being birds of mature pine forests, of old and open woodland, but they often nest in dead small trees such as birch suggesting perhaps that they prefer rather open woodland containing a mixture of large pines and other trees. Yarrell[412]

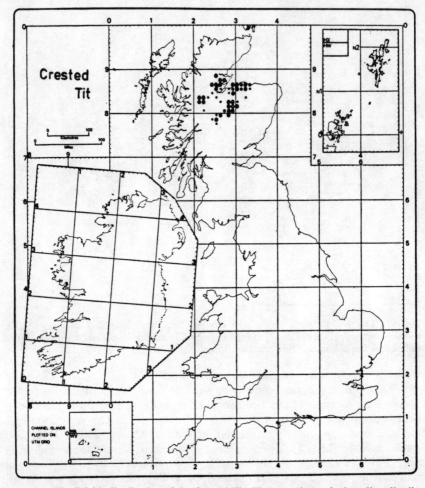

FIG. 12. The British distribution of the Crested Tit. The map shows the breeding distribution of the birds plotted on a 10km grid, the largest dots denoting proved breeding. Although largely confined to mature forests, there is some suggestion that the species may be spreading as new forests become mature (from Sharrock 1976).

says that Crested Tits 'seem partial to woods where firs and oak trees are mixed' since they often nested in holes in the oaks. Yarrell and Newton[413] quote Gray as saying that prior to the highland clearances the woodland was mostly composed of a mixture of 'Scotch firs and oaks'. Hence the new Spey forests appear to be different in composition from those felled two centuries ago.

Apart from these contractions and slight re-expansions of their range little is known in Britain of the status of the species and possible changes in numbers, though at times it is susceptible to severe winter weather. However, on the Continent, there have been some considerable changes during this century; again some of these can be associated with re-afforestation[177], but there also seem to be other changes in abundance which cannot so clearly be associated with changes in the woodlands. One possible reason for this is that there too the Crested Tit seems quite vulnerable to hard weather in winter and may fluctuate in numbers in relation to the winter weather, taking perhaps two or three years to recover from a severe winter.

Even within its restricted range the Crested Tit is never very common. The pairs are usually separated by long distances making it difficult, if not impossible, to calculate breeding densities or territorial boundaries. They seem to seldom occur at densities of more than one pair per 50 acres (20 hectares) and usually they are considerably less abundant than this[52].

The detailed feeding ecology of the Crested Tit has not been studied in Britain so a diagram of feeding stations as shown for the other species is not available. Detailed studies of this species have been made in Norway[145, 148]. In summer it is primarily found in spruce and pine (foraging at all levels) but spends about a quarter of its time searching on the ground. In winter, thick snow makes the latter impossible and so the birds divide their time between the spruce and pine. At both times of year the birds spend more time in the spruce than in the pine[230]. In addition Crested Tits concentrate their foraging on the larger branches and the trunk while the Coal Tits spend more time in the outer branches.

As far as is known the Crested Tit is extremely sedentary. Although it may visit bird tables in adjacent gardens during the winter and may become quite tame in hard weather, it seldom seems to wander far. Its limited breeding distribution and the lack of records outside this area tend to support this view. The birds appear to spend most of their lives paired within their territories.

Laying usually commences in late April or early May and the species is almost always single-brooded; genuine second broods have been recorded, but seem very rare. On the Continent they may be much more frequent, up to 60% having second broods. The nest-site is usually in a rotten stump, though in addition they are recorded as having nested in the base of an old nest of a bird of prey, in squirrels' dreys or in holes in the ground[261].

The Crested Tit excavates a nest-site for itself in rotten wood. The nest itself may be in almost any species of tree, provided that it is rotten enough to excavate in; even old fence posts have been used[409]. Nest-boxes are sometimes used, but usually ignored in favour of natural sites. An excavated hole is not usually used in two successive years. As with the Willow Tit, the birds prepare a new site for each year, even if the new site is in the same tree as the one they used the previous year. The nest has a moss foundation and the cup is lined with fur, wool or hair, though feathers may be used at times. Both excavation and nest building are done almost exclusively by the female.

In Scotland the full clutch is usually in the region of 5–6, though larger ones have been recorded. Within Europe, there seems to be a decline in clutch-size as one goes northwards. Reasonable samples give the average clutch in southern Germany as 6·3, in Switzerland as 5·9 and in Sweden as 4·9[226, 134, 93]. This needs further checking since many other species, including the Blue Tit, show the reverse trend. The fledging period has been given as 21–22 days, a little longer than for some of the other species though data are not easily collected.

The diet is similar to that of the other tits, being almost exclusively insects in the summer and including a lot of seeds and berries in the winter, especially conifer seeds. In Norway, the species collects and stores a large amount of food[148]. Much of this is spruce seeds, but considerable numbers of insect larvae may be stored also; these are usually incapacitated but not killed; up to 20% or more of the food stored may be animal rather than plant.

CHAPTER 6

THE MARSH TIT – *Parus palustris*

In appearance the Marsh Tit is much less striking than the species we have looked at so far; it is a rather plain brown bird with a black cap and pale cheeks. This alone is sufficient to separate this species easily from all the other British species except one – the Willow Tit – though on the Continent both Sombre and Siberian Tits are also similar. The Marsh Tit is only separated from the Willow Tit with practice and with difficulty. The juveniles of the two species cannot always be reliably identified even in the hand.

The Marsh Tit has a glossy black cap and a small black bib. The whole of the upperparts are a uniform, unspotted brown and the wing is also uniform, dark brown. The underparts are dull white with a touch of buff on the flanks. The sides of the face are creamy white.

The Willow Tit is basically similar in appearance and the differences between the two species are small. The main differences in plumage are as follows:

1. The crown of the Willow Tit is a very deep chocolate colour, not black, and lacks the rich gloss of the Marsh Tit.
2. The dark cap of the Willow Tit appears to extend a little farther down the nape than is the case in the Marsh Tit.
3. In association with the extended cap, the whitish cheeks appear to extend further towards the back of the head in the Willow Tit than in the Marsh Tit.
4. The edges of the flight feathers in the Willow Tit are pale cream; in the closed wing this can cause the bird to show a pale patch on the wing, not visible in the Marsh Tit.
5. The flanks tend to be a slightly warmer colour in the Willow Tit than in the Marsh Tit, giving it a slightly richer brown appearance underneath (as opposed to the grey appearance of the Marsh Tit).
6. The bib of the Marsh Tit is small with sharply defined edges while that of the Willow tends to be less neatly defined, more diffuse and slightly larger.

None of these differences is completely reliable and each may at times be difficult to see, especially since the birds are often in the poor light of deep cover. If the bird can be examined in the hand, the differences are clearer, but examination of a series of specimens is needed in order to acquire experience of the differences; all are only a matter of degree. In the hand, there is a further difference; the tail of the Marsh Tit has a squarer tip than that of the Willow Tit. The outer feathers of the Marsh Tit are some 2–4 mm.

shorter than the inner ones, those of the Willow Tit some 5–6 mm. shorter[409].
This is a fairly reliable way of differentiating the two species since there
seems to be little overlap in these measurements.

A microscopic examination of the head feathers of the Marsh and Willow
Tits shows that there are differences in the number of barbs on the feathers
of the two species. The shape and positioning of the barbs also differ (fig. 13).
However, once again the separation is not complete and there is some overlap
between the two species.

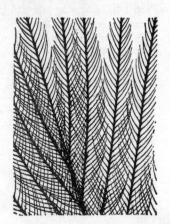 

FIG. 13.   Enlargements of the crown feathers of the Willow Tit (left) and the Marsh Tit
(right). The main difference lies in the number of barbs along the quill and the amount of
curvature, especially in their distal ends (from Tucker 1935).

There are no known external morphological differences between the two
sexes, nor is it possible to distinguish birds in their first year from older ones.
In the United States, methods for determining the sex of the closely related
Black-capped Chickadee have been suggested with the observation that the
same technique can be used on Marsh and Willow Tits[427]. However, the
reliability of this method has been questioned[418]. As in the other tits, the
primary coverts are not moulted by the juveniles but, as in the Crested
Tit, the feathers of the juveniles are so similar to those of the adult that the
two age classes cannot be separated.

Juvenile Marsh Tits can be distinguished from older ones by the differences
in the crown feathers. They are duller and lack the glossy black of the adults.
However, another difficulty arises in that this difference from the adults
makes the young Marsh Tit very similar to the young Willow Tit; the young
of the two species cannot be reliably separated in the early part of the post-
fledging period. Only when the tail is fully grown can the difference between
the measurement of the outer tail feathers be used, but until this time the
young may not be separable. Tucker's study[383] of the structure of the head
feathers showed that those of the young Marsh Tits are very similar to those

of Willow Tits of all ages and hence his technique cannot be used at this stage.

The two species are so very similar that one sometimes wonders how the birds themselves manage to tell each other apart. The answer seems to lie in their calls; here the two species are quite distinct. The song of the Marsh Tit is a series of 'chip' notes; these may be given slowly as separate 'chups' or more quickly when they run into each other and become a trill[250]. Another song of the species – described occasionally as the Marsh Tit's 'nightingale' song – a rich 'yu-yu-yu' – is usually given during courtship and may be a prelude to coition[248]. A display flight just prior to coition has also been observed[350].

The best-known call of the Marsh Tit is a loud, rather explosive 'pitchou' which, like the song, has no equivalent in the Willow Tit (for calls see p. 60). However this call is given almost exclusively by the established territory holders (both male and female) and never by the young[250].

The Marsh Tit's distribution is slightly odd in that, although the birds reach as far east as Japan, there is a major break in its distribution, no birds living in the area between longitudes 52°E and 85°E (fig. 14); such a situation clearly has potential for eventual speciation, inasmuch as interbreeding between birds from these two areas is not at all likely to occur. Throughout this range, with a few exceptions discussed in chapter 9, the Marsh Tit is a bird of broad-leaved deciduous woodland. As a result its distribution tends to be slightly more southerly than that of the Willow Tit which prefers coniferous woodland.

Within Britain also, the Marsh Tit does not spread quite as far north as the Willow Tit (fig. 15). The latter occurs widely in southern Scotland, but the Marsh Tit only just extends into the country, with a few pairs breeding in Berwickshire, and a record from Roxburgh. The Marsh Tit is also scarce in western districts of England and Wales and absent from Anglesey, Isle of Man and the whole of Ireland (where introductions were attempted but were not successful[21]) and all the western isles. British Marsh Tits are recognized as a separate subspecies (*P. p. dresseri*) from those in adjacent Continental Europe (*P. p. communis*).

This is an extremely resident species. Apparently the birds pair for life and seldom wander outside their territories, even when hard weather has forced most of the other tits to leave the woods[120, 250, 356]. Even if they attach themselves to a feeding flock that passes through their territory, they will drop out as the flock crosses the territorial boundary[250]. There are few ringing recoveries at any distance and the species does not appear to take part in irruptions.

The most detailed British study, carried out in Bagley Wood near Oxford, showed that Marsh Tits have territories of about six acres in extent (2·5 hectares) though the size varied markedly[347]. In Germany rather larger territories of 5–6 hectares are used[232].

The Marsh Tit's liking for broad-leaved woodland has already been

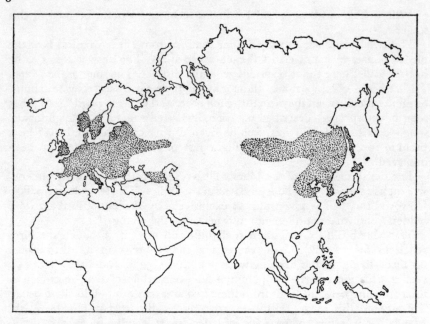

FIG. 14.   The world distribution of the Marsh Tit, *Parus palustris*. This species is primarily confined to broad-leaved woodlands.

mentioned; it is rare in conifer plantations in England and Wales. Marsh Tit is not a good descriptive name for the species since it is frequently found away from damp areas. It probably does have a liking for rather open woodland with a rich understory since this is where much of its feeding is done[158]. However, it has been recorded as commonly feeding on the canopy of sessile oaks in the Wyre Forests[410]; Yapp considers the Marsh Tit to be rare in the sessile oakwoods of higher country as well as in birch and conifer.

In the more northerly parts of their range – in southern Scandinavia – the Marsh Tit is very rigidly confined to its favourite habitat – broad-leaved woodland[342]. In Britain it occurs most frequently in open, rural wooded gardens and in orchards. The preferred feeding sites of the Wytham Marsh Tits are shown in figure 16. From this it can be seen that the species tends to forage low down in the canopy or on the ground.

The breeding season is similar to that of the other species of tits. In southern Britain in a normal year Marsh Tits start to lay in the second half of April. Based on a sample of 80 nests in Wytham the Marsh Tit is the second of the tits to start; it begins to lay, on average, about a day after the Coal Tit and a day before the Blue Tit[90]. Repeat clutches are recorded but there does not seem to be any good evidence for second broods; certainly they are rare.

Marsh Tits nest in holes in trees, often low down, and may enlarge

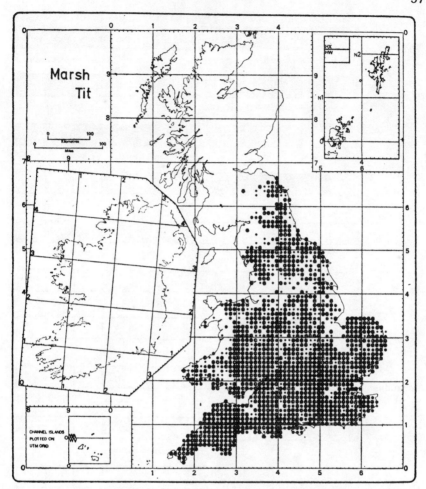

FIG. 15. The British distribution of the Marsh Tit. The map shows the breeding distribution of the birds plotted on a 10 km grid, the largest dots denoting proved breeding. Note how the species becomes scarcer in the north and west and is absent from Ireland (from Sharrock 1976).

natural cavities to some extent. They do not, however, excavate a hole in the same way as does the Willow Tit, but merely enlarge an existing one. Records prior to the beginning of this century which suggest they excavate a complete nest are unreliable since the Willow Tit was not recognized as a different species until then. A further complication is that Marsh Tits may occasionally take over the nest-holes of Willow Tits after the latter have excavated them[50, 108]. For unknown reasons, Marsh Tits do not readily

58 BRITISH TITS

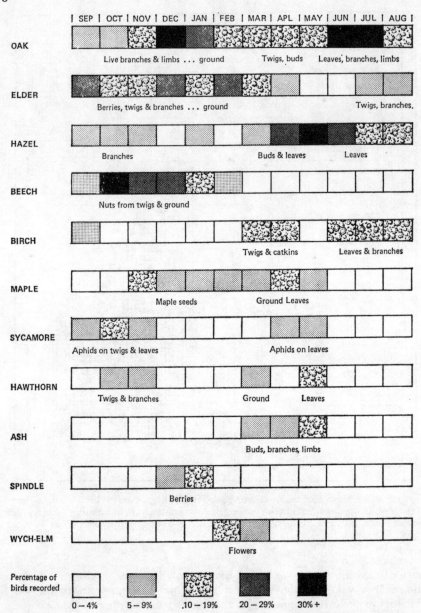

FIG. 16. The main feeding sites of Marsh Tits in Marley Wood, Oxford, showing the proportion of the time spent in each tree species in each month. From September–March Marsh Tits fed more often in elder and rather less in oak than the other tits, and about as often as Coal Tits on beechmast. In elders, Marsh Tits fed on the berries in September, then from

take to nesting boxes so that only a very small proportion of the birds in any given area will be found nesting in them.

The nest itself is variable, but often similar in appearance to that of a Blue Tit in that feathers may be used to line the nest in addition to hair. The foundation is moss. The clutch is usually in the range of 7–9 eggs; in Wytham the average is 7·7.

Food is similar to that of other species, insects in the summer and many seeds in the winter. The Marsh Tit has a relatively strong beak and probably opens more hard seeds than any other British tit except the larger Great Tit[310]. In particular the species feeds heavily on beech mast when it is present. I have seen it taking the fruits of the spindle *Euonymus europaeus* more frequently than any other species and Gibb[119] makes the same point. The Marsh Tit also stores food more regularly than most other British tits, except the Coal Tit[223, 305, 306]. During the summer it depends less on the insect larvae on the oaks than many of the other tits, taking more of its food from the shrub layer.

---

twigs and branches, and finally from the ground in February and March. In oaks they fed mostly from live branches and limbs. Apart from elder, beech and oak, which lasted for most of the winter, Marsh Tits fed from a long succession of less important foods and sources, as follows: (a) burdock seed, July–April; (b) honeysuckle berries, mostly in September; (c) aphids from sycamore leaves and twigs, September–November; (d) twigs and branches generally, September–January; (e) maple seeds, November–March; (f) spindle berries, December–January; (g) the ground, January–April; (h) elm flowers, February–March; (i) birch twigs and catkins, March–April; (j) ash buds, branches and limbs, March–May; and finally (k) leaf-buds of hazel, maple and sycamore, April–May (from Gibb 1954a).

CHAPTER 7

THE WILLOW TIT – *Parus montanus*

As described in the previous chapter, the Willow Tit is extremely similar in appearance to the Marsh Tit and the differences between the two species are given there.

Because of the great similarity between Marsh and Willow Tits it was not realized that the latter existed as a separate species in Britain until 1897[186]. A detailed description of the discovery is given by Simson[332]. The Willow Tit was the last British species to be recognized and even then, though quite detailed descriptions of some of the differences were given by some authors[314], many observers were unwilling to accept that there were two so similar species. A number of years passed before there was general acceptance. An unfortunate result of this is that no records of either Marsh or Willow Tit prior to this time are acceptable since they could refer to either species. However, some early descriptions of 'Marsh Tits' plainly refer to Willow Tits[234, 244].

Initially, this species was thought to be conspecific with the North American Black-capped Chickadee *Parus atricapillus*, and was so named. However it is now held to be a separate species and given the name *Parus montanus*, but many earlier references to it (from the time of its discovery up until the 1950s and 1960s) will be found under the name of *Parus atricapillus*.

The plumage differences between Marsh and Willow Tits were dealt with in the previous chapter. As with the previous species the males and females cannot be separated on external morphological grounds nor can the first-year birds be distinguished from older ones. The colour of the head of juvenile birds is more similar to that of the adults of this species than in the Marsh Tit and hence separating juveniles from adults is more difficult. However, a bird in heavy body moult in July or August but not moulting the flight feathers should be a first-year bird since, as with the other tits of this age, the flight feathers are not moulted at this time. Even so, caution is necessary since the adult tits tend to complete their wing moult before their body moult (p. 189) so that in the late summer a bird in body moult only could be either an adult which had completed growing its new set of flight feathers, but not yet completed its body moult, or a juvenile.

As mentioned the most distinctive differences between the two species are their calls. Both the song and the normal calls of the Willow Tit are clearly distinguishable from those of the Marsh Tit. These are well described by Foster and Godfrey[108]. The full song is not frequently heard since, as in the Crested Tit, pairs are often out of earshot of each other and under such circumstances singing is less frequent. The song is a sweet warbling which contrasts with the chipping trill of the Marsh Tit. The most commonly heard call notes are the thin 'zee-zee-zee' or 'zi-zurr-zurr-zurr', deeper, more nasal and slurred than any note of the Marsh Tit. This call is very distinct from any made by the Marsh Tit and may be heard at any time of year[170]. Several authors have also drawn attention to the harsher 'chay' or 'tchay' note, often repeated several times. This again is quite different from any of the Marsh Tit's usual utterings. It is equally worth stressing that the Willow Tit has no note similar to the very distinctive 'pitchou' of the Marsh Tit.

According to Morley[250] the female Marsh Tit does not sing, but both sexes of the Willow Tit sing, at least at times[108]. The female Willow Tit uses a begging call that is distinct from those of other tits; described as 'eee-da-da'[108]; Nethersole-Thompson notes that this species has a special call associated with prospecting for nest-sites.[263].

The distribution of the Willow Tit is shown in figure 17. It is found throughout large areas of the Palaearctic in a range somewhat to the north of that of the Marsh Tit since it occurs in the coniferous woods and even the more northerly birchwoods while the Marsh Tit is confined to the deciduous woods farther south. Several races have been described and the British Willow Tit, *Parus montanus kleinschmidti*, is recognized as being distinct from that on the nearby Continent, *P. m. rhenanus*. At least one representative of the northern race *P. m. borealis* has been recorded in Britain[409]. In Central Europe the situation is complicated in that alpine and lowland Willow Tits are separable in some areas. They have different songs. However, where the two forms meet they interbreed freely and so cannot be considered separate species[370]. Apparently the alpine birds are highly resident, staying at high altitude the whole year round so that relatively little mixing occurs[220].

Within Britain, the detailed distribution is not perfectly established for two reasons. Firstly observers have not always been able to distinguish Willow Tits from Marsh Tits reliably and, in addition, it seems as if the species may have a patchy distribution anyway (fig. 18). It is absent from all the Scottish islands, from the Isle of Man, Anglesey and Ireland. It is widespread, though patchy in much of southern Scotland (where the Marsh Tit is very rare). It is rare in the north of Scotland but has been found in the birchwoods of Ross-shire, though seems considerably scarcer in the Highlands than it used to be. It is known to be much commoner than the Marsh Tit in parts of Wales (and this may be the general situation) if not throughout most of Wales. It is also commoner than the Marsh Tit in areas of extensive pine plantations[127]. There are insufficient data to provide a feeding niche diagram as given for the other species in Wytham. The Willow Tit feeds low down, spending much of its time in the shrub layers of the woodland, but very rarely comes down on to the ground, which the Marsh Tit does freely. In some other areas the Willow Tit is much commoner than the Marsh Tit; this is especially so where there is not much extensive woodland, since the Willow Tit occurs throughout farmland as long as there are small

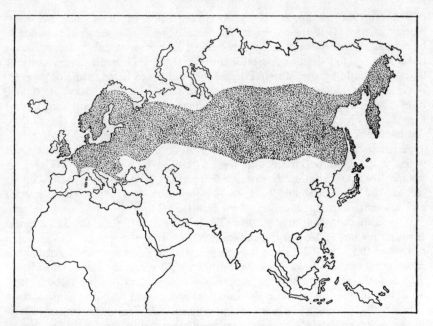

FIG. 17. The world distribution of the Willow Tit, *Parus montanus*. Although it is found in habitats similar to those of the Marsh Tit, it also occurs in coniferous forests and so extends considerably farther north than the other species.

patches of trees, but Marsh Tits do not. This may be true over much of England.

The Willow Tit is usually thinly distributed even in those areas where it occurs most abundantly[44]. In Wytham, Foster and Godfrey[108] reported that there was usually only one, sometimes two, pairs in an area of some 27 hectares of woodland. It does not often seem to reach higher densities than this in Britain, though in Germany territories may average 5–6 hectares[232].

Over most of its range the Willow Tit is a bird of conifers and mixed woods and the Marsh Tit one of broad-leaved deciduous woods[342]. However, this does not wholly fit with the British situation. Although the Willow Tit occurs in conifer plantations (whereas the Marsh Tit does not do so frequently) and its range is more extensive in Scotland than that of the Marsh Tit, it is also frequently found in low-lying areas devoid of conifers. Indeed, in southern Britain, it might be said to be the species more deserving of the name 'marsh tit' since this describes the habitat of the Willow Tit better than that of the Marsh Tit. These usually include rather scrubby areas of elder, *Sambucus niger*, alder, *Alnus glutinosa*, or birch, *Betula verrucosa*, although the species may also spread into orchard and rural gardens. Often, though not always, these are moist areas.

As far as is known, British Willow Tits are highly sedentary. However,

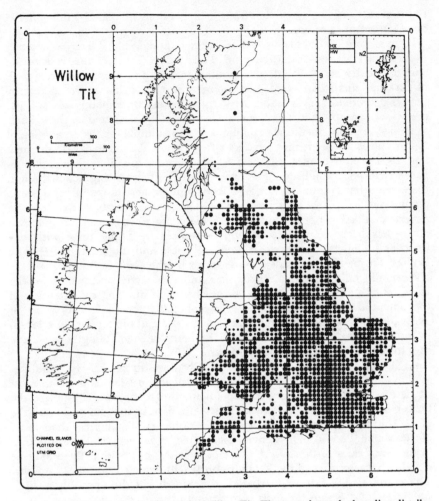

FIG. 18. The British distribution of the Willow Tit. The map shows the breeding distribution of the birds plotted on a 10 km grid, the largest dots denoting proved breeding. Note that the Willow Tit becomes scarcer in the north and west, and is absent from Ireland. The dots in central and northern Scotland represent very small populations that appear to have existed in these areas for some time (from Sharrock 1976).

there are reports on the Continent of Willow Tits wandering quite widely in autumn, apparently even in an irruptive manner[68, 160].

The time of breeding is roughly similar to that of other species of tit in that clutches are usually started in the second half of April or early May. However, in Britain there are no quantitative data; in Germany it may be the last of the tits to breed[407]. Second broods have not been reliably recorded, though late first clutches may occur quite frequently, some as a result of the birds being evicted from their previous nest-site by other tits[108] or of losses from predation.

Among the British tits, only the Crested and Willow Tits completely excavate a new nest-hole each year. The Willow Tit does this in a rotten stump, usually only a few feet above the ground and usually in dead trees of a rather small diameter (possibly because they occur more commonly than larger ones). This habit may to some extent explain this species' presence in damp areas; small, rotten trees are often neglected by the forester so such areas may have some small dead trees suitable for the excavation of nesting holes. So set is this behaviour that they will even excavate the new hole in a stump containing the nest-hole from a previous year, still apparently in good condition. They very rarely nest in nesting boxes, though there are a few records of Willow Tits occupying nest-boxes in young pine plantations where there is no suitable dead wood for them to use. The American Black-capped Chickadee – which also always excavates its own nest – has been induced to occupy nest-boxes by filling these with dry wood chippings; the birds then 'excavate' these and use the boxes[193]. The Willow Tit may be persuaded to use boxes by the same technique.

Normally only the female excavates and she carries away most of the wood chips – presumably to reduce the chance of drawing the attention of the potential predator to the nest; exceptionally the male may assist in excavation[409]. Willow Tits seem particularly shy and inoffensive, in relation to the other tits, since there are several records of their losing newly-made sites to other tits, usually Blue or Marsh.

As in the excavation, the female usually does almost all the building. Willow Tits use much less moss in nest construction than is found in most tit nests. The nest is usually lined with some of the wood chippings; the birds may collect scales off buds and these are used in the foundations of the nest[1, 50]. The eggs, in my experience, are rather more spherical than those of the Marsh Tit and more heavily pigmented. However, the measurements in the Handbook of British Birds[409] do not bear this out so that these may be merely characteristics of the Wytham birds with which I am most familiar. The clutch-size is similar to that of the Marsh Tit, but possibly a little smaller, with 7–8 eggs the most common number.

Diet has not been well established, again largely as a result of difficulties of separating Marsh from Willow Tits in the field. In general it seems similar to that of the other species. It feeds predominantly low down on the trees, often foraging on dead wood and most frequently on birch and elder[119]. Neither Gibb nor I have found it taking beech seed, although the Marsh Tit does this in quantity, and Gibb also noted that all the year round this species searched for food on the branches, limbs and boles of trees much more than the Marsh Tit.

In general it seems as if the Willow Tit's slightly more slender beak makes it less suitable for dealing with strong nuts and seeds than the stouter beak of the Marsh Tit. The latter species hammers open a lot of seeds in winter, but the Willow Tit does not seem to do so; this may account for the lack of records of it feeding on beechmast. The slightly finer beak may be related to its being a bird primarily adapted to coniferous woodland (p. 86).

In Scandinavia and Germany the Willow Tit commonly stores food[148, 232]. It probably does this regularly in Britain as well but, as with so many aspects of this bird's life, there is insufficient information. In the Breckland, the Willow Tits regularly store food[127], but elsewhere there have been relatively few records. In at least some of these the storing seemed to be only a temporary phenomenon since the birds had been seen collecting the stored food again as soon as they had depleted the supply of peanuts from the bird table[156, 157].

CHAPTER 8

THE LONG-TAILED TIT – *Aegithalos caudatus*

THE Long-tailed Tit is 'the odd man out'. As previously stated it is less closely related to the *Parus* tits covered by this work than the latter are to each other. This is clear from many aspects of its appearance and behaviour. Hence this rather longer chapter, which covers some of its special habits in some detail. A number of studies have been conducted in Europe; in particular, I shall refer to those of Lack and Lack[212], Riehm[308] and Gaston[116]; in Japan an important series of papers has been published by Nakamura[257, 258, 259, 260]. I shall refer to these papers frequently during this chapter.

PART I

The Long-tailed Tit differs markedly in its appearance from the other tits and can easily be distinguished from them by its small size, long tail and the absence of a black cap or crest; in addition the pink in the plumage is diagnostic.

The head, with the exception of a broad black eye-stripe, is white. The underparts are dirty white with a slight pinkish tinge to the belly and the flanks. The upper parts, including the tail and wings, are basically blackish with the exception of the rump and scapulars which are pink. The flight feathers have a varying amount of white on their outer edges; this usually gives rise to a distinctive white patch on the closed wing. If the tail is fanned (which it rarely is) it can be seen that the outermost three pairs of feathers are very much shorter than the rest and strongly marked with white. From the underside this can even give the impression of a white tail. Seen close to, the rims of the eyelids are either orange or pink; the colour seems to vary in the same birds on different occasions, but the reasons for the variation are not fully understood.

The juvenile bird is much duller than the adult; it lacks the pink colour completely and the black colouring of the adult is replaced by brown. In addition the juvenile has brown sides to the face (instead of white) and for some considerable period after leaving the nest the tail is markedly shorter than that of the adult.

Except by observing their behaviour, it is not possible to tell the sexes apart in the field, nor can this be done in the hand though the females have on average shorter wings. However, during the nesting period, the female can usually be distinguished from the male by her bent tail, the result of long periods in the close confines of the nest. Unlike the other tits, the Long-tailed Tit undergoes a complete moult a few weeks after leaving the nest and acquires wing and tail feathers similar to those of the adult at this time; hence it is not possible to distinguish first-year birds from older ones. However it is possible to distinguish some of the first-year birds by the technique of examining the skull ossification[366]; this method seems valid at least until October or November.

Except during the breeding season Long-tailed Tits are almost invariably seen in small parties often of 8–20 or more birds. They have a characteristic undulating flight and call; this is a sharp 'tsirrip' or 'tsup', usually repeated several times. Once heard it is easily recognized. Gaston describes three main calls. One he calls a rattling 'schnurr' which varies markedly in length and intensity. He says that this is given when the birds seem generally excited and is often associated with lengthy flights (over 20 metres). A second call, a slightly metallic 'pit', is given when the birds are feeding and generally undisturbed. The third call, a high-pitched 'eez-eez-eez', is often given during short flights and also by isolated birds trying to make contact with others.

A proper song has been only doubtfully recorded, but the birds do have a slow butterfly-like display similar to that described for the Blue Tit (p. 155). A hovering 'flycatcher display' is performed during nest-site selection. It consists of a vertical flight followed by the bird dropping back downwards; often this is carried out near the nest-site. In addition there is another display whose function is not clear. Gaston calls it the 'plunge-flight' since it occurs when a bird drops suddenly from the top of the tree into the bushes beneath. The bird may give the 'schnurr' call loudly and may be followed by the rest of the flock. The full significance of a number of these displays is not understood and this species would undoubtedly repay further study.

As with several of the other British tits, the species ranges from Ireland to Japan (fig. 19) and several subspecies are recognized. The British birds are recognized as a separate race *A. c. rosaceus*; this is quite similar to some of the birds *A. c. anemoricus* found in north-western France. A number of other subspecies have been recognized in western Europe, of which the northern Long-tailed Tit, *A. c. caudatus* is possibly most relevant to us in Britain; this is a pale bird with a completely white head (plate 5). Several birds of this type have been recorded in Britain and it is not clear as to whether these are immigrants or whether they are mutant forms thrown up by the local populations. Since white-headed birds occur at low frequencies in the German breeding populations[360] it is possible that they might also occur in British birds. However, these white-headed birds have usually been noted in the eastern and southern coastal counties where immigrant tits of other species are most common so that it seems more likely that these particular Long-tailed Tits are immigrants also.

Although therefore some birds may move, the British subspecies is highly resident and there are only rare records of ringed birds travelling more than a few miles. On one such occasion, the distant movement involved a party most of which moved together. Eight birds were ringed at Donna Nook in

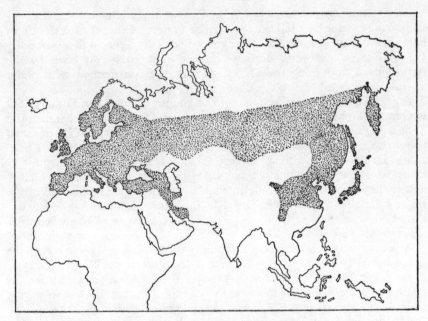

FIG. 19.   The world range of the Long-tailed Tit, *Aegithalos caudatus*.

Lincolnshire in late October and seven of these were recaptured together at Gibraltar Point, 27 miles SSE only four days later.

Within Britain the species is widespread in woodland, though absent from most of the outer islands, the majority of the Hebrides and from both Orkney and Shetland (fig. 20); like several of the other species it becomes scarcer in northern Scotland where the woodlands thin out. It is absent from the fell woods of England and Wales and scarce in conifer plantations[410].

The Long-tailed Tit also frequents hedgerows and gardens of the outer suburbs. It rarely, however, comes to bird tables, though if one or more of a party break with this tradition, the whole party may visit the table regularly for much of the winter and even succeeding winters. The habit may equally suddenly die down again.

The numbers of Long-tailed Tits fluctuate markedly from year to year owing to their susceptibility to cold weather, numbers being reduced dramatically during a cold winter and only rising again after a run of mild ones. In recent years, the Long-tailed Tit was severely reduced in numbers during the hard winter of 1946–47[375].

The same thing happened during the exceptionally hard winter of 1962–63 (the coldest winter in central Britain for about 200 years). Long-tailed Tits vanished from Wytham, and possibly may have been extinct as a breeding species there in the summer of 1963. It took four or five years for them to become numerous in Wytham, but in 1971 after a series of mild winters

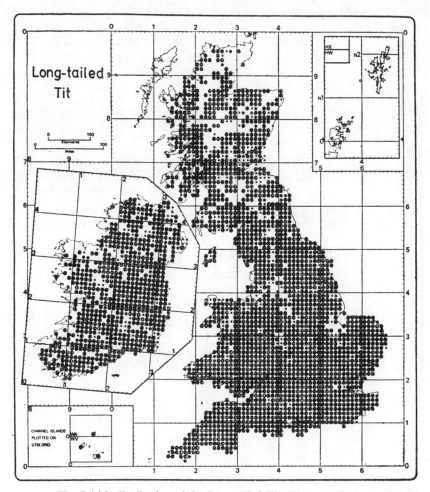

FIG. 20. The British distribution of the Long-tailed Tit. The map shows the breeding distribution of the birds plotted on a 10 km grid, the largest dots denoting proved breeding. The increasing severity of the winter as one goes north and on to higher ground, may explain the scarcity of this species in certain areas (from Sharrock 1976).

Gaston was able to find 78 birds in his study area of about 250 hectares, representing a breeding density of about 15 pairs per 100 hectares. If this held over the whole wood (about 400 hectares) then the population increased from nil in 1963 to about 60 pairs in 1971. Similar fluctuations have been recorded in many parts of the country. The species' scarcity in areas of northern Scotland may in part be due to the harder winters there[410].

Such violent fluctuations can result in difficulties in defining its habitat preferences, breeding densities and range, for unless areas are studied over

a series of years, the observations may not be representative. In his study
area in Japan, Nakamura[258] recorded winter populations in one study area
varying in number between 30 and 140 birds per 100 hectares. However,
as we have seen, fluctuations in Britain can be much greater than this. The
Lacks recorded populations in Wytham over a series of years (1949–51 and

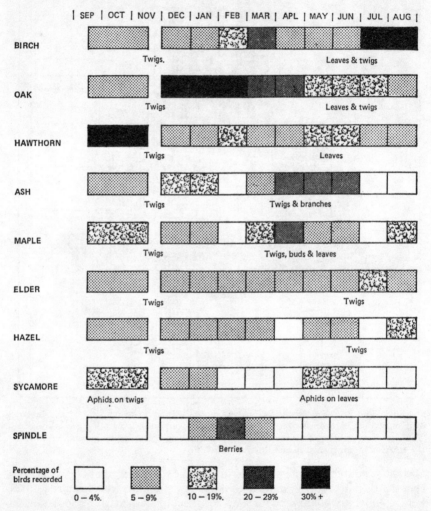

FIG. 21.   The main feeding sites of Long-tailed Tits in Marley Wood, Oxford, showing the
proportion of time spent in each tree species in each month. Long-tailed Tits fed primarily in
hawthorn twigs from September–November, and in oak twigs from December–April; oak
twigs were slightly less popular from March onwards, when they were replaced by twigs of
birch, maple and ash. Other foods or sources were (a) twigs generally, all winter, and (b)
spindle berries, late January–early March (from Gibb 1954a).

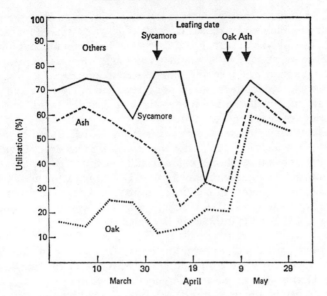

FIG. 22. The percentage of time spent by Long-tailed Tits in oak, ash and sycamore in relation to the date at which the trees burst into leaf (denoted by arrows above). Note how much more the tree species is used once it is in leaf (from Gaston 1973).

1955–57), these varied between 5 or 6 pairs in one 80-acre (32 hectares) area to 9 pairs in 65 acres (26 hectares) in a particularly good area.

The Long-tailed Tit is usually found amongst the thinner twigs of the trees, often pecking in and around the buds. It practically never comes down to the ground in its search for food. Figure 21 shows the feeding sites of the Long-tailed Tit in Marley. They have a preference for hawthorn bushes in the autumn, oak in the middle of winter and birch, maple and ash after the beginning of March. During midwinter, the birds spend 90% of their day feeding, covering some seven kilometres within their home range and spending some two to three minutes in each tree. During concentrated feeding periods, they move at a speed of about four metres a minute; clearly they do not thoroughly examine each tree at this speed. Larger flocks travel faster than smaller ones. Gaston has shown how the birds alter their feeding habits in the spring in relation to the time at which the different tree species come into leaf (fig. 22). In March, as in Gibb's study, he found that the birds foraged a great deal of the time on ash. However, when the sycamore leaves opened the birds switched to feeding there more than in ash. Later still when the oak leaves opened the Long-tailed Tits switched to these, spending 60% of their total time foraging there.

The Long-tailed Tit is the earliest breeder of all the tit species, and starts laying in late March in southern Britain. Because of its complex and elaborate nest, it may start building long before that, often in late February in the south[50]. A high proportion of nests is lost to predators so that many of the late broods are likely to be repeat clutches of pairs that have lost an earlier nest. From an analysis of nest record cards, the Lacks found that fewer than 10% of clutches in southern Britain were started as late as May. There seems to be no good evidence for genuine second broods.

The nests are commonly found in two sorts of sites. They may be placed – usually high up – in the fork of a tree, tight against the trunk or they may be in a clump of twigs and branches of a bush – usually low down. In the latter case a thorny site is often chosen such as in brambles, hawthorn or gorse, possibly in order to make the site less easily accessible to predators. These two types of site are not of course rigidly separate. Although the latter type may be low down, often about head height, some nests are placed in a similar position in a clump of needles high up in a pine; in addition some of the lower sites on trees such as hawthorn may be close to the trunk. There are a few records of nests in holes in the ground[295, 367].

In their study the Lacks showed that there was a bimodal distribution of nests, with more nests high up and low down than at intermediate heights. They also noted a tendency for nests to be situated in the hedges around woodland. Gaston also noted a preference for nest-sites in scrub, or hedges and bushes outside the wood and observed that these were much more successful, some 22% of the nests in such places producing young as opposed to only 4·5% of those within the woodland.

Similarly, the Lacks noted that high nests were invariably unsuccessful and wondered why the Long-tailed Tits built there at all. Working in Wytham some twelve–thirteen years later than the Lacks, Gaston found many fewer nests more than six metres from the ground than were found in the earlier study (table 1). It seems possible in view of the Lacks' observations that during the intervening years the birds have changed their nesting habits so as to reduce their use of high sites. The predator believed responsible for the losses of nests in high sites is the Jay, whereas mammals (possibly weasels or mice) are probably responsible for many of the losses of lower nests. It would be interesting to know whether the Long-tailed Tits in different geographical areas show nesting habits related to the pressures of different kinds of predation.

In all, the Lacks reported that 86% of the nests they studied were taken by predators, while Gaston reported that 84% of nests failed, again largely as a result of predation. While these figures may seem extremely high, they compare closely with that of 84% for nesting losses in the Blackbird in Wytham[345]. It should be remembered that birds that lose a nest are likely to make one or more attempts with repeat clutches and may well succeed with one of these. In particular many of the Long-tailed Tits' nests are taken by predators at a very early stage; in Gaston's study 43% of the nests lost to predators were destroyed before laying had commenced. First nests may take up to twenty days to build, but replacement ones contain fewer feathers nd may be built much more quickly. Laying may start as soon as the cup-

PLATE I. *Above left*, the Ben Vair Forest with Sgurr Dhonuill (3284 ft) in the background. Much of Scotland was cleared of forest during the heyday of sheep farming. Re-afforestation provides new habitats for tits, the Coal Tit especially benefiting from conifer plantations. *Right*, a mature pine plantation in Scotland, the home of Crested Tits which need dead trees in which to excavate their nests; a pair nested in the stump in this picture. *Below*, at the beginning of last century much of Wytham Wood was grazing land with large trees. After the Enclosure Acts woodland developed around the large oaks.

PLATE 2. *Above left*, the Coal Tit is the smallest of the true tits in Britain and has the finest beak. The Great Tit is the largest British tit. The black band on the male's belly, *above right*, is much broader than the female's, *below*, particularly between the legs.

Table 1. The proportion of Long-tailed Tits' nests built at different heights in different years in Wytham. The apparent change may be connected with the lack of success of the higher nests (from Gaston 1973).

| | | Height above ground | |
		less than 3 metres	more than 6 metres
1955–7	first nests	4	7
	repeats	12	4
1971	first nests	25	0
	repeats	21	4

base is completed, long before the nest has a roof. The Lacks record one nest without a roof that already contained five eggs.

The nest is very different from those of the other British tits though similar in some respects to that of the Penduline Tit in other parts of Europe. The purse-like structure is made of fibrous material, with a single entrance hole on one side near the top. The entrance hole is slightly springy and, particularly early in the nesting cycle, tends to partially close after an adult has passed through it. The basic nest structure is made of moss woven with cobwebs and hair, but the outside is covered with greyish lichens so that the whole is beautifully camouflaged, especially against a tree trunk. The overall size is about six inches deep by four inches in diameter. One of the features that has attracted much attention is the lining of the nest; prodigious numbers of feathers are brought in for this. Owen[277] counted the feathers in six nests; the number varied from 985 to 2084 with an average of 1558. Both members of the pair build the nest and both roost in it from the time it is sufficiently built to do so until the time the young fledge. Corroborating this, there are records of severe late snow-storms during the night, after which both adults have been found dead in the nest – apparently unable to get out.[14] The Lacks report that the break-up of the roosting parties (see below) can be related to the date at which each pair completes the roof of its nest; once this is on the pair stop roosting with the flock and spend the night inside their nest.

The clutch is quite large, numbering about 8–12 eggs with an average of 9·4 in southern Britain and 9·9 in Yorkshire. Larger clutches seem to occur in the north of the species' range, with an average of 11·1 in Sweden. Still larger clutches are not infrequently recorded[409], but these may be the product of more than one female since there are not infrequently more than two birds at a nest (see below). Similarly, though normally only one egg per day is laid, there are a few records where more than one egg is laid each day[262]; again intensive observation would be required to determine whether or not two females were involved. Late clutches are smaller than early ones.

The food of the Long-tailed Tit is not well known, but it takes many fewer seeds in winter than the other tits, possibly because of its weaker bill. It does not, for example, take beech mast as do most of the other tits and even seems to have some difficulty in dealing with berries such as those of spindle. The insectivorous diet may be one reason for the Long-tailed Tits' being more susceptible than the other tits to periods of hard weather. In addition to its weaker bill this species differs from the other tits in not having much dexterity with its feet. It cannot hold an object under a foot in order to hammer at it with the beak. Instead it has developed a different method for dealing with the larger food items; it hangs upside down from the branch by one foot, holding the fruit in its other foot while eating it. This method is used for eating larger objects such as small pieces of peanut[152]. In spite of this, the Long-tailed Tit is not well adapted to dealing with large or strong morsels of food. This accords well with its main feeding niche on the outer twigs of trees when almost all the food taken is very small[28].

PART II

The Long-tailed Tit has several habits that are so unlike the other tits that it seems best to deal with them separately here rather than to try and include them later.

Winter parties

Characteristically Long-tailed Tits go around in parties outside the breeding season. These parties are of such a size (six to eight upwards) that they probably consist of one or more families that have stayed together since the summer, but this may not always be so, since some of the smaller parties are composed mainly of adults; possibly these may be aggregations of failed breeders. Occasionally these parties may contain large numbers of birds and Witherby[409] gives records of parties of up to 50 or more individuals, but these are very unusual. The birds stay together in these parties throughout the winter, only breaking up in the pre-breeding phase. However, because the Long-tailed Tits start to build their nests early in the season, the break-up may occur as early as the beginning of February. After this time, they may be encountered mainly in pairs except towards dusk when they gather together into parties for roosting. At times the parties seem to have quite regular daily routes. Gaston and Nakamura have shown that a party tends to remain in a set area during the winter and hold group territories; at times quite violent inter-party conflicts occur at the edges of these territories. In Wytham these flock territories had an average size of 25 hectares while five such territories in Japan averaged 21 hectares.

The advantage of being in these flocks during the day may be that the individuals learn food sources that they would not otherwise discover by the mere fact that there are more birds hunting for food (p. 109). Certainly on odd occasions after one bird has tried a new source of food many others that had previously not taken that food, may start to do so. In the winter of 1958–59 I was trapping tits in Wytham using small wire funnel traps, baited with fat, in several different parts of the wood. In Marley I was catching Long-tailed Tits frequently while I was not catching them in other parts at all. One day in March I caught three Long-tailed Tits in another area, 1·5 kilometres from Marley; these birds were ones that I had been trapping regularly in Marley. As soon as these three started to visit the traps in the new area, many of the local birds started to enter them also. Thereafter, I caught Long-tailed Tits regularly in both the areas for the rest of the winter, though not in other areas of the wood.

The Long-tailed Tit gains another important advantage from living in parties. This species does not roost in holes in trees and since it is very small it has to use a lot of energy during the long, cold winter's nights in order to maintain its body temperature (p. 120); doubtless it is during the night that many of them die in winter. In order to reduce the difficulties of surviving overnight the birds roost huddled up together in small clumps, so helping to keep each other warm (plate 6).

Shortly before dusk the birds become uneasy and active. All of a sudden they become silent and then fly some distance away in a fairly straight line and then enter a thick piece of shrubbery, such as a hawthorn tree. Once there, they gradually close up on one another until they form a small ball with their tails sticking out[139]. They may use the same place night after night if they are not disturbed; doubtless this is advantageous in that if a bird loses contact with the party it can still regain the group at nightfall and so benefit from the extra protection afforded by huddling together. How close the birds huddle may depend on the temperature since looser clumps of birds have been reported in the spring; in the closely related Bush-tits the birds stay about two inches apart unless the temperature drops below freezing when they huddle close together[336]. The birds in Riehm's study area frequently bathed some half an hour to an hour before going to roost.

While these reasons for being in groups throughout the winter may be adequate, there may be other more subtle ones which we do not fully understand. The main reason for this suggestion is that, although the Long-tailed Tit's behaviour is unusual in Europe, elsewhere, and especially in the tropics, many other species hold group territories. Most of these birds are passerines and most are largely insectivorous. This convergent behaviour occurs in a wide range of different families and must therefore be of considerable advantage to all these species.

In spring the parties break up into pairs; some pairs may be formed earlier, or even maintained from the previous year. For large parts of the day the pairs move about on their own though they rejoin the parties for roosting. In one year in Wytham, when a party that I had been trapping regularly throughout the winter, broke up, I started to catch birds only in pairs. In almost every case the 'pair' (I could not tell for certain that they were pairs) included one member of the winter party and one unringed bird, indicating that there is a certain amount of movement during the spring and that not all pairs are formed within the groups. Gaston working with a larger sample found the same, though possibly to a slightly smaller extent. In his case, however, he knew the sexes of all the individuals and in every case (out of nine) the bird that moved into a group territory was the female and the bird that remained within the group territory was the male. Hence it seems that during the 'spring instability phase'[258] males remain within their flock territory whereas females more readily move, or are more readily accepted by another flock. Gaston also noted that the pairs took up nesting areas within the area occupied by the flock in which they (or at least the male) had spent the winter. According to him and the Lacks they did not appear to defend territories in the normal sense at this time (about mid-March); the males rarely attacked another bird unless it wandered too close to the pair. However, both Riehm and Nakamura mention that the separate pairs hold and defend territories. How these territories are maintained is not clear in that they seem to overlap considerably; possibly adjacent pairs will not indulge in territorial disputes if they have come from the same winter flock whereas if they are from different flocks they may continue to defend the group territory boundaries.

The nesting period

The nests are elaborate structures that take a considerable amount of time to build. As soon as the nest has a roof, the pair starts to roost inside the newly built nest; up until this time they roost with the party. It may still be cold at night at this time (about mid-March) so that presumably the birds do not forsake the communal roost until they have the alternative of a well-constructed nest. The pair may roost in the nest from this moment on until the young leave the nest, perhaps some two months later[277].

The early nests may take a considerable time to build; the Lacks noted that the early nests took about three weeks to build and that the birds did more building in warm weather than in cold, in the morning than in the afternoon and in the early stages of building than the later ones. The latter may be because of the need to complete the outer shell of the nest as quickly as possible since it is better camouflaged then than when only partly built; certainly many nests are destroyed by predators during building. The Lacks also noted that the birds built repeat nests (those replacing early lost ones) more quickly than first nests and this has been quantified by Gaston (fig. 23) who showed how the rate of building of the outer shell varied throughout the season; in addition Riehm has noted that fewer feathers are put into the later nests. It is not known whether later nests are built more quickly because of the urgency to breed before the season ends or whether because the birds have more time to spare for building since the days are longer.

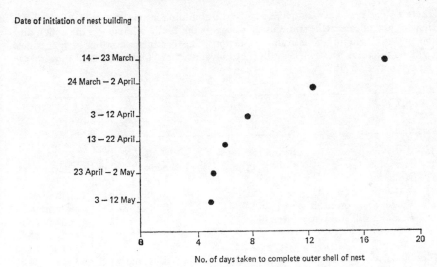

FIG. 23. The speed of nest-building in relation to the date at which nest-building started. The points denote the number of days from the start of nest-building to the completion of the outer shell of the nest (from Gaston 1973).

Nest-building

The building of the complicated nest has received some attention, in particular it has been described in detail by Tinbergen[381] and by Thorpe[374]. The latter, using Tinbergen's observations, emphasises the long series of different behaviour patterns that are necessary in order for the bird to be able to complete so intricate a structure. The actual building involves 'only a repertoire of relatively few simple movements.' However, while the number of movements may be small, they must be done in a set order and only in that order. In addition the correct materials must be used in conjunction with the correct movements at each stage and there are four basic types of material – moss, spiders' web, lichen and feathers.

After the birds have chosen a site for their nest, they start to put pieces of moss there; although much of this may fall off they continue until some pieces stay there. When sufficient moss has adhered to the site, the birds switch to collecting spiders' web which they pass back and forth across the moss until it sticks when they bind it to the branch. Collecting the moss and spider's web in alternating bouts and binding them together continues until a little platform is built. Then the birds start to behave differently; they sit in the middle of the platform and tuck the new moss around themselves. Collection of moss and web continue in alternating bouts and the bird now weaves them into the sides of the nest, turning as it weaves so as to produce a circular nest. Tinbergen describes two weaving motions, a sideways action

Table 2. The necessary activities involved in building a nest of the Long-tailed Tit showing the releaser (the stimulus that triggers the bird's behaviour), the action and the material sought or used in the action. The complete nest-building involves eighteen releasers and fourteen distinct movements or combinations of movements (from Thorpe 1956b).

Releaser	Action	Object Sought and/or Manipulated
1a. Territory	Searching	Nest-site
1b. Nest-site	Collecting	Moss ⎱ 1b and c alternate
1c. Nest-site	Placing	Moss ⎰ until:
2a. Tufts of moss in fork	Collecting	Spider's silk ⎫ 2a, b and c
2b. Spider's silk on moss	Rubbing	Spider's silk ⎬ alternate a
2c. Spider's silk stuck to moss	Stretching	Spider's silk ⎭ number of times, then back to 1

[Periodical alternation of actions and object manipulation in (1b+c) and (2a+b+c) until platform built.]

3a. Platform	Collecting	Moss
3b. Platform	Sitting	
3c. Action of sitting	Placing material on rim	Moss
3d. Moss on rim	Sideways movement of bill (sideways weaving)	
3e. Moss on rim	(2a+b+c)	
3f. Moss on rim	Vertical movements of bill (vertical weaving)	
3g. Curved nest rim or cup outside bird's body	Steady rotation of body during building.	

[Periodical alternation of actions and object manipulation in (1b+c) and (2a+b+c) and (3a+b–f).]

4a. Nest-cup	Breast pressing	
4b. Nest-cup	Trampling with feet	
4c. Nest-cup	Turning	

[Periodical alternation of actions and object manipulation in (1b+c), (2a+b+c), (3a–f) and (4a+b+c).]

5a. Nest-cup more than about one-third built	Collecting	Lichens
5b. Outside of nest-cup unevenly or incompletely covered with lichen	Weaving from inside	Lichens

Releaser	Action	Object Sought and/or Manipulated
5c. Outside of nest-cup unevenly or incompletelycovered with lichen	Weaving from outside	Lichens
5d. ditto	Actions of 2b and 2c from new positions, i.e. outside cup	
[Periodical alternations of all five sets of actions.]		
6. Cups about two-thirds built	Change of movements (especially 3g) so as to leave an entrance hole. Special weaving and other movements on the rim of the entrance hole	
7a. Completed dome	Collecting	Feathers
7b. Completed dome	Lining	

followed later by a vertical one when the sides of the nest have grown higher. The cup-shaped nest is completed with the help of two further movements, 'breast-pressing' – in which the bird pushes itself outwards into the nest sides – and 'trampling' with the feet. By these actions, the Long-tailed Tits arrive at a well-woven cup-shaped nest similar to that of other birds.

At this point the birds bring in a third material – lichen. This is woven into the outside of the nest only. The birds do this in two ways, by leaning over from inside and also by clinging – sometimes upside down – to the outside of the nest. After much of the surfacing has been completed, the birds continue to build up the walls of the nest (still intermittently adding lichens, though to the outside only) until the sides of the cup are about three-quarters finished. At this point the weaving movements change, especially that of turning around inside – so as to leave an entrance hole on one side. Exceptionally, two entrances may be built[309]. Also, the sides of the nest are now getting so high that the bird can no longer easily reach the top from a standing position; as a result the added material tends to lean inwards and in this way the dome is formed. Special extra weaving movements are associated with the building of the entrance hole and the strengthening of its rim.

When the dome has been completed and the exterior completely covered with lichens the birds stop collecting moss, spider's web and lichens and collect feathers for the interior. As mentioned earlier, very large numbers of these are brought in and woven into the sides of the interior of the nest, providing a soft, insulating lining to the nest.

Thorpe has pointed out how complicated this nest-building activity is and stressed how each activity can only commence once a certain stage of nest-building has been reached. Each stage acts as a sign or 'releaser' to the bird to start a new behaviour. Thorpe's sub-division of the series of patterns of behaviour is shown in table 2. He points out that the whole series of activities – searching, collecting, rubbing, weaving, sitting, pressing, trampling, turning and lining have to be combined with other activities and in addition the four different materials must be correctly used.

The Long-tailed Tit's nest is far more complex than those of the other tits, but the latter's more simple nests involve a number of similar activities of collecting moss, turning, weaving and trampling it into position followed by doing the same with a lining material such as fur, hair or feathers. However, not only are the number of different movements fewer, but neither camouflage nor cohesive spiders' web are necessary.

Extra birds at the nest

The breeding cycle is not dissimilar to that of other tits except for one important feature. It is not at all uncommon for there to be more than a pair of birds at a nest; three or four birds have been relatively frequently recorded (the Lacks list many references to such observations.) However, most of these are isolated instances and it is not so easy to determine how frequently there are more than two birds at a nest. Gaston found that there were 'supernumeraries' at eight out of ten of the broods he studied, though at two of these they were not apparent until the young had fledged.

The status of these additional birds is not clear. Some at least are birds that have lost their own broods and instead of having a repeat brood join the parents at another nest. For example, a Long-tailed Tit that had lost its brood has been recorded helping to rear an adjacent brood of Great Tits[329]. In Gaston's study, many of the birds were colour-ringed and in one case extra birds arrived at a nest shortly after a nearby nest had been destroyed by a predator. Both males and females may be found helping at other nests.

The extra birds may not always be ones that have lost their own nests since more than two birds have been recorded at some nests right from the beginning of the breeding season. Casement[54] records three birds roosting in the nest during incubation at a relatively early nest (15 April). At some such nests it has been thought that the extra bird was a male but Witherby[409] mentions several cases where exceptionally large clutches (of around twenty eggs) have been found and in such cases it seems likely that two females were involved.

A special display is associated with these extra birds at the nest[257, 308]; Gaston calls this the 'hover display'; it involves a steep upwards flight, followed by a short hover and a slow fluttering descent. A 'tic' call may be associated with the flight, though at other times the bird is silent. Typically, the display is given very near to the nest and by both the owners of the nest and by the supernumerary birds. The display may start shortly after the young have hatched. Supernumerary birds were not noted until the display had been recorded and the display is much more frequently given at a nest where helpers are present than at those where there are no helpers.

The significance of the display is not at all clear. In some cases the new arrivals may be driven off while in others no fighting occurs and the extra birds appear to be tolerated. Riehm considers that the function of the display is to distract predators, but in view of the fact that it is given conspicuously near the nest this seems unlikely. Indeed an observer familiar with the display can locate a nest by it, though it does not seem probable that a predator would learn to do so.

An interesting explanation for the behaviour of supernumerary birds has been put forward by Zahavi[414] working with another bird, a babbler, where the territory is also defended by a group. Zahavi argues that each bird faces competition throughout its life from others of its kind and stands the best chance of surviving (or of leaving surviving offspring) when there are fewest competitors. In order to leave successors, a bird must try to breed. However, if circumstances prevent this happening (as in the case of the Long-tailed Tit that has lost its nest) then the next best thing a bird can do is to prevent his neighbour breeding since, by doing this, the bird reduces the numbers of its competitors and so increases its chances of surviving to breed another year. One way to do this is for the bird to appear to help its neighbour and so get access to its nest, though in fact the bird does so in such a way that it attracts predators to the neighbour's nest; therefore 'helpers' are not helpers at all.

However, there are many problems associated with this view. In the case of the Long-tailed Tit in particular, the parents give the display frequently themselves and presumably would not do so if it were not advantageous. Gaston counted the number of feeding visits per hour at nests with and without helpers and found that there was little difference – 21·4 compared with 20·5 visits per hour, respectively. However the reason that there was no difference was because the parents slowed down their feeding rates, coming only 16·3 times an hour (two birds) to the helper's 4·1. The parents had therefore to work less hard. These observations were made in a single year; there might well be years or times of year when the parents could not easily raise a brood without a helper. As Gaston says, 'the display is so distinctive that it is difficult to believe that it does not have an important function. As it pinpoints the nest very accurately and exposes the adult itself to predation, it must have some compensatory value.'

CHAPTER 9

ECOLOGICAL DIFFERENCES
BETWEEN SPECIES

IT is now commonly accepted that different species of animals have different niches – their requirements are different from those of other species. No two species could ever be exactly equal in their abilities to perform a certain task; one would be less good than the other and so less successful. At times of shortage, the less successful species would suffer heavier mortality or raise fewer young than the other. Natural selection has therefore favoured those individuals of a species which tended to specialize and to do things better than other species. In this way the specializations of each species have evolved to such an extent that, as a result of competition, two similar species scarcely ever occupy similar niches, but displace each other in such a manner that each takes possession of certain peculiar kinds of food and modes of life in which it has an advantage over its competitor[117].

For some time this view was known as Gause's Hypothesis but, in fact, it had been demonstrated before by others and is usually known now as the theory of 'competitive exclusion'[153]; the situation has been reviewed for birds by Lack[216] who discusses the tits as a particular example.

Competitive exclusion is not easy to demonstrate, but there are occasions when a species behaves differently when in the presence of a second species from the way that it behaves in the absence of the other species; the change is likely to result from competition between the two. One such case is known in the tits and will be mentioned later.

If each species shows different feeding specializations and these enable each to survive, one might expect such differences to be most apparent when conditions for survival are most threatened by food shortage, namely in winter.

In this chapter I shall examine some of the evidence that the different tit species have different niches and see in what ways these differences may reduce competition between the species. It is normally held that there are three basic ways by which species can avoid or reduce interspecific competition. Usually, food is likely to be the resource for which different species may potentially compete, but this need not always be so. Firstly the different species may live in different parts of the world and so not come into contact either at all, or at any rate not frequently. Secondly, they may live in the same general area but avoid coming into contact with one another very much – for instance, by having specializations which largely restrict them to different habitats. Thirdly the two species may live in the same habitat,

82

but reduce competition by taking different foods. The European tits show all these three ways of reducing competition.

1. Ranges which do not overlap

Since so many of the European tits may be found in the same geographical areas, clearly not all the tits avoid competition in this way. There are, however, three species of tits which occur in Europe but which have more restricted ranges than those tits we see in Britain; these only come into contact with some of the other species over small parts of their ranges. Relatively little is known about these three species and, as they do not occur in Britain, they will not receive much attention in this book. But they deserve some mention and are worth further study.

The Siberian (or Lapp) Tit, *Parus cinctus*, occurs only in the northern forests of Eurasia where it is almost wholly restricted to coniferous woodland (fig. 24). Only two other species of tit occur in this area, the Great Tit and the Willow Tit. The Great Tit is not common at such latitudes and in winter seems to be dependent on getting much of its food from the vicinity of houses and so does not compete to any extent with the Siberian Tit[339]. Hence the Siberian Tit only overlaps with one other species to any significant degree.

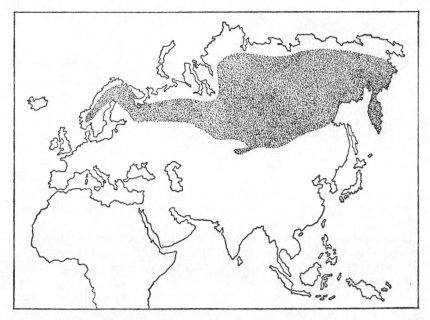

FIG. 24. The range of the Siberian Tit, *Parus cinctus*. This species primarily occurs in high latitude coniferous woodland.

The second case is that of the Sombre Tit, *Parus lugubris*, a relatively large tit (though still smaller than the Great Tit) which is found in the Balkan peninsula and whose range extends beyond Europe through Turkey into Iran (fig. 25). It is mainly found in forests in mountainous regions,

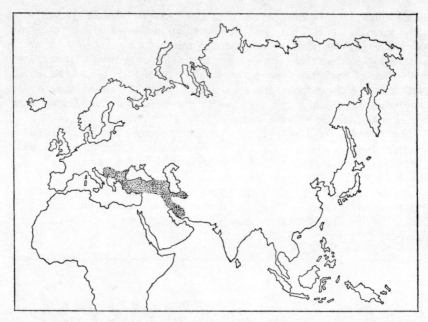

FIG. 25.   The range of the Sombre Tit, *Parus lugubris*. This species has a restricted range in south-west Europe and the Middle East.

breeding mostly in relict woodland especially of *Quercus pubescens*. It stores food and eats many seeds[227]. It seems to live mainly in the lower branches of trees in the bush and shrub layers of the forests. In such places it might compete with the Marsh Tit or the Great Tit both of which feed in these sites. However, both these species are scarce in the areas occupied by the Sombre Tit and any overlap which occurs is likely to be small. The Sombre Tit maintains large territories and, in contrast to the other European tits, is a cautious, rather retiring bird.

The third case concerns the ranges of the Blue Tit and the closely similar, though paler, Azure Tit, *Parus cyanus*. The ranges do not greatly overlap at present (fig. 26) and the two species could be said to replace each other, their combined ranges being similar to that of many of the other European tits. In the period 1870–1900 the Azure Tit spread westwards into eastern Europe but has since retreated again; suggesting that it has difficulty inhabiting this area, perhaps as a result of competition with the Blue Tit[216, 342]. During the westwards spread of this species, hybrids between it and the Blue

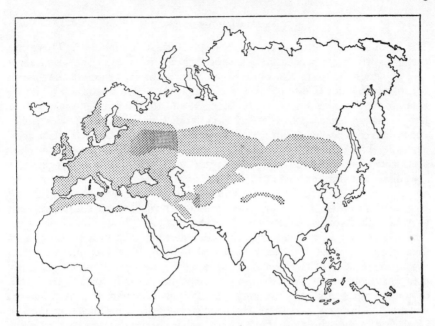

FIG. 26. The ranges of the Blue Tit, *Parus caeruleus*, and the Azure Tit, *Parus cyanus*. The main area of overlap is in central Europe, but the western edge of the Azure Tit's range has varied markedly and there has not always been as much overlap as shown here.

Tit were reported – normally a rare occurrence between any of the tit species[297]. However, there are further complications; initially the two species had relatively poor isolating mechanisms inasmuch as they frequently inter-bred and produced hybrids, the so-called *Parus pleskei*. Hybrids between the two species still occur where the two species overlap[394], but apparently much more rarely than they used to[388]. How much reduced hybridization is due to an increase in isolating mechanisms, to specialization into different habitats or to the withdrawal eastwards of the Azure Tit is not clear. Indeed even the statements about changes in frequency of hybridization between the two species must be treated with caution since none of the field obser-vations are sufficiently quantitative to make firm comparisons[368].

There is also a further reason for the occurrence of hybrids; at the edge of a species' range it often happens that the sex ratio is very unequal and if so, the sex that preponderates may be liable to take mates of another closely related species in the absence of those of its own. Again, however, there are no reliable data on the sex ratio of Azure Tits in the area of overlap. What-ever the details, it remains true that the ranges of these two species do not overlap except in one relatively restricted area and there, as discussed below, the two species tend to live in different habitats.

2. Habitat Separation

The habitats of Eurasian tits have been studied in detail[342]. There are certain fairly clear separations, through choice of habitat, between some species which occur in the same areas. For example, amongst the British tits, Coal Tits and Crested Tits occur predominantly in conifers (as, farther north, does the Siberian Tit). The Blue Tit and the Marsh Tit, on the other hand, clearly prefer broad-leaved woodland. Several other species prefer broad-leaved woodland, but occur in conifer as well, the Great Tit is a good example. The Willow Tit inhabits both conifer and mixed woods though it also occurs in pure birchwood, at the northern extremes of its range.

While these differences in habitats are quite clear they are not, of course, absolute. One may find Coal Tits nesting in broad-leaved woodland and Blue Tits in conifers. However, when this happens the birds are less numerous than in their favoured habitats[205]. It is also surprising how often, when such exceptions occur, the birds will be found nesting near to a single tree of their preferred type. Thus in a conifer plantation, Blue Tits may be found near a small patch of birch or as in our largely broad-leaved woodland study area at Oxford, the Coal Tits often nest not only near to an isolated patch of conifer but actually in the only nest-box on a conifer. In broad-leaved, deciduous Marley Wood there are usually only one, sometimes two, pairs of Coal Tits in the whole 66 acres, whereas there is usually one pair to every eight or ten acres in pinewoods[77, 214, 376].

The Coal Tits that nest in the 'wrong' habitat are usually quite successful with their broods, but the same is not true of Blue Tits with their broods in conifer. Their poor nesting success probably results from the fact that the food supply and its timing is different in conifer from that in broad-leaved woodland; this will be discussed in chapter 15. Some Blue Tits breeding in the conifer plantations of the Brecklands of East Anglia were even found to be feeding their young on larvae from oak trees on the edge of the plantations up to half a mile away. Although they were finding plenty of food in these trees, their journeys took them so long that they were still unable to feed their broods adequately.

The ranges of the Azure Tit and the Blue Tit overlap to some extent, but their habitats differ. The Blue Tit, as already mentioned, is a bird of broad-leaved woodland and occurs most frequently in oakwoods, while the Azure Tit occurs most frequently in low-lying, riverine forests. In more easterly parts of its range, in Central Asia, the climate is drier and riverine forests may be the main forest types in grassland areas; it is to these that the Azure Tit seems best adapted.

There is a morphological difference between those species that prefer broad-leaved woods and those that prefer conifer. The birds that live in conifers have relatively longer, thinner beaks than those that live in broad-leaved woodland (table 3). This difference is attributed to the need to probe into conifer needles. Needles grow in small clusters (the number de-

Table 3. Typical weights (in grams) and measurements (in mm) of males of European *Parus* species. All figures are averages for the areas stated. Dimensions vary from country to country with a tendency for each species to be larger with a proportionately shorter beak in colder regions. C=conifer, B=broad-leaved woodland (from Lack 1971).

	Habitat	Weight	Wing	Culmen from base	Beak-depth	Culmen/wing	Depth/culmen
ENGLAND							
P. ater (Coal)	C	9·3	60	10·8	3·7	0·18	0·34
P. caeruleus (Blue)	B	11·4	64	9·3	4·4	0·145	0·47
P. major (Great)	B	20·0	76	13·0	5·2	0·17	0·40
P. montanus (Willow)	C/B	10·1	60	10·6	4·0	0·18	0·38
P. palustris (Marsh)	B	11·4	63	10·4	4·3	0·165	0·41
SCANDINAVIA							
P. cinctus (Siberian)	C	13·7	68	11·7	4·0	0·17	0·34
P. cristatus (Crested)	C	11·0	64	11·5	3·6	0·18	0·31
EUROPEAN USSR							
P. cyanus (Azure)	B	—	69	10·1	5·2	0·145	0·51
BALKANS							
P. lugubris (Sombre)	B	(16·7)	76	12·6	c. 5·3	0·165	0·42

pending on the species) from a single base and a bird could probably reach small insects hidden among them better with a thin, pointed beak. Further, Snow records that the insect prey in conifers in winter is smaller than that in broad-leaved woods and Coal Tits take smaller insects than the other species, so perhaps a finer bill is better for collecting these. The differences between the beak shapes in the two types of woodland holds over wide areas of Eurasia and also in North America (fig. 27).

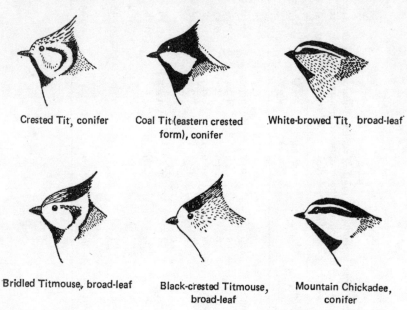

Crested Tit, conifer   Coal Tit (eastern crested   White-browed Tit, broad-leaf
                           form), conifer

Bridled Titmouse, broad-leaf   Black-crested Titmouse,   Mountain Chickadee,
                                   broad-leaf   conifer

FIG. 27.   The species living in broad-leaved woodland have stouter beaks than those which live in conifer. The upper row are Old World species of *Parus*, the lower are New World ones (from Snow 1954b).

Some particularly striking support for the correlation between beak shape and habitat comes from measurements of Coal Tits which live in broad-leaved and coniferous forest. Table 4 gives the bill measurements for Coal Tits in a variety of different habitats. In addition, the Blue Tit occurs in conifer in the Canary Islands where it is the only tit species; the Blue Tits there have long, pointed beaks and these may be an adaptation to living in conifer[206]. However, there are difficulties in accepting this suggestion; throughout all the Canary Islands, for example, the Blue Tits have the same shaped beak although not all the islands have conifers[342].

There are also other correlations with habitat. In the presumably more rigorous northern areas Coal, Marsh and Blue Tits are found in a much narrower range of habitats than farther south in Europe[23, 94, 298]. The reverse is true of the Willow Tit which is more restricted in habitats in the

PLATE 3. The Marsh Tit, *left, above and below*, and the Willow Tit, *right, above and below*, are extremely similar and are difficult to identify except by call. In the hand they can be separated by the length of the outer tail feathers. As shown in the lower photographs, these are almost as long as the rest of the tail in the Marsh Tit, but 5 mm or more shorter in the Willow Tit.

PLATE 4. The Blue Tit, *above left*, and the Crested Tit, *right*, are largely confined to Europe and eastern Asia. The Crested Tit is primarily a bird of conifers, while the Blue Tit prefers broad-leaved woodland. Blue Tits are also the commonest tits in gardens and frequently use nest-boxes. *Below*, the Long-tailed Tit is the smallest British tit. It differs from the true tits in that it does not nest in a hole, but makes a beautifully woven nest, usually in thick cover and surfaced with camouflaging lichens.

Table 4. Beak shape of Coal Tits in different habitats.

Habitat	Locality	Beak index	Relative beak-length	Relative beak-depth
Entirely or mainly conifer	N. Scotland	0·32	0·18	0·057
	Alps	0·32	0·18	0·058
	Central Sweden	0·34	0·18	0·060
Mainly broad-leaved	England	0·34	0·18	0·061
	Ireland	0·34	0·18	0·062

Beak index is the ratio of depth to length, relative beak-length and relative beak-depth are the ratios of beak-length and beak-depth to wing-length (from Snow 1954b).

south-western parts of its European range, but which occupies a wide range of habitats in the north, including mixed woods, pure conifer and the northernmost birch forests.

These differences in habitat preference can be shown in the aviary where Coal Tits will search preferentially among coniferous branches, Blue Tits amongst broad-leaved deciduous ones. Such differences are apparent in hand-raised young birds[280]. Doubtless at least part of the difference results from morphological differences which make it easier for each species to perch in a different manner (plate 7).

In several groups of birds it is well established that one species is kept out of a particular area or habitat by the presence of a close relative; where, however, the relative is absent, the species may occupy that habitat from which it is excluded elsewhere. Such observations strongly suggest that some form of competition causes different species to stay apart in their separate habitats, though exactly how this comes about is not known. In most cases the tits occupy the same habitats and even where one species is missing, the other species do not appear to alter their way of life, suggesting that their niches are now well established and competition between them is limited.

There are exceptions to this[342]. The very similar Marsh and Willow Tits usually occupy different habitats, broad-leaved and coniferous or mixed woods respectively. In five areas of the world the Willow Tit is absent but the Marsh Tit present (Pyrenees, West Jutland (Denmark), the Caucasus, the area from west Yunnan to the southern Chin Hills of Burma, Korea). In all but the first of these, the Marsh Tit is found commonly in the conifer habitats occupied elsewhere by the Willow Tit. It can hardly be coincidence that the Marsh Tit occupies this habitat only where the Willow Tit is absent. The reverse situation, namely the Willow Tit occupying the habitat of the Marsh Tit in the latter's absence, does not seem to occur, though only three areas are known where this could happen (Tian Shian, parts of Western

China, main island of Japan); in all of these the Willow Tit is found in its typical habitat but not in broad-leaved woodland[342].

There may be other cases where the tits interact with one and other. During the period since about 1966, Great Tits have become rather less common and Blue Tits more abundant; one wonders whether these two changes are related. Further, the Coal Tit is commoner in deciduous woodland in Ireland, where Marsh and Willow Tits are absent, than in England where these two species are present; all three species feed in rather similar ways in broad-leaved woodland[129]. Other recent studies also suggest possible interactions between tits and other insectivorous birds, particularly warblers [421].

The feeding habits of the Long-tailed Tit do not conflict with those of the *Parus* tits; again it is the exception. The Long-tailed Tit has a very deep and very narrow beak, rather like that of a miniature Puffin. This species obtains a lot of its food from the cracks in the twigs and small branches of oaks; probably depth of beak is not important here, but it is critical that the beak be narrow enough to slip into the crevices. The reason for the relative depth of beak in this species does not seem to be known; it is certainly not a powerful one inasmuch as it does not bite hard. It eats almost only insects and does not compete greatly with the other species in Britain. On the Continent, however, it must at times overlap with the Penduline Tit, though any possible interactions do not seem to have been studied.

3. Segregation by choice of food

A number of studies have been made of the feeding strategies of the tits. Such studies are greatly complicated by the fact that the birds may feed in different places at different times of year. This is particularly true of the birds that feed in broad-leaved, deciduous woodland; here the trees lose their leaves in winter and so become poorer feeding places. Detailed studies

Table 5. The feeding stations of tits in Marley during the winter. The figures show the percentage of the total time spent by each species in each station (from Lack 1971).

	Coal	Blue	Great	Willow	Marsh
NOVEMBER– APRIL					
Ground	17	7	50	0	16
Branches	24	8	16	50	30
Dead parts	11	16	6	12	7
Twigs, buds	24	34	5	27	19
Leaves	4	3	4	4	2
Elsewhere	20	32	21	7	26

of the feeding of the British tits have been made by Gibb[119] and Hartley[158].
Table 5 shows the proportion of time that each species spent feeding in
different sites during the winter in Marley. Even on this simple criterion
some differences show up between species. Blue Tits in particular spend a
greater proportion of their time hunting their food amongst the twigs and
buds than do Great, Marsh or Willow Tits. The Great and Marsh Tits search
the ground, lower branches and trunks, while the Willow Tit searches also
to a great extent low down, but rarely actually on the ground itself. The
feeding habits of these species in Wytham (with the exception of the Willow
Tit for which there is insufficient information) are summarized in figures in
chapters 2, 3, 4, 6 and 8. Examination of these figures shows considerable
differences between the species. The details will, of course, often be different
in other woods where the available trees and foods will differ. Nevertheless
the broad differences seem to hold for other areas.

Other differences show up in the height above ground at which the birds
feed (table 6). Once again both Blue and Long-tailed Tits feed high up in

Table 6. Average height (in feet) of bird above ground when feeding in trees (from
Gibb 1954a).

Species	November/ December	March/ April	All months
Great Tit	29·5	19·7	25·6
Blue Tit	34·2	31·4	31·4
Coal Tit	34·4	33·1	32·5
Marsh Tit	25·5	26·0	23·5
Long-tailed Tit	31·9	29·4	27·8

the trees; even though the Marsh Tit also feeds amongst the branches and
twigs (table 5) these tend to be the lower ones, within about twenty feet
of the ground. The figures in the species chapters show the tree species which
each species of tit visited most frequently. Again differences are apparent.
The Coal Tit, it will be remembered, shows a strong preference for feeding
in conifers though it cannot do so in Marley where there are virtually none;
the Blue Tit concentrates its efforts on the oaks. The differences between
species are most marked in hard weather when each species becomes even
more specialized than at other times[119]. Differences between the foraging
heights of the different species have also been shown in Japan[273].

While one may infer that different species are taking different foods from
observations that birds are feeding in different places, the examination of
the gut contents provides positive proof (table 7). The Coal Tit takes
mostly very small items (less than 2 mm) while the Blue Tit takes more of the
slightly larger range (3–4 mm). The mean size of the Marsh Tit's prey is
larger still, while only the Great Tit takes a high proportion of the largest
items.

Table 7. The size of insect prey taken by different species of tits. The data are based on stomach analyses of birds collected in mature oakwood in the Forest of Dean, Gloucestershire (based on Betts 1955a).

| Size-range | % of prey of each size | | | |
	Coal Tit	Blue Tit	Great Tit	Marsh Tit
0–2 mm	74	59	27	22
3–4 mm	17	29	20	52
5–6 mm	3	3	22	16
>6 mm	7	10	32	11

The data in table 7 are only for the insect portion of the tits' diet. Differences also exist in the types of seeds that are eaten. The most striking difference is perhaps that most to be expected. Only the Great Tit is strong enough to be able to hammer open the large hard nuts of hazel *Corylus avellana*; it also takes a great many more other large seeds such as acorns *Quercus robor*, sweet chestnut *Castanea sativum* and wood sorrel *Oxalis acetosella*. The Sombre Tit also opens seeds, wedging them into cracks so that it can hammer them open. The Marsh Tit is probably the next best at dealing with seeds, taking a wide variety of smaller seeds and fruits; mention has already been made (p. 59) of this species' tendency to take the seeds of spindle. Coal, Crested and Willow Tits also take large numbers of seeds for storing – the first two tend to take the seeds of conifers; several authors have noted that the Willow Tit takes large quantities of seeds of dead-nettles (*Galeopsis* spp.).

The Long-tailed Tit takes relatively few seeds except small ones such as those of spindle and honeysuckle; its beak does not seem strong enough to open stronger seeds. It is perhaps largely the Long-tailed Tit's greater dependence on insect food in winter, compared to any of the other species, that results in its suffering most in a hard winter. Species which can live on seeds may be expected to suffer less under conditions which rapidly kill off many of the insects.

Only two species of tits, Willow and Siberian, are found in conifers in northern Scandinavia during winter (excluding the Great Tit which, as mentioned, occurs largely around human habitations) and these also forage in different ways. The Siberian Tit searches each tree very thoroughly before moving on to the next whereas the Willow Tit looks only briefly at each tree before flying to another. While direct evidence of the food taken is lacking, it seems likely that the different methods lead to the two species finding different foods. Another difference is that the two species segregate by habitat to some extent, the Siberian Tit being found mainly in conifers while the Willow Tit occurs also in the birch forests[216, 338].

Haftorn has also shown that in Norway the tits feed in different places in the winter (fig. 28). The Coal Tit feeds almost exclusively in the outer twigs

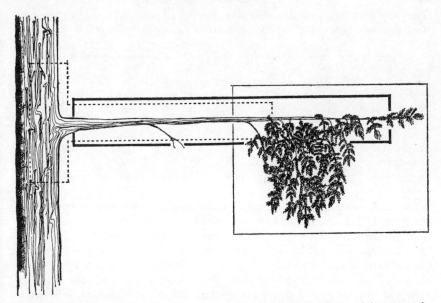

FIG. 28. The typical feeding areas of tits in Norway. The Willow Tit (- - - -) forages on the trunk and base of the branches, the Crested Tit (——) along most of the branch and the Coal Tit (——) amongst the needles. The three species store food in their respective feeding areas (from Haftorn 1956b).

and needles of pine or spruce, while the Crested Tit spends almost half its time in spruce searching the inner parts and branches rather than the needles; when in pine it spends 62% of its time in these positions. Similar observations have been made in Germany, where in addition, the Crested Tit is said to go into pine more than the Coal Tit[230]. The Willow Tit spends less of its time in the conifers than either of the other two, but when there feeds to a greater extent low down and in the inner parts of branches, or on dead branches than either of the other two. In addition the Willow Tit is more of a vegetarian in the winter than the other two species, taking a higher proportion of seeds and fewer insects.

SUPERABUNDANCE OF FOOD

The preceding tables show that differences between species, though marked, are not absolute. The feeding behaviour of different species becomes more alike when food is abundant than when it is scarce. This happens for the tits mainly on two occasions – in summer when caterpillars are abundant on the trees and in winters with a good crop of beechmast (seed of *Fagus sylvaticus*).

Table 8 shows the places where the different species find their food in

Table 8. The feeding stations of tits in Marley during June–August. The figures show the percentage of the total time spent by each species in each station (from Lack 1971).

	Coal	Blue	Great	Willow	Marsh
Ground	0	0	2	0	5
Branches	23	2	4	22	12
Dead parts	16	5	1	17	15
Twigs, buds	4	2	2	6	7
Leaves	56	90	84	50	48
Elsewhere	1	1	7	5	12

summer. At once a major difference can be seen between feeding in summer and winter. The Great and Blue Tits take their food from the leaves almost to the exclusion of all other sites; the other species take about half their food from the leaves though they feed in other places as well to a much greater extent than the Blue and Great Tits. At this time there is a very rich supply of caterpillars on the leaves of the trees; over 100 species have been collected from the Wytham oaks and some of these are very abundant. The most common of all, the Winter Moth, *Operophtera brumata*, may reach levels of over 1000 per square metre.* Exceptionally a large tree may carry half a million caterpillars; at densities such as this the tree may be defoliated.

With such large numbers of caterpillars in the trees it is perhaps only surprising that any of the tits hunt in other places for their food. Observations show that the ground feeding species, such as the Great Tit, move up into the trees about April when the first small caterpillars appear in the breaking buds. 'In April came a sudden change. The Great Tits had gone upward, leaving the ground, and did not now differ in feeding levels from Blue Tits'[158]. After that, all the tit species spend a great deal of their time amongst the leaves. It is normally held that all the species feed on this glut of caterpillars, but this cannot be wholly true. As can be seen from table 8 the Coal, Marsh and Willow Tits find about half their food elsewhere and in addition the Marsh and Willow Tits take longer to return to the nest with food than do the Great and Blue Tits; the feeding rate of the Marsh Tit is about once every four minutes, that of the Willow Tit about once every four and a half minutes whereas in Blue and Great Tits the feeding rates may reach, or even exceed, one visit per minute. However, Marsh and Willow Tits also bring back more items per visit than do Great and Blue Tits. A considerable amount of the food which the Long-tailed Tit brings back to its nest is different from that being fed by Great and Blue Tits to their young; in addition this species also tends to bring more items per visit

*Measured as that number of caterpillars which fall down to pupate into a trap one metre square on the ground; this is, effectively, the number of caterpillars living in a column of the tree over each square metre of ground and which survive to pupate.

than the single items brought by Great and Blue Tits. The size of the food items collected also affects the feeding rate; where particularly large larvae are brought even Great Tits may only make about one hundred feeding visits to the nest per day, a very low figure for British oakwoods[57].

While both Great and Blue Tits take a lot of caterpillars from the oaks at this time, their breeding seasons and the number of second broods they have are subtly different and, in all probability, they too are taking slightly different diets or collecting food from slightly different places. A striking pointer to such a difference between the two species occurred in Wytham in 1961. In that year there were few caterpillars and, for reasons unknown, the numbers of Great Tits were very much higher in Marley than in the rest of Wytham; the numbers of Blue Tits were similar in most areas of Wytham. The Marley Great Tits plainly had difficulty raising their young in this year and lost many from starvation (table 9). Nestling Blue Tits survived as well in Marley as in other parts of Wytham and about as well as in other years. Presumably the two species were taking different foods, or the same foods in different ways or places. While there is no doubt that Blue and Great Tits feed more similarly in summer than in winter, the actual differences merit further study.

Table 9. Nestling losses in Wytham in 1961 (from Perrins 1965).

| | Marley | | Great Wood | |
	No. young	% lost	No. young	% lost
Great Tit	403	16·4	197	3·0
Blue Tit	330	4·8	329	2·7

The other time at which there is a temporary superabundance of food is when the beech produces its heavy crop of seed. This happens in some years but not others. When there is a crop it tends to be a heavy one and many species of birds, as well as some small mammals, may feed on it all winter. In Wytham, the Coal, Great, Blue and Marsh Tits feed heavily upon it (and it is extremely important to them (p. 142)). The Long-tailed Tit does not take it; probably the small, rather blunt beak is not able to open the seeds. (None of the species can open the hard woody cupule around the seeds, they only break into the seeds once the cupule has opened.) In Wytham the Willow Tit does not seem to take beechmast either. This may be because the Willow Tit lives mainly on the lower slopes of the wood, whereas most of the beech is on the top of the hill where the Willow Tit may not go often enough in order to find it. However, there are also a few beeches at the bottom of the hill within close range and yet it does not seem to come to this rich food supply with the frequency of other species.

Even while eating the beechmast there are some differences between the species in the ways they take the seed. In particular, whereas the agile Blue

Tit can get the seed before it falls by swinging on the slender twigs, the Great Tit cannot easily do so and tends to concentrate on fallen mast. This difference can, on occasions, have important implications for the Great Tit since, if there is thick snow, it may be unable to reach the buried seed while the Blue Tit can still obtain it from the branches. In the hard winter of 1962–63 this had an important effect (chapter 16); many Great Tits perished in a period of unusually thick snow, while many more of the Blue Tits survived the difficult time. Great Tits search for the seeds on the ground a great deal more than other species (table 10) even early in the autumn, when few have fallen. At this time the three smaller tits, Blue, Coal and Marsh, take most of their seeds from the tree before they have fallen. However, by January when the majority of the seed has fallen, all four species search for them on the ground, though the Great Tit is the only one which, to any great extent, turns over leaves in the search (table 10).

Table 10. Behaviour of tits searching for beechmast. The figures show, for birds feeding around beech trees, the percentage of birds on the ground. The figures in parentheses show the percentage of birds on the ground which were turning over leaves in their search (from Gibb 1954a).

	September/ October	November/ December	January/ March
Great Tit	45 (0)	42 (9)	93 (51)
Blue Tit	17 (0)	43 (2)	76 (14)
Coal Tit	0 (0)	38 (0)	84 (0)
Marsh Tit	28 (0)	35 (0)	80 (0)

In Scandinavia, where many species store food to help them through the harsher winter, the birds also flock to any rich seed crops that occur in autumn. In a series of papers Haftorn has shown that Coal and Crested Tits commonly store the seeds of spruce, *Picea abies*. In Britain, with a milder winter, the habit of storing food seems to be less frequent though Coal, Marsh and Willow Tits regularly store food. If one watches at a bird table where large numbers of Blue and Great Tits are feeding on peanuts, one may see Coal Tits coming underneath the table and taking away small pieces of nut, returning shortly afterwards to collect more. Being considerably smaller than either of the other two species they often do not even try to compete with them but are content to pick up the pieces that fall to the ground. These they take away to store. A further point is that in Britain birds may store food in the ground[305, 306] while in Scandinavia it always seems to be stored in the bark of trees – from where it can be retrieved even in mid-winter when the ground is covered by deep snow. The three species, Coal, Crested and Willow Tit, store large quantities of seeds; they store these in the same general areas as they hunt, i.e. the Coal Tits among the needles, the Willow Tits on the trunk and on top of the larger branches, the

PLATE 5. The Long-tailed Tit's nest starts off cup-shaped, but the sides are gradually built up until a dome is formed, leaving only a small entrance in one side. The outside is bound together with spiders' webs and covered with lichens; the inside is lined with feathers. These photographs (taken in Holland) show a pair in which one bird has the pale head of the northern race.

PLATE 6. Roosting. Many tits roost in the safety of holes, but some roost in thick foliage. The Coal Tit, *above*, often roosts in clumps of conifer needles. Long-tailed Tits, *below*, usually roost clumped together in parties, which enables them to keep warm. They frequently roost in the same place for many weeks.

Crested Tit in areas intermediate between these two. The Coal Tit also tends to store its food at higher levels in the tree than the other two species and is the only one of the three which often tries to hide the stored food by covering it with bits of vegetation.

SEGREGATION BY NESTING SITE

The tits not only show specific differences in their feeding habits, but they also show different preferences for nesting sites. This has not been investigated in Britain but in Germany such differences have been demonstrated by presenting the birds with a choice of different types of boxes at different heights on the trees[225].

As might be expected the Blue Tit, which tends to forage in the tops of the trees, prefers to nest high and chooses boxes fifteen metres or more above the ground. The Great Tit, which feeds lower, chooses sites that are between 3·5 and 7 metres from the ground. In addition to having different height preferences, the Blue Tit tends to prefer a smaller box than the larger Great Tit. Since the Great Tit can often successfully dispossess the smaller Blue Tit of its nest-site, one of the reasons why the Blue Tit chooses a smaller site may be to reduce the chance that the larger and stronger bird will come and take it; in addition, the smaller hole will tend to reduce the likelihood of a predator being able to enter.

The Coal Tit shows differences from the Great and Blue Tits in choice of nesting site. It prefers boxes at nine metres or above and also prefers small boxes, but in addition whereas the Blue and Great Tit select boxes with a round entrance hole, the Coal Tit prefers one with a narrow slit as an entrance; the reason for this choice is not known, but a bird may be able to squeeze through a long slit of narrower width than the diameter of the smallest hole it can enter; possibly such sites are even less easy for other tits – or weasels – to enter.

These three common species also show differences in the species of tree on which they prefer to nest. As mentioned earlier, the Coal Tit prefers to nest in a box on a coniferous tree when one is available. The Blue Tit shows a marked preference for a nesting box on an oak while the Great Tit is much less commonly found in boxes in such sites; in Wytham it seems to prefer a box on a smaller tree such as a hawthorn *Crataegus monogyna*. These three species do not normally excavate much of the hole, but rely on finding one of sufficient size.

The Marsh Tit differs from the above three species in that it usually nests close to the ground and does not seem to be particularly interested in using nest-boxes – though it does so on occasions. Its typical nesting site is quite small, often in a hollow branch or crack in a stump low down, near the ground. This it may partially excavate in order to get a large enough hole.

The Willow Tit and Crested Tit differ from all other British tits in that they almost always excavate a complete nest-site each spring. They do this

D

usually low down in a hollow rotten branch or trunk of a smallish tree. They may even excavate a new site in the same stump as in the previous year, even though the original site seems in good condition. As a result of this specialized habit the Willow Tit does not normally accept nesting boxes at all and Crested Tits do so only rarely.

The same habit is found in the American Black-capped Chickadee. However, it was found that this species could be induced to nest in nesting boxes by the simple expedient of filling the box with wood chips[193]. The bird can then satisfy its apparently essential 'urge' to excavate by removing the wood chips! The same technique works with the Willow Tit in Britain. Why these two tits should have this habit of always making a new nest-site is not clear, but it does seem as if the Willow Tit may not always be successful at obtaining sites in competition with other species. In the case of two recently completed Willow Tit nests that I have found, both were taken over by Blue Tits, which successfully raised their young in the Willow Tits' nests. Other researchers have had the same experience[50, 108, 178]. Possibly also, the Willow Tit, by making a new hole each year, reduces the bother from parasites which are often present in old nests (p. 155). Whatever the reason, the Willow Tit has this one markedly different nesting habit from all the other British tits except the Crested Tit; this species has similar habits, but in Britain the two species do not commonly occur together.

As with the differences in food and feeding sites, these preferences for different nest-sites are by no means absolute. Given little or no choice, the different species will accept similar types of nest-site. When natural sites are very scarce all species (except the Willow Tit) accept nest-boxes of the same size put up in similar positions and in young conifer plantations, where there is no rotten wood, even the Willow Tit may sometimes use a nest-box.

The Long-tailed Tit does not nest in nest-boxes but makes its own nest in a thick patch of branches in a gorse or bramble bush or against the stem of a hawthorn or in the crutch between the branches of a larger tree. These nests are beautifully surfaced with lichens, are well camouflaged and often very hard to see, even when they are built in early spring before the young leaves are fully open.

The forms of segregation which I have discussed have of course been brought about by evolution. Over long periods of time, natural selection has favoured those individuals of a species which have evolved ways of life which differ from those of other species; in this way, interspecific competition has been avoided. For the most part, these adaptations have resulted in the birds of different species going about their daily lives without direct conflict. However, there are activities which do result in marked interactions between species.

FIGHTING FOR FOOD AND NEST-SITES

While each species tends to feed in different places and so reduce interspecific competition, it does not follow that they never compete for food nor that they will not try to take food from one another. If a tit sees another with a large morsel of food which it might hope to wrest from it, then frequently the first bird will attack.

These 'supplanting' attacks are more likely to be successful if the food item is large or still attached in some way. If the potential victim has the food already in its beak, it may fly away without losing it.

Supplanting attacks are most frequent in the middle of the winter – when one might expect the birds to be most hungry[119]. Of the attacks noted, 90% of those involving a Blue or Great Tit were with another member of the same species, while this was true for only 63% of Marsh Tit attacks and 27% of the Coal Tit ones. Hence interspecific fighting for food was more important to the Coal Tits than to either Great or Blue Tits. There is a hierarchy in these species: Great and Blue Tits are about an equal match for one another but both are dominant to Marsh Tits and all three species are dominant to Coal Tits[165].

These attacks may seem a minor part of the birds' lives, but this is not always so. During the period November to February, Gibb noted that Great Tits were attacked on an average of five times per hour, Marsh Tits six times, Blue Tits fifteen times and Coal Tits twenty-three times. Hence some birds could stand to lose (or gain) important amounts of food, especially since the attacks usually occurred (and were more likely to succeed) over the larger food items.

Similarly, when nest-sites are scarce there may be a great deal of violent conflict for them both within and between species. Normally, as with the food, the smaller species are subordinate to the larger ones and may well lose a site at which they are established if a stronger bird wants the site. In both winter and summer, the aggressiveness of the Blue Tit makes it, often, a match for the much larger Great Tit. Although the Great Tit usually wins, the Blue Tit may do so especially if it is well established at the site.

The Blue Tit becomes progressively more aggressive to the Great Tit the further its nesting is advanced[359]. Nevertheless, a Great Tit holding a particular territory often appears to dominate the Blue Tit and chase the latter off from its selected site. Usually the Blue Tit merely retires and returns when the Great Tit has departed. In one case a male Great Tit freely entered the nesting box throughout the nest-building and the Blue Tit seemed powerless to stop him.

Possibly the rather quiet display at the nest of the Blue Tit (compared with that of the Great Tit) may be the result of its trying to avoid drawing attention to its nest[359]. Certainly the dominant nature of the Great Tit (and of the Blue Tit over the other tits) may well be a major reason why the other species try to select sites with entrances too small for the Great Tit or in some other way unattractive to the more dominant species.

COMPETITION WITH OTHER SPECIES

So far I have discussed some of the ways in which the different species of tits reduce interspecific competition. It would be of considerable interest to know how much the British tits – which form such an important part of our woodland avifauna – interact with other woodland species. Such information is very hard to obtain but, if available, might help to explain why it is that there are so many species, and individuals, of tits in Europe compared with elsewhere in the world. Why are there for example many fewer species, and individuals, of tits in any piece of woodland in the United States?

Two possible reasons for the differences between western Europe and the United States have been suggested. Firstly, in the north-eastern States the winter is very much harsher than in much of western Europe. Although Black-capped Chickadees live in the area in winter, one should perhaps be comparing that part of North America with parts of Europe nearer to the Arctic Circle where, as we have seen, only the Siberian Tit and the Willow Tit are to be found away from man. However in the western areas of the United States, along the Pacific seaboard, the winter is much milder than in the eastern States. Yet even there it is unusual to find more than two species of tits in any one habitat. Hence the severity of the eastern winters cannot be the only reason for fewer species of tits.

The second possible explanation is that in the United States there are very many more other small insectivorous birds in summer than is the case in Europe. In particular, there are large numbers of warblers of many species, several of which are to be found in most woodland habitats. Has competition from these birds made it difficult for the tits to radiate into several different niches in each habitat and so be as common as in Europe? In one study area in the United States, where warblers are scarce, tits are unusually abundant.[420] Evolution of the species of tits happened in the past and this question cannot easily be answered now. However, if the tits do interact with the other species then perhaps they arrived in Europe and were well established before the warblers came, whereas the reverse might be true in North America.

CHAPTER 10

HOME RANGES, TERRITORIES AND COMMUNICATION

IN this chapter I shall look at the tits' activities around the year, in particular their movements and their interactions with others of their kind. Their behaviour towards other birds varies markedly according to their own internal state at that time. Once again, this chapter will be predominantly about Blue Tits and Great Tits; they have been much more intensively studied than most of the other species and in addition, since they are more numerous, interactions between individuals are much more frequent and hence more easily observed. However, the behaviour of Coal and Marsh Tits and, more recently, that of the Long-tailed Tit has also been studied in considerable detail. Both Crested and Willow Tits are so thin on the ground that interactions between, say, pairs in the breeding season are relatively infrequent and, inevitably, less is known. Many workers have noted that, with these two species, each pair seems so far away from the next that interactions do not appear to occur at all. As a result of this, the edges of territories are ill-defined; without another bird to sing against, the birds tend to be relatively silent and the observer cannot easily determine where the edges are. Some authors have even doubted whether the Crested Tit has a song!

THE AREA COVERED DURING THE YEAR

During the late summer, after the breeding season is over, the parent birds moult. At this time the adults of most species are relatively quiet and often solitary; although they remain in the general vicinity of the nesting place, they do not abide by the territorial boundaries that were fixed earlier in the year and, indeed, during the course of the day the area they cover may be considerably greater than their territories.

This is not, however, true of the Marsh Tit. Once this species acquires a territory it seems to remain within it for life[249]. Neither the males nor the females leave the territory even when their mate dies; they remain on the site and eventually a bird from a wandering party will come and pair with the bereaved bird, though this may take several months. The Plain Tit, *Parus inornatus*, of the United States also seems to be remarkably faithful to its territory the whole year round[85] but none of the other British tits seem to be as rigidly attached to their territories as the Marsh Tit. In all species, the territory holders are at their least aggressive during July and August, the period of the moult.

The young, too, moult in late summer though it will be remembered that they have a less complete moult, changing only the body feathers not the major flight feathers at this time. Young birds are less likely to be found alone than are adults, often being in parties composed almost wholly of juveniles. These are not necessarily family parties from the breeding season, but mixtures of young from several different broods. Since at this time many of the birds have not moved far from their birthplace the flocks may well contain several young from the one brood and others from adjacent broods.

Within a few weeks of leaving the nest the young start to wander considerably and those from different areas of woodland become thoroughly mixed. Most of this wandering appears to occur between late July and early September, by which time, in Britain, many of the young birds have settled down in the general area in which they will live. Ringing recoveries suggest that the large majority of the birds moving at this time travel less than ten miles. We estimate that in the Wytham breeding population some 30–40% of the birds were not raised on the estate; in all probability the large majority of the immigrants arrived in Wytham during this late summer period. Nevertheless, some local movement occurs throughout the winter, especially if the weather is severe.

As autumn approaches and the adults complete their moult, the birds become more vocal. By September there is a general resurgence of territorial behaviour, some birds singing loudly and defending an area of the wood. As with some other species of birds, this resumption of sexual activity may exceptionally lead to attempts at breeding. However, in the tits these are extremely rare. Often it appears that only the adults (birds that bred earlier in the year) indulge in territorial activity at this time. Groups of young birds may be observed moving around the woods as they have been doing previously; only a few young Great Tits settle down in autumn, and most do not do so till spring[190]. This resurgence of territorial behaviour in autumn is common in a great many species of birds and wanes as winter approaches. It has been held that this activity is an important one in that it helps regulate numbers of birds that will be present during the following season and we shall return to its significance later (p. 239).

In autumn, the birds may settle down to spend the winter in an area or they may move elsewhere. On the Continent, many more birds move away from the areas in which they bred or were raised than is the case in Britain[190]. In some study areas on the Continent a few birds arrive for the winter, presumably from farther north, and then depart again in spring.

As described later in this chapter, tits (except the Long-tailed) roost solitarily, usually in small holes. In the day, however, they join up into small flocks often containing several species. These flocks contain a similar composition of individuals from day to day and may move over a fairly constant area. In the morning, awakening birds gather together into flocks in which they spend the day. The area over which the birds move during the day is usually considerably larger than a summer territory and has been called the bird's 'domicile' or home range[77, 190]. As mentioned earlier, some birds may move distances of two to three miles from woodland to urban areas for the day to get food, but it seems likely that when they do they will still retain a regular 'beat', covering a fairly standard route on most days. Once a bird has got to know the area and is able to find food in it, there is an obvious advantage in continuing to feed there.

If one has a well-stocked bird table in the garden, one tends to see a number of tits there at any one time. However, until one traps and rings the birds one can get no real appreciation of the numbers involved. On several occasions in and around Oxford I have caught more than a hundred different individual tits at a single bird table during the course of a morning. Many of these birds seem to wander over large areas, visiting one particular site only infrequently. If the weather remains reasonable this set routine may continue for the whole of the winter with the birds visiting regular, well-established feeding places. However, if the food supplies disappear or if the winter becomes very severe, then the birds' routines may be upset and they may have to wander farther afield. At times of very heavy snowfall, for example, many tits may desert the woodland in their search for food (though Marsh Tits usually remain resolutely in their territories). The birds that come into the wood after milder weather has returned contain many of the old, familiar birds, but also a number of newcomers. Doubtless under such severe conditions some of the birds have perished while others perhaps have moved a long way and are now taking up residence in a new site. In Wytham, some of the birds that come into the wood after a cold spell – and a few that arrive at the beginning of spring – are very dirty. We believe that these birds have been spending their time in the city and have only just come to the woods.

In species such as the Blue Tit some birds at least are paired within the flocks. Likewise Great Tits may pair while in the winter flocks and, although they do not hold a territory at this time, the male may defend a small area around his mate as she moves through the wood, keeping other birds away[165]. The pair usually leaves the flock together as it breaks up in the evening[64]. They often roost close together; the birds go to the female's roosting hole, where the male sees his mate to bed, often accompanying this by a short burst of singing and some sexual chasing. The male then goes to roost near by; in the morning he may come and wait outside his mate's hole until she emerges. The male continues to see his mate to her roost in the spring when she is roosting in the future nest-site[11]. A very similar night-time routine has been recorded in the Marsh Tit so that it may be widespread within the group[249].

Territorial behaviour begins at any time during the winter if the weather is mild enough. The males sing in their future territories for varying periods of the day, though usually mainly in the early morning. They then leave the territory and join the foraging flocks for the greater part of the day. As spring approaches, the birds spend progressively more and more of their time singing and defending the territory. However, if the weather suddenly becomes cold again, territorial behaviour may cease since the birds have to forage more earnestly for food.

The males continue to defend their territories through the egg-laying and incubation period. Once the young have hatched the parents are so busy collecting food for their young that territorial behaviour may cease abruptly and may not recur until the autumn. If, however, the birds go on to have a second brood, then the male may be territorial again while his mate is laying and incubating.

When feeding the young, the territorial boundaries are to a considerable extent ignored and the adults forage wherever they please; obviously they tend to feed as near the nest as possible in order to save themselves unnecessary and time-consuming flights. Often they may take much of their food from a very limited area – much smaller than the whole of the territory that they previously laid claim to. After the young have left the nest, the family party appears to wander almost anywhere without regard to territorial boundaries. Once again the parent birds usually forage near to their hungry young, but now the focus is one of moving fledglings, in contrast to the stationary nestlings, so that the focal point for their activities moves slowly around the wood.

ROOSTING

The majority of the *Parus* tits roost in holes though, especially in summer, birds may roost in thick foliage. This latter habit is probably particularly common amongst individuals which live in coniferous woodland where there is dense foliage all the year round. At least some Coal Tits roost in the same bunch of needles for long periods. A wide variety of sites for roosting have been described; almost any nook or cranny seems acceptable. At times the birds may use the nests of other species such as the Blackbird. Having found a safe roosting site, the birds tend to use it for a considerable period. Even many of those birds that leave the woodland during the day to 'commute' to urban areas to feed return each night to their chosen site in the wood to roost[198]. The roosting site is normally within the bird's territory and is presumably taken up some time during the bird's first autumn of life when it has settled into a home range.

For the Great Tit the preferred roosting hole is much smaller than the preferred nesting site so that the birds may have to give up their small winter site as spring draws near. Females may roost in the future nest-hole for some weeks before breeding commences.

The birds roost solitarily; even the members of a pair do not normally roost together. The bird fluffs its feathers up into a ball and covers its beak and legs in order to reduce heat loss. In view of the length and severity of the winter nights in some areas it seems slightly surprising that the members of a pair do not huddle together at night in order to help keep themselves warm. Further, some species such as the House Sparrow, *Passer domesticus*, build nests in which to roost. By so doing the birds keep themselves considerably warmer than if they just roosted in an open site. Why do the tits not build themselves a warm nest in which they could snuggle down at night? There seems little doubt that they would keep themselves warmer by doing so and hence need to find less food during the day (p. 120). The advantages seem so obvious that there must be some disadvantages in so doing.

In many areas the nights are extremely cold. Willow Tits in central Siberia may roost in tunnels in the snow where they gain some protection from the lowest night temperatures. Apparently some of the tunnels they use are those made by small rodents. The birds have to dig their way into, or out of, the burrows after heavy snowfalls[415]. In Scandinavia also, small birds use burrows in the snow for roosting and tits may be among the species that use these tunnels[362].

Recently it has been shown that the closely related Black-capped Chickadee of North America may be able to lower its body temperature by as much as 10–12°C at night. By going torpid in this manner the bird may be able to save itself around half the energy that would otherwise be necessary for overnight survival[56]. Although relatively little is known about this behaviour, it may be quite widespread. Both Willow and Siberian Tits may lower their temperature at night, apparently becoming torpid. They take a considerable time to wake up after being disturbed[150]. Roosting Great Tits have also been shown to have a lowered basal metabolism than when active during the day[354].

FLOCKS AND FLOCKING

During much of their annual cycle many tits are found in flocks; in fact this is the normal situation outside the breeding season and, for the young at least, during the moult period that follows. The flocks usually contain a mixed group of species including birds other than tits; Treecreepers and Goldcrests are common additions to the flock.

The flocks may have fairly regular routines in that the composition of a flock at a certain time and a certain place seems relatively constant. Similar observations can be made from watching colour-ringed birds at bird tables; here some individuals may appear predominantly at a certain time of day and in company with certain other birds, suggesting that they have a regular 'round' of feeding sites.

In some species the individuals in the flocks (of mixed species) change as the flock moves along. As the flock crosses the boundary between the territory of one pair and the next, the pair whose territory the flock leaves drops out from the flock while the pair in whose territory the flock now is joins it. Hence, while the species composition may remain fairly constant, the individuals in the flock are constantly changing. This happens with the Marsh Tits which own territories[250]. They join a flock only within the limits of their territory and drop out when the flock moves farther afield. Similar detailed work has not been carried out with the other tits, but it would not be at all surprising if something similar occurred, at least for the well-established territory holders, since these seem more tied to their territory than are the younger birds.

Many reasons have been put forward to explain the functions of flocking and these fall broadly into two divisions. One suggestion is that the flocks serve to facilitate the finding of food[401], the other is that a number of birds are more likely to notice the approach of a predator than is a single bird and hence it is safer to be in flocks[397].

The former theory suggests that it is of advantage to an individual (especially one which does not know of a reliable source of food) to join a flock (or in some species a breeding colony or a communal roost); since some members of that flock are likely to know of good feeding sites, the individual that does not can follow them and learn where food is most readily available in the vicinity.

It is not clear that this would always be true in the case of the tits since they often feed in a loose flock composed of several species widely dispersed over many trees, picking up a mixed diet of insects and seeds. However, where there are highly localized supplies of large quantities of food such as beechmast (or nowadays a well-stocked bird table) many of the birds must initially learn the location of these sites by seeing other birds flying there.

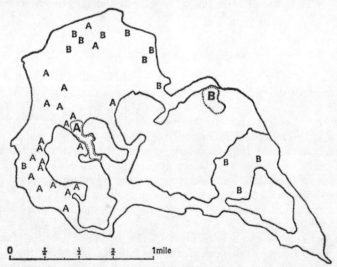

FIG. 29. The winter feeding areas of breeding Great Tits in Wytham. In the winter of 1960/61 many tits came to feed at beech trees in the areas marked A & B. The smaller letters show where the birds subsequently bred. Note how the birds tended to go to the nearest site for food. The bird marked B in the bottom left hand corner was only caught once at site B very early in the winter (from Perrins 1963).

In Wytham, birds are drawn to a beech with a good crop from a wide area (fig. 29) and can sometimes be seen flying directly towards such sites; a tit that did not know the whereabouts of a plentiful supply of food could easily follow.

However, the birds may also gain some protection from predators by being in a flock. There is a very distinctive alarm call given by small birds in the presence of a predator which puts all other birds on their guard[236, 240]. Goshawks *Accipiter gentilis* are more successful at catching Wood Pigeons *Columba palumbus* when these are alone or in small flocks than when they are in large flocks[183]. Hence it would not be at all surprising to find the tits were safer in flocks than when alone.

Where mixed flocks are concerned, such as is often the case with tits, it seems more likely that the advantage is one of avoiding predators rather than of finding food. Since many of the species in mixed woodland flocks are taking different foods there would be little advantage in the birds staying together if they were trying to learn where the food supplies were. Since they all give – and recognize – similar alarm calls when a predator approaches, even different species can gain advantage from being in the same flock.

In addition to the increased number of eyes on the look-out for predators, a further advantage of being in a flock has been suggested. When a predator attacks it may be confused by many birds flying in different directions and may not be able to 'make up its mind' which to attack. This seems likely to be one of the advantages of being in a very dense flock such as is found in Starlings *Sturnus vulgaris* or some of the waders, or in the Coot *Fulica atra* which may be attacked by the White-tailed Eagle *Haliaeetus albicilla* but it is less clearly the case in the looser flocks of tits in woodland.

The alarm call given when a small bird sights a hawk is of a type that is very difficult to locate (fig. 30). Hence the bird that gives it is not in very grave danger of drawing the hawk's attention to itself by giving the call. However, it has been suggested that the bird must run some small risk by giving it and so would be better off not calling at all; any advantage could only be to other members of the flock. There is another possible interpretation[288]. On two or three occasions, I have approached a trapped tit which has given the 'hawk alarm' call to me (they do not usually give this call where humans are concerned). On each occasion the effect that the call has had on me has been to make me look around for another bird, even though subsequently I was reasonably certain that the call could only have been given by the trapped bird. The call may therefore not only be difficult to locate but also ventriloquial in that it seems to come from another place so that it appears as if another bird is present. If the call has the same effect on a hawk then it would be of benefit even to a lone bird to give the call since it may baffle the hawk by presenting it with an apparent 'choice' of prey – as it did to me. At such times 'split-seconds' make the difference between life and death so that even the slightest hesitation on the part of the predator could be an advantage to the tit.

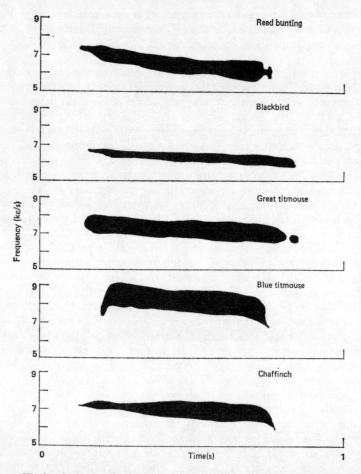

FIG. 30.   The hawk-alarm calls of tits and other birds. The figures are diagrammatic repro-
ductions of sound spectrograms. The high, thin 'tseee' of these alarm calls is difficult to locate,
at least to the human ear. Presumably hawks find the call equally difficult to locate and this
is why similar calls have been evolved by different species (from Marler 1955).

It is also relatively easy to see how such a call could have been evolved. A
bird must sometimes take some risk in order to help its mate or young to
survive, at such times there is no need to wonder whether the bird should
endanger itself; it may have to in order to prevent the loss of its family (and
hence the inheritance of its characteristics by succeeding generations). If
an individual could give a call that both warned the family of an approaching
hawk and did not enable the hawk to locate the caller, this would be of great
advantage. Hence, through natural selection, calls should have evolved

qualities which make them as difficult as possible to locate. If, in addition, they could have evolved a ventriloquial quality so as to confuse the predator even when the bird was on its own, then there would seldom if ever be a disadvantage in giving such calls, even outside the breeding season and away from one's relatives.

An interesting series of observations have been carried out in the laboratory on feeding behaviour and flocking[203]. In these studies Great Tits were kept in cages and released into a larger aviary in numbers varying from 1–4. In the large aviary, food – in the form of mealworms – was provided but this was covered over in a series of different containers. The birds had to look into these containers and often also had to remove some covering material before they could obtain the food. The observers noted two main points. Firstly the birds tended to collect food more quickly when they were in company with other birds than when they were alone (table 11). Secondly,

Table 11. Searching rates (measured as number of visits to feeders per 5 minutes) of birds in groups of four and on their own (from Krebs et. al. 1972).

	Bird in group of four	Bird alone
No. of visits	387	430
No. visits/5 min	10·7	8·4

after one bird had found food in a given site, the others could be observed looking in similar sites (table 12). This evidence suggests, perhaps, that both the suggested explanations for flocking are true; birds in flocks have to spend less time looking round for possible predators and, in addition, they can observe the sites where other birds are finding food and look in similar places. If, as seems likely, certain foods are mainly in certain types of site then these sites will be found more quickly when more birds are searching together. The birds are quick to learn from one another which sites are proving most profitable. Doubtless the dispersion pattern of the food would affect this – the more clumped the food the more likely that it would be profitable for a bird to search near to another which has already found an item. Such an explanation holds also for mixed species flocks; in these also birds of different species would note where a bird found food and then search in similar places[204].

Tits are well known for their habit of opening the tops of milk bottles and drinking the cream. It seems reasonably certain that this is a habit which most birds have learned by watching others. The habit is a relatively recent one and has been well documented. It was first recorded in Southampton in 1929, but thereafter spread relatively rapidly from several centres[105]. Similarly the habit has been recorded in other western European countries including Holland, Denmark and Sweden, where it also spread

Table 12. The 'copying rate' of individuals trained in two different ways (from Krebs et. al. 1972). Copying rate is measured as the percentage of a bird's visits which were within the same 10-second period as another bird's visit to the same perch. Note how the copying rate changes in relation to whether the birds had been accustomed (prior to the experiment) to find food as single, dispersed items or in clumps.

	Copying rate	
	Following clumped training	Following dispersed training
Bird 1	15·3	8·9
2	19·0	8·3
3	16·8	12·2
4	17·3	4·0

outwards from a few centres[166]. At times many birds come down to the bottles. There are even records of flocks following the milk delivery vans along the road and opening bottles each time the milkman left to deliver milk. There can be little doubt from the manner of spread that this is an example of a feeding habit that was passed on from one individual to another, each bird observing the behaviour of others and then copying it. It is likely that tits also learned that peanuts were a source of food by seeing others take them. The same is doubtless true for natural foods as well.

TERRITORIES

By taking up territories, the birds ensure that they are spaced throughout the available habitat. There have been many discussions as to the function of territory in animals and the effect that territorial behaviour has on the total population. In particular, people have been concerned as to whether such behaviour limited the number of birds breeding in a particular area and so, by preventing other birds from establishing themselves, set a limit to the breeding population. The regulation of numbers in the population is discussed later (chapter 17) where some aspects of territorial behaviour are considered in greater detail; however, here I shall discuss some other observations on the territories of tits.

As one might expect, adult birds that bred in the previous season tend to re-occupy the same area in a subsequent year. The exact area is not always the same since the boundaries are modified in relation to interactions with the owners of adjacent territories, but the core of the territory is frequently the same. The size of the territory of the Great Tit may be related to the age of the bird in that it becomes progressively larger as the birds grow older[82].

In the Coal Tit the time at which the birds take up their territories has an important bearing on the size of the territories[77]. Irrespective of age, the birds that settle earlier in the season take and maintain larger territories than late-comers. If one assumes that the birds that are first able to take up territories are the fitter and most vigorous ones, then again this is to be expected.

How many birds fail to get a territory? This is a crucial question since it has an important bearing on the regulation of population size, but it is not easy to answer. A relatively small number of experiments have been undertaken. In the Bean Wood, an outlying area of Wytham, the territories of colour-ringed pairs of Great Tits were mapped. When the owners and the extents of these territories were known (in mid-March), the pairs were removed from half the territories. Within hours these territories were reoccupied by almost exactly the same number of pairs as had been removed (fig. 31). This observation suggested a considerable number of birds have been unable to obtain territories in the face of competition from those already resident.

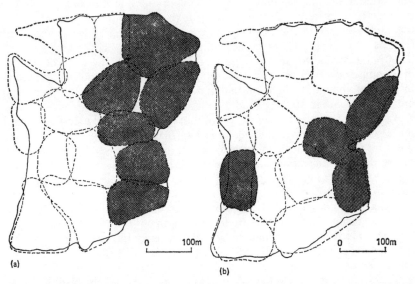

(a)

(b)

FIG. 31.   The replacement of removed birds. Six pairs of Great Tits were removed between 19 and 24 March 1969 (a, stippled areas). Within three days, four new pairs had taken up territories in the wood (b, stippled areas). There was some expansion of residents' territories during the removal so that after replacement territories again formed a complete mosaic over the wood (from Krebs 1971).

In an attempt to discover where these surplus birds came from, a further study was made the following year. The birds were colour-ringed and their territories mapped as before. The pairs occupying territories in the surrounding area, mainly hedgerows, were also colour-ringed. When some of the pairs from within the wood were removed, exactly the same thing happened as in the previous year – they were once more immediately replaced. However, the replacing birds were almost all ones that had held territories in the adjacent hedgerows. As soon as space became available in the wood they had immediately vacated their hedgerow territories and these were not re-filled.

From these studies one is tempted to conclude that there were no birds without territories, though some were holding territories which they were prepared to leave immediately another, presumably better, site became available. Nonetheless, previous to the experiments, the hedgerow birds had been prepared to accept such sites rather than try to force their way into the woodland area. Presumably this would have been too difficult against the opposition from the woodland territory-holders.

A similar sort of situation has been noticed in Holland where observations were made in two habitats for a series of years (fig. 32). These were areas of adjacent strips of oakwood and pinewood. The numbers of Great Tits fluctuated more markedly in the pinewoods than in the oaks. This was interpreted as meaning that in years of high numbers the oakwoods, being the preferred habitat, were filled first and the latecomers were faced with the choice of trying to force their way into a small territory in the more favoured oakwoods or accepting a larger territory in the less favoured, but more empty pinewoods. Although the latter habitat was not so favourable for raising young, it might be better to have a larger territory there than only a small one in the oakwood.

Again there was no conclusive proof that birds were excluded from breeding altogether. However, in the American Black-capped Chickadee, where there may at times be a non-breeding surplus, not only do some birds fail to breed, but amongst breeders the most dominant birds in the winter flocks are most likely to get the best territories, to breed earliest and to have the largest clutches[133].

Other workers have also removed territorial tits during the early part of the breeding season. When a number of pairs of Coal Tits were removed from the middle of a plot where most of the territory holders were known and colour-ringed, the removed birds were not replaced[77]. Once the birds have started nesting they seem disinclined to move. A small number of breeding pairs of Great Tits were removed from Wytham just after the birds had commenced breeding; there was no replacement[404].

I have tried the alternative experiment, namely that of bringing birds into the area in spring and trying to add them to the breeding pairs. Some at least of these birds are known to have stayed and bred. However, the territory holders in the areas into which they were introduced were not studied in sufficient detail to know whether the additional birds squeezed themselves in between existing territory holders or evicted some of them.

In a study of the territorial behaviour of the Great Tit, Hinde[165] noted there were often areas between territories which were apparently suitable

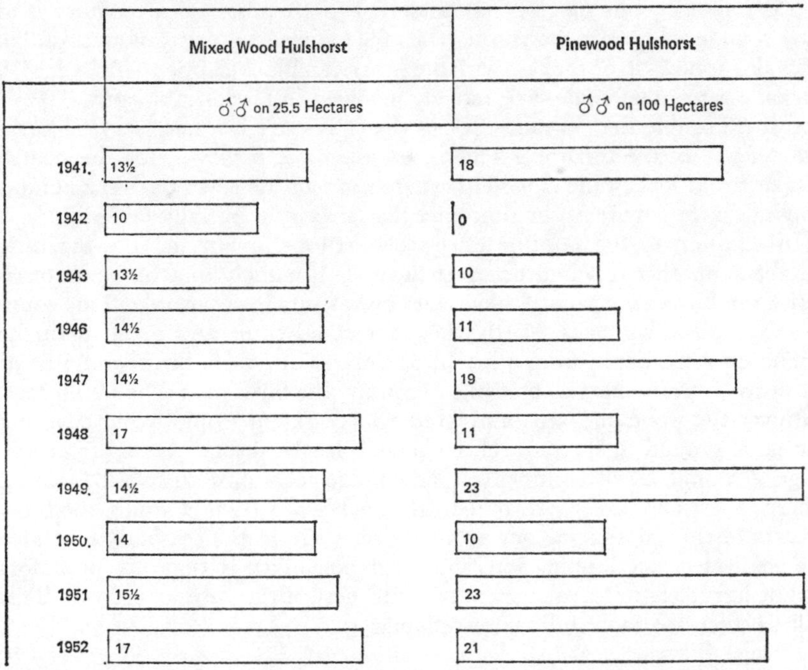

Mixed Wood Hulshorst		Pinewood Hulshorst	
♂♂ on 25.5 Hectares		♂♂ on 100 Hectares	
1941.	13½		18
1942	10		0
1943	13½		10
1946	14½		11
1947	14½		19
1948	17		11
1949.	14½		23
1950.	14		10
1951	15½		23
1952	17		21

FIG. 32. Fluctuations in numbers of pairs of Great Tits in mixed wood and adjacent conifer. Note that the number of pairs in conifer varies more than the number in the mixed wood (from Kluijver and Tinbergen 1953).

(and indeed were occupied in other years) but which remained unoccupied. He saw no apparent reason why there should not have been room for other birds had any been looking for territories. A similar situation was noted for the Marsh Tit where there was much unused woodland[347]. The majority of Marsh Tits do not hold territories during the period June to January when they then take up one by pairing 'with a bereaved territory holder or occupying an unused area'[249, 250].

Some young male Great Tits do not succeed in getting a territory, though not necessarily because they are excluded by other males. The evidence is to some extent circumstantial, but there is a shortage of young males (compared with young females) in the breeding population, apparently because there are fewer old females than old males in the population and the old males are more successful than young ones in obtaining mates. The result is that there are not enough females for all the young males to be able to obtain a mate (p. 224). These birds do not normally appear to have a territory. All territories mapped seem to contain a pair of birds that successfully build a nest. If the males without mates do have territories it seems that they must be small, rather transient ones.

Such observations suggest that possibly a prerequisite of a territory is to have a mate; only paired birds may be able to defend a territory successfully. This also appears to be the case with the American Black-capped Chickadee[271]. In some cases the females are actively involved in territorial disputes[135, 173] and it is possible that in some species their presence is a necessary factor in the defence of the territory. This is not the case, however, for the Marsh Tit, or for at least some Coal Tits where some of the early territory holders may not have a mate at the time that the territory is initially taken up.

In addition to the possible effects of territory in limiting the breeding numbers, another function has been suggested, namely that by being territorial the birds are spacing themselves out as much as possible. This could have several advantages. Firstly the pairs could court and breed with the minimum disturbance from other birds since each pair of birds would be as far away from the next as possible. Secondly, the birds would be well spread out over the woodland area and so to a large extent would avoid covering the same ground in their search for food. Clearly, if food was short at any stage it would be of considerable advantage to a bird to avoid foraging where others had already searched. Although when feeding young the birds are not territorial, spacing out at an earlier stage in the season will reduce the chances of overlapping later. A third possibility is that the predators will be less likely to learn to search for tits' nests if they are spaced out. This will be discussed more fully later (chapter 18).

DOMINANCE RELATIONSHIPS AND AGGRESSION

Territorial birds develop an 'understanding' of one another whereby each remains dominant in its own territory, but becomes submissive once it crosses the boundary into its neighbour's territory. Provided a bird does not try to vie with the territory holders it is often allowed to pass through a territory unmolested; feeding parties of non-territorial Marsh Tits are often joined by the territory holders while they cross the territories (though in the Plain Titmouse in North America, they appear to be excluded from the territories[84]). However, an adjacent territory holder may be recognized and pursued from a territory even if it is not being aggressive.

Outside the territorial system there are marked dominance relationships or 'peck orders' both within and between species at several times of the year. The interspecific relationships are basically correlated with size; the Great Tit is usually dominant to all other species. The dominance order is usually Great Tit, Blue Tit, Marsh Tit, Coal Tit[165]. Such relationships hold over all aspects of the birds' year, the more dominant species being more likely to win food or nest-sites from the subordinate species. Nevertheless they are not perfect; probably everyone has seen a Blue Tit defeat a Great Tit in a dispute at a bird table. Conflicts over nest-sites are to some extent affected by the stage in the nesting cycle of the two contesting species. A Great Tit is normally dominant to a Blue Tit over a choice of nest-sites, but is less likely to succeed if it tries to take a nest-site from a Blue Tit which is well-established at that site and is, say, already laying eggs. As mentioned, Willow Tits often seem to lose their nests to the more aggressive Blue and Marsh Tits.

Since the Blue Tit is more likely to lose in contests with the Great Tit, it is perhaps not surprising that it may show a greater response to an increase in the number of nesting boxes than does the Great Tit; the latter swiftly takes the boxes which it needs and, if these are in short supply, the Blue Tits may not find sufficient. However, if the number of boxes is increased, the numbers of Blue Tits nesting in them may rise since they were short of sites while there may be no change in the numbers of Great Tits.

Within any species there is a marked tendency for old birds to be dominant to young birds and for males to be dominant to females. This may be noticed in the frequency with which male and female Great Tits can be caught at bait, since the females come much less frequently[275]. In other species the females and the first-year birds are more likely to move away from their home area during winter than are the males or the older birds. This is probably also true for the tits.

Within a given age or sex class of any of the species there is also a hierarchy, built up presumably on the strengths of the birds in previous encounters. When such pairs of birds meet, the subordinate usually gives way to the dominant swiftly. There is rarely any actual physical encounter, but the victors tend to be larger than the vanquished. Although the subordinate bird may appear to lose by this behaviour, it would probably lose more if it were to do battle. Not only would it be likely to receive injuries but also it could waste considerable time that could otherwise be spent in searching for further food. The problems associated with such strategies have been more fully described elsewhere[241]. At least one factor influencing a Great Tit's position in the hierarchy is its weight, heavier birds being dominant to light ones[115].

Aggressive behaviour can be noted in fledglings; within about a week of leaving the nest the stronger birds are starting to threaten other young. It has been suggested that such aggression may be at the root of the dispersion of young birds in late summer. In years when there are many young, some will be forced to leave as a result of constant chivvying by others; if so, then this behaviour could play an important part in population regulation. Detailed observations on many aspects of aggression are sadly lacking, but it should be noted that on the Continent young from late broods, especially second broods, wander more than those of first broods; this observation would be compatible with the suggestion that the older young from first broods were able to settle in vacant spaces before those of later broods, so forcing more of the latter to search for a home elsewhere.

CALLS, SONGS AND DISPLAYS

Tits are very vocal birds and many calls and songs have been described. Some of the main calls for each species have been given in chapters 2–8. No fewer than 20 vocalizations and 15 visual displays have been described in the Carolina Chickadee *Parus carolinensis*[337] while as many as 40 distinguishable calls have been recorded from a single individual Great Tit[135]. Particularly detailed studies have been made of the Great Tit[135, 165, 173].

Len Howard made an outstanding study of Great Tits under highly unusual circumstances. Her birds were so tame that they followed her into the house, roosted there and plainly depended on her for a great deal of their food. Under these conditions of great intimacy, Howard learned to recognize considerable numbers of birds by their appearance, behaviour and calls. She claimed to be able to recognize a wide variety of displays and 'moods' in those birds she knew well. This work is a striking example of how a person who knows an animal well can recognize a large number of different behaviour patterns and even small differences in these between individuals. If an experienced observer can note so many differences, how many more can probably be recognized by another member of the species?

A number of the calls that have been described are known to be associated with specific activities. The song itself is, as in many other species of birds, normally associated with territorial activities and is mainly given by the males, though female Great Tits can sing well and the female Willow Tit sings frequently[108]; in one observation the female Great Tit only sang when her mate was ill[135]. In late winter, song is heard mainly in the early morning in mild weather but it increases in frequency through the day as spring approaches. It recurs in autumn during the brief period of territorial resurgence at this time.

As described earlier for the Great Tit, individuals may have a repertoire of song, switching from one to another during the course of a bout of singing. According to Gompertz each male Great Tit tends to have at least four different song-types, usually of at least three different tempos. The reasons for changing from one song to another are not understood, but two males when singing against one another tend to use the same type of song; if one changes, the other follows[135]. There is some evidence that, the more varied the song, the more effective it is in deterring intruders[422].

Individuals appear to be able to recognize the songs of several neighbours. When the territories have been firmly established in late spring, the birds do not respond to the songs of their familiar neighbours as intensely as they do to the songs of strangers[202]. If one makes a tape-recording of Great Tit song and plays it to a group of males away from where it was recorded then one can easily see the response of the established territory holders to this strange song. Obviously they respond to the new song as being from a possible interloper, whose presence is a greater threat to their territory than is an established neighbour.

The distinctive 'pink' call of the Great Tit and 'pitchou' call of the Marsh Tit, described as the main calls of these species in the field guides, are in fact given almost only by established territory holders[135, 250]. The Great Tit call may be complementary to the song, being given most frequently at times when singing is less common. The main difference between these two species is that the female Great Tit does not normally give the 'pink' call whereas both sexes of Marsh Tit commonly give the 'pitchou' call.

Both inside and outside the breeding season, the birds have a series of contact calls which may be used to enable the pair or the flock to keep in touch with one another even when they are out of sight. A different contact note is given by the juvenile Great Tits, and a similar sort of call appears to exist in the other species. The young also have begging calls, one of which is used in the nest and a different one during the period when they are still dependent on their parents after leaving the nest. Everyone must have heard the rather high-pitched and rapid 'tsee-tsee-tsee' calls of young fledgling tits which fill the woods in June and early July. This begging behaviour is only seen in the young for a few weeks after fledging, often only for a few days. It is accompanied by a slightly crouched position (an upright posture usually means a threat, so that crouching makes clear that the bird is not threatening), a rapid fluttering of the wings and often a slight spreading of the tail. An almost identical display is given by the female in spring when she begs her mate for food. This behaviour occurs most frequently during the period when she is forming eggs, when it often accompanies coition, and when she is incubating but also it may be seen briefly after the young have just fledged even when no second brood is produced. Presumably at this time the female is often in a physiological state which would permit a second brood if ecological conditions allowed (p. 183). The behaviour of the male feeding the female is usually referred to as 'courtship feeding', but this is a very poor phrase since courtship and pairing take place long before and the feeding is associated mainly with those nesting activities where the female needs more food than she can get herself (p. 172).

In addition to the high intensity alarm given in the presence of a bird predator such as a sparrowhawk, the tits have a series of other alarm calls which are given under different conditions; Gompertz lists six variations in the Great Tit, mostly forms of churring. These include a lower intensity call when the danger is apparently less severe; some of these may be given when humans are present. Several authors have noted that these calls will immediately silence the nestlings[30].

Three other calls are given under conditions of danger. One I have already described (p. 107). In addition a captured bird may give a long-drawn-out distress call. When this happens other birds tend to swoop down to see what is the matter. The normal effect of this may be that, while being mobbed by other birds, the predator is distracted, so giving its captured prey a chance to escape. Large young may give this call when being handled by an observer at the nest; adult Blue Tits (but only very rarely adult Great Tits) will respond by diving close to the observer using a very shallow quivering wing-beat that is almost a glide and uttering a high-pitched buzzing sound. This display is quite striking and again is presumably done in order to distract the would-be predator from the young. In the same way that a ground-nesting species may use a 'broken-wing' display to draw the predator away from the nest, the Blue Tit may hope to lead the observer away.

A further type of call is uttered by the incubating female if disturbed[136]. Great Tits commonly use this call which is most easily described as a sharp hissing note accompanied by a beating of the wings. This has often been likened to a snake's hiss and it has been presumed that potential predators mistake it for a snake. However, snakes are rather rare in Britain and it seems unlikely that most weasels in Wytham would ever have met one. The noise may in fact sound like a threatening weasel[199]. This would be far better known to most predators in British woodland and so would be far more likely to frighten them. While the effect it has may not be permanent and so not save the nest it does give the female a good opportunity to escape. It is surprising how effective the call is, making the approaching animal jump back. Occasionally I find, when visiting a nest-box, a female that sits tightly and in order to see how many eggs she is sitting on, I have to roll her slightly to one side. Even though I know that under these circumstances the bird is highly likely to hiss, nevertheless the moment the bird hisses my hand still gives an involuntary jump (plate 15)!

Tits also have a series of warning calls and scolding notes which are used to warn other birds from coming too close. The use of these calls is often accompanied by threat postures against the offending bird. As in other animals these displays usually involve the exaggeration of some striking portion of their plumage. In the Great Tit, the bird may stretch itself up tall and display the striking black and yellow underparts. Other species make use of their striking head patterns often augmenting this by raising crown feathers to make the head look larger still; this movement can be even more striking in the crested species. Many of these threatening actions can be clearly observed when there are a large number of individuals feeding at a bird table. They may be accompanied by a forward thrust in which the mouth is opened but no sound comes forth, or by a variety of hisses, churrs or chatters.

Finally the Long-tailed Tit has some displays which are worthy of mention here. One is a hovering flight accompanied by a buzzing call. This is given close to the nest and may at times be used by a knowledgeable observer to locate the nest once the call is known. The curious thing about this call is that it seems to be given when adult birds are accompanied by additional birds at the nest. As described in chapter 8 it is not uncommon for there to be more than a pair of Long-tailed Tits feeding the young; at least some of the additional birds may be failed breeders from another nest. It appears that the display is usually given when one of these additional birds is at the nest and its functions are not understood[116, 308].

In addition to the hover display, the Long-tailed Tit has a display called the 'plunge flight', a rapid dive from the canopy, often quickly followed by others in the party[116]. This was also noted in spring when two pairs met. Gaston also describes a 'flycatcher display' when the bird flies up a few feet into the air and then drops back with the tail up and the wings partially spread; this display was seen mainly before nest building commenced. None of the *Parus* tits are known to have similar displays to those described here for the Long-tailed Tit and their functions are not adequately understood.

This group of birds is therefore highly vocal and their many calls undoubtedly convey far more to each other than we yet appreciate. There is much scope for further study.

FOOD REQUIREMENTS, FEEDING
RATES AND WEIGHTS

THIS chapter and the following one deal with foods and feeding habits. It also covers the amount of food the birds must get and the time that they have to spend feeding. The following chapter is concerned more with the feeding behaviour of the tits in relation to the types of food they take. A few feeding habits which are particularly relevant to other aspects of the tit's biology are treated elsewhere; the feeding niches have been covered in chapter 9, the feeding of the female by the male during the early stages of breeding is included in chapter 14 and the feeding rates and energy requirements of broods are covered in chapter 15; some aspects of food quality are discussed in chapter 18.

WINTER FOOD REQUIREMENTS

Being small, active, warm-blooded animals, tits need considerable amounts of energy and hence must be able to find food reasonably easily at all times of year. Food provides the fuel for all the body's needs: for growth and the replacement of worn tissues, for maintaining body temperature and for the energy necessary for an animal's activity. A small warm-blooded animal, such as a tit, requires a considerable supply of energy in order to maintain itself – especially if the weather is cold. Small objects lose heat to the surroundings more easily than large ones since their surface area is large in relation to their volume and the greater the difference between body temperatures and the surroundings the faster is the heat loss. High activity also demands large supplies of fuel. As we shall see, the combined demands of these requirements result in the tits having to search for food very busily through long periods of the winter. Like most small birds, the tits do not normally build up sufficient reserves of fat in their bodies to enable them to survive for several days without feeding*. In general it is probably true to say that they must obtain enough food each day to enable them to survive for that day and, in addition, to build up sufficient reserves to survive the night – since they cannot feed from dusk until dawn. The modest reserves they carry probably enable them to work on a 'trade gap' – where expenditure exceeds income – for at best only a very few days. However, such reserves may be essential for survival on very wet, windy or cold days, when feeding

*As we shall see, the smaller tits require about 10 Calories of energy per day, the Great Tit about 20. Since a gram of fat yields about 9 Calories, the birds would have to store many grams of fat if they were to last several days without food; this they do not do.

is difficult and energy demands high. Not surprisingly, therefore, the tits spend a lot of their day feeding in order to satisfy their considerable energy requirements.

We know of these qualitative changes in the energy demands of the birds from a wide variety of studies[361]. However, more specific measurements have only been made on certain aspects of the tits' lives and many gaps remain to be filled.

The winter food requirements of tits have been calculated by observing how much food the birds ate in captivity. The birds were kept in outdoor aviaries, so that they experienced both the natural winter temperatures and natural day-length. They were fed on a diet of seeds and locally collected insects, though not all the insects came from the branches of the pines where the birds normally feed. The calorific values of the diets were established and the energy requirements of the birds calculated by observing the amount of food eaten. Table 13 shows the results of these observations.

Table 13. The daily energy requirements of different species of tits (from Gibb 1957).

Species	Energy requirements per day (K. cals)	Energy requirements per gram of body weight per day
Great Tit	19·7	1·0
Blue Tit	10·8	1·0
Coal Tit	11·7	1·3

As might be expected, the much larger Great Tit required more food than either of the other two species, though it is odd that the Blue Tit consumed less than the slightly smaller Coal Tit. In both the Great and Blue Tit, the birds required less food at higher temperatures. With small laboratory samples such as these there is considerable variation in the results. At least one possible source of error lies in the activity of the individual bird, the more active the bird the more energy it will need. This might well account for the observed difference between the Blue and Coal Tits. Furthermore, captive birds with adequate food supply may not have had to use as much energy as wild birds in their search for food; the latter will fly considerable distances during the day (see below) and so require considerable supplies of energy for this activity alone.

Birds have such a wide range of activities that it is difficult to extrapolate laboratory measurements of energy requirements to natural situations. For example while the bird may be active in the aviary for the same amount of time as in the field, it is not likely that it will fly so far and flying demands large supplies of energy. Further, the amount of flying that a bird does must vary at different times of year; probably the energy requirements of the parent birds reach a maximum when they are feeding young, since they can seldom do so much flying at other times of year. When there are nestlings to feed, individual Great Tits may be making as many as 400 visits to the nest with food during the course of a 15- or 16-hour day.

Other estimates have been made of the energy requirements of laying and incubating birds. By measuring the oxygen uptake of a female Great Tit during incubation it has been shown that she needs considerably more energy for incubation as the temperature goes down since at lower temperatures she must put more heat into the eggs to keep them warm (fig. 33).

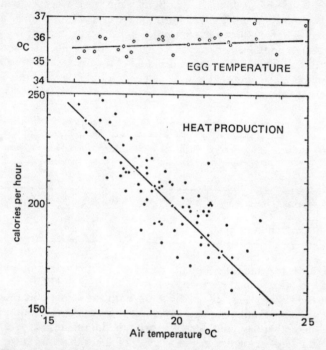

FIG. 33.   Heat production and egg temperature of an incubating Great Tit in relation to air temperature. Note that although heat production rises markedly at lower temperatures the temperature of the eggs remains fairly constant. In the field the air temperature at night is often much lower than that shown here so that the energy requirements of the incubating female will be correspondingly higher (from Drent 1972).

However, these figures were collected from a female incubating at a temperature higher than that normally found in a nest-hole in the field; some measurements taken in Wytham by myself at lower temperatures give higher figures.

Apart from the feeding rates to nestlings, which are discussed later (p. 146), direct measurements of energy requirements have not been made at many stages of the tits' annual cycle; indeed because of the problems associated with varying amounts of activity at different times of year, they would be difficult to make. However, some idea of the difficulty that the tits have in getting sufficient food can be obtained by observing the proportion of the daylight hours that they spend feeding, and this has been done several times[103, 119, 125, 189]. Figure 34 shows the situation in Wytham; in addition, in February the Long-tailed Tits spend 90% of the day feeding[116]. Similar results were obtained for the birds feeding in the pinewoods of the Breck[127]; in mid-winter, the Great Tits spent about 75% of the day feeding, the Blue Tit 85%, the Coal Tits 90%, the Long-tailed Tits 95% and the Goldcrest virtually 100%.

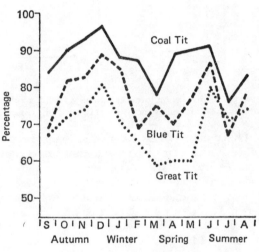

FIG. 34. Percentage of the day spent in feeding. Note the high proportion of time spent feeding in midwinter and in the nesting season and that the smaller the species the greater the proportion of the day spent feeding (from Gibb 1954a).

Several trends are apparent from these data. In mid-winter, when the days are shortest and the weather coldest, the birds spend a greater proportion of their time feeding than in any other season of the year except the nestling period. In addition, the smaller the species, the higher the proportion of the time it spends feeding because (as discussed above) it needs relatively greater amounts of energy to maintain its body temperature.

Other trends are probably also associated with the difficulties encountered in finding sufficient food in winter. The Great Tit gets up earlier and goes to bed later in relation to sunrise and sunset in mid-winter than at other times (fig. 35)[92, 189]. Hence the birds work a proportionately longer day when the days are shortest. Between species, there is a tendency for the smallest to get up earliest and go to bed latest – again a relatively longer day in the

smaller species. Observations similar to these of Kluijver's have been made
for the Great Tit in Wytham where the order of getting up and going to
roost could be related to body size in the three species Great Tit, Nuthatch
and Great Spotted Woodpecker, the first named being on the wing for the
longest day, the last for the shortest[165].

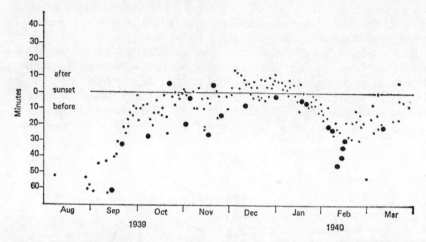

FIG. 35.   Time (in minutes) of retiring to roost, plotted with sunset as a base line. Heavy
dots indicate rainfall at the moment of retiring to roost (from Kluijver 1950).

Other observations have been made along these lines by observing the
order in which birds come to feeding tables; however, these are open to other
possible interpretations since some of the birds may well have fed elsewhere
before arriving at the feeding sites or they might be coming different distances.
Hence the species arriving at one bird table came in the order Blue Tit,
Great Tit, Marsh Tit, Nuthatch and left in the order Nuthatch, Great Tit,
Marsh Tit, Blue Tit, both nearly right in terms of body size, but the Coal
Tit arrived last and left first[237].

Large variations in the times of going to roost and of getting up between
different individual Great Tits were reported by Len Howard[173]. Doubtless
variations also exist in the wild, but in mid-winter they are likely to be
overshadowed by the need to feed for most of the day. Howard's birds were
well fed (by her) and often apparently spent the night indoors where,
being warmer than outside, they would not use so much energy overnight.
On both counts, therefore, Howard's birds could afford to take life more
easily than those having to feed in woodland.

The fact that the birds spend less of the time feeding later in the winter
may not mean that they need less food at this time, but merely that the day
is longer. As always there is a time element in feeding behaviour since time
is limited. Although the days get gradually longer from mid-winter to mid-
summer, it does not follow that the birds have an equally increasing amount

of time to search for food; other duties may prevail. As spring approaches the male must defend his territory and the female must build the nest, form and lay the eggs and later incubate them. The female may need up to 40% more food in order to be able to form her eggs[318]. When building and incubating she has less time for feeding; for example an incubating female may spend 15 minutes on the eggs and have 5 minutes off for feeding[301]. At such times her mate may have to help her to collect sufficient food (p. 172), a factor which further reduces the time that the male has for feeding himself.

The other time of year at which the tits feed for such a high proportion of the day is when they have young to feed. Both the parent birds spend most of the day foraging at this stage (fig. 34), even though at this time of year there are some sixteen hours of daylight in central Europe compared with about eight hours in mid-winter[119, 189]. The parent birds also rise earlier and go to roost later in relation to sunrise and sunset at this time of year than at any other time during the summer.

At most times of year the birds tend to concentrate their feeding into early morning and evening and slacken off around midday when they may rest or preen; in mid-winter the smaller species find little or no time for activities other than feeding. This slackening off period in the middle of the day shows up in the weights of the birds.

THE DAILY WEIGHT CHANGES

Weight changes of birds can be due to a wide variety of causes and an internal examination of a bird may be necessary to ascertain the cause which is responsible. Changes in weight may result from changes in fat reserves, changes in food carried in the digestive system, changes in the size of the reproductive organs (especially in the female) or, during the laying period, to the presence or absence of eggs inside the female.

Other body organs may show seasonal changes in weight, though few of these are likely to be sufficiently large to affect field observations. However, the digestive system of the Bearded Tit (which switches from a diet of small seeds in winter to one of insects in summer) is about twice the weight in winter that it is in summer[352]. The main change is in the weight of the gut wall which becomes more muscular in winter – possibly in order to be able to grind up the harder diet taken at that time of year. Examination of a small number of Blue Tits suggests that similar changes in the size of the digestive system occur in this species also. A change of diet from insects to seeds may pose problems for the birds. Though little is known about this, the enzymes required for efficient digestion of the different foods are likely to be different, and the periods when the bird changes from one diet to the other may be critical to its survival.

There are marked changes in the weight of tits during the course of the day at least in winter[275]. Birds lose weight overnight; their weights increase from 0900 hours to 1630 hours but the increase does not occur steadily throughout this time. During the middle of the day when the birds reduce their rate of feeding their weights stay steady or even decline (fig. 36). Both Blue and Great Tits are about 5% heavier at dusk (1600 hours) than at 0900. Kluijver[191] weighed Great Tits as they started to roost, kept them overnight and weighed them again in the morning; he noted that they lost 1·7 grams (10% of the total) overnight. Hence probably the birds weighed by Owen[275] had already put on some weight before 0900. Owen also showed that Coal, Marsh and Long-tailed Tits were heavier in the afternoon than in the morning, though he had insufficient data to plot changes as for the Great and Blue Tits.

Diurnal changes in weight have been reported for many species[19]. Birds tend to lose more weight overnight in cold than in mild weather (since they use more fuel to maintain the body temperature), and so have to feed more in order to maintain their weight. However, the tits do not merely feed harder after a cold night in order to replace reserves that have been used, but they tend to feed harder during the day throughout a cold period, in order to increase their reserves so that they can survive the cold nights more easily. Hence many birds tend to be heavier during the day during cold weather than during mild weather, the opposite of what one might expect. Similarly Norwegian Great Tits are lighter in mild weather in winter than they are in cold weather[143].

Table 14 shows the weight changes of individuals during weather of varying severity. Obviously such increases during cold weather can occur

Table 14. Weight variation in relation to changes in air temperature. The average temperature is calculated from the average of the maximum and minimum temperatures for the period concerned. The figures in parentheses give the numbers of weighings (from Owen 1954).

	1951 26 Nov.–8 Dec.	1952 26 Nov.–8 Dec.	Difference
Average temperature	42·4°F	31·8°F	10·6°F
Average weight (grams)			
Blue Tit	10·60 (23)	11·64 (54)	+1·04
Great Tit	19·66 (79)	20·72 (27)	+1·06
Coal Tit	8·75 (8)	9·23 (28)	+0·48

only if food is plentiful enough for the birds to be able to feed up sufficiently during the day. If food is short and they cannot do this then the birds may be in difficulties; if the weather is very cold for a long period they may die. During a cold spell in Holland, Great Tits with access to food from bird tables increased in weight by an average of one gram during the cold weather, while those birds that did not have access to such supplies lost weight by 0·4 grams[191]. Several other factors affect the weight of tits; in particular, during cold weather, the weights of Great Tits increased in

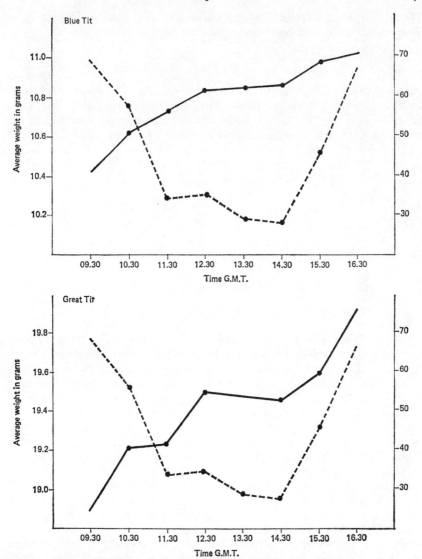

FIG. 36. Diurnal variation in weight in Blue (upper) and Great Tits (lower). The measurements were taken during January and December. The solid line shows the weight changes during the day, the dotted line shows the feeding activity of the birds as measured by the numbers of birds entering the traps each hour (right hand axis) (from Owen 1954).

oakwoods but not in pinewoods; the birds in oakwoods had higher fat reserves than those in pinewoods[16]. It was thought that this was because there is more food in oakwoods than in pinewoods with the result that the

Great Tits in the former habitat could find sufficient to increase their reserves while those in pinewoods could not.

ANNUAL VARIATIONS IN WEIGHT

Annual variations in weight have also been studied and some of these occur as a direct result of changes in the size of body organs (fig. 37); in March or early April the female's reproductive organs grow considerably in size and for a brief period the female is a little heavier than the male.

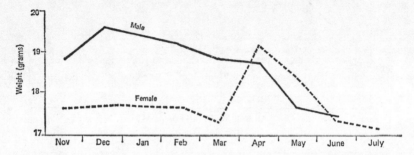

FIG. 37. The annual changes in body weight of Great Tits (from Kluijver 1952).

As breeding is about to start, the female forms eggs and when she goes to roost she carries a fully-formed egg that she will lay the following morning, as well as three other eggs which, although very much smaller, have started to develop. At this time she is considerably heavier than at any other time. In the Blue Tit where a normal winter weight may be about 10 grams, the laying females may weigh as much as 15 grams, an increase of 50%. At the end of laying her weight decreases sharply since she is no longer forming eggs and during the incubation period her weight may decline still further as the reproductive organs diminish in size. There is also a further reduction in weight during the nestling period since the female 'loses condition' at this time due to the hard work of raising young; at dusk the female Blue Tit's fat reserves are usually about 1·0 grams during most of the breeding season whereas at the end of the nestling period they may be as little as 0·5 grams, only a little more than she needs to keep alive overnight (fig. 38).

In many small birds there is a slight increase in weight during the moult possibly as a result of more fluids being mobilized during feather growth; this has not been studied in tits, but in the Lesser Redpoll *Carduelis flammea* a bird of similar size to the tits, there is a higher blood volume at this time[100]. The weights of the tits increase gradually during the autumn reaching a peak in November or December[143, 190]. In mild winters, there is a gradual decline in weight thereafter (fig. 39) though such a decline would not be noticeable in the early stages in colder winters, and for the reasons described above sharp changes in temperature will affect the general trend. These

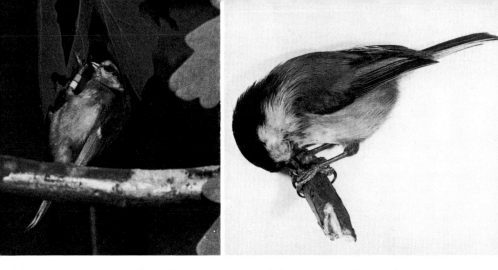

PLATE 7. Feeding. Most tits can hang onto foliage by wrapping their toes around twigs or needles. The Blue Tit, *above left*, can hang on a large leaf by pressing its toes onto opposite sides of the leaf. In winter tits are omnivorous, but most specialize on seeds. Many tits hammer open seeds with their bills, usually with the upper mandible only. Here, *above right*, the species is the Willow Tit. Tits are also frequent visitors to gardens where they take food put out for them by man, *below left*. Tits are less popular when they open milk bottles to drink the cream, right. This habit has spread from area to area by birds copying each other.

PLATE 8. In summer tits mainly eat insects. When feeding the brood the parents often bring prey at the rate of one a minute. *Right*, enlargements from a 16 mm film in which an electronic flash and a camera were mounted in the wall of the nest-box on the side opposite to the nest entrance, and a watch placed beside the entrance. The entering bird triggered the camera. Note how rapidly the visits were made. *Below*, feeding and intelligence: tits are quick to learn how to reach food. Here a Great Tit, *left*, holds loops of string under its feet to enable it to pull up food it could not otherwise reach. A Blue Tit, *right*, has learned to pull out matchsticks from an apparatus so that the seeds fall down into the tray beneath.

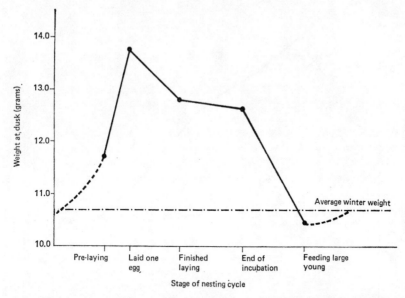

FIG. 38. Weight change of female Blue Tits during the breeding season. The increase in weight prior to laying is largely due to an increase in size of the reproductive organs. During the laying period, the females also carry a fully formed egg (weighing about 1·3 grams) and yolks of further eggs. The low weight towards the end of the nestling period results from the reproductive organs having been largely resorbed and the birds carrying less fat than at any other time during the breeding season – a reflection presumably on how hard they are having to work.

changes in weight are reflected in the feeding activity of the birds; tits come to bait or bird tables far more freely in cold than in mild weather.

The extra weight is fat which is laid down early in the winter when food supplies are still reasonable. This can serve as an insurance against winter scarcity or bad weather later on. These longer-term changes in weight, as opposed to those changes which occur in relation to the weather at the time, are adaptations to the kind of weather that might be expected at that time of year and the reserves necessary to survive such weather.

Several authors have suggested that the lower weights in the later part of the winter are a result of food shortage then. Winter foods are mostly seeds or insects, neither of which reproduce rapidly at this time (though new insects may become available). Food supplies are being continually drawn upon by the birds and so becoming progressively reduced. Hence, in spite of a gradual lengthening of the day, late February might be the most difficult time of year since food might be scarcer then than earlier (p. 136). However, such a suggestion is not wholly in accord with data such as those in figure 34 where the feeding intensity of the birds is lower in February than it was earlier in the winter. This subject requires further study; doubtless there is

E

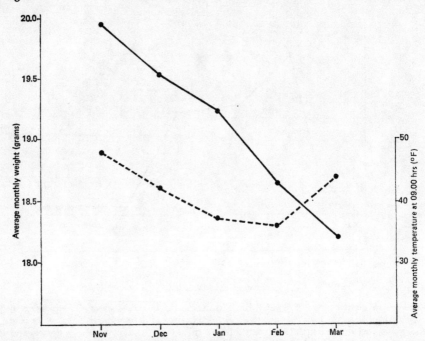

FIG. 39. Winter changes of weight in the Great Tit (solid line). The mean monthly temperatures are given by the dotted line (from Owen 1954).

considerable variation between years. In the very mild winter of 1960–61 in Wytham it was almost impossible to catch any tits at bait since they had ample supplies of beechmast. Further, by early February, the flocks feeding under the beeches had greatly diminished and the birds were getting sufficient food in relatively short visits to the beech trees; already the males were spending a great proportion of the day singing, a situation that by no means exists in every year! Hence, once again, generalizations are dangerous since so much depends on the weather and the amount of food available.

CHAPTER 12

FEEDING HABITS AND IRRUPTIONS

THE tits take a wide variety of foods. With the exception of the Long-tailed Tit (which is almost wholly insectivorous) they can be considered as being insectivorous during the summer and eaters of fruit, seeds and some insects in the winter. However, the diets of different individuals may vary strikingly; in winter some become almost wholly seed-eaters while others, such as those living in the Breckland conifer plantations (p. 133), remain largely insectivorous. Almost all the summer food of the tits is insects. Whether or not the birds do any good to man (p. 255), they certainly do little harm. Although the tits have been recorded taking seeds or fruits wanted by man such as, for instance, garden peas, or attacking the flowers of fruit trees in spring, this allegedly harmful habit needs further study. In at least some such cases, closer examination has shown that the birds were taking insects from damaged fruits[97, 114]. Further, Great Tits seem to take infested acorns, in preference to undamaged ones; apparently they can distinguish these from healthy ones by tapping them. Even apart from the possible good done by taking infested seeds, the seeds the tits take are not of great importance to man; even when they take seeds from potential forest crops such as beech or spruce the proportion taken is usually negligible[149]. However, the presence or absence of these crops has a marked effect on the tits and it is for this reason that I have included a discussion of the latter's movements in this chapter.

A food source for tits that may have been largely overlooked is nectar. There are only a few records of tits taking nectar or honey. But on the few occasions when it has been put out for them, they have taken it with enthusiasm. Blue Tits in particular will learn to take sugar solutions from humming-bird type feeders[351] and have been recorded taking the sap of trees[256]. Further studies of the amount of nectar taken by birds in the wild would be useful.

FEEDING METHODS

Tits are perpetually inquisitive and frequently investigate strange objects[123]. Presumably in this way they find new sources of food. Apart from being very nimble and able to perch in a wide variety of positions they use their feet a great deal to hold food – particularly large objects – while preparing it for eating; they also show considerable ingenuity when it comes to reaching food in difficult sites.

About twelve days after they have left the nest the young birds start to use their feet for pulling at things[6]. They may manipulate threads, rubber bands and other small objects and so gradually learn to co-ordinate the use of feet and beak. In contrast to the Chaffinch *Fringilla coelebs*, the young Great Tit shows an instinctive tendency to use its feet in this way and gradually, through practice, the birds become more expert[168, 391, 392].

The tits are well able to handle large food items; a tit flies up to a branch with the food, places it on the branch and then holds it there with one or both feet[124, 393]. Individual birds show 'handedness' – the tendency to use one foot in preference to the other. If the food item is a seed or fruit, the bird will hammer and tear it until it has succeeded in removing the outer casing and will then eat it. Large insects such as caterpillars are usually held under one foot with the head inwards (towards the other foot), the head is pecked hard (to break the mandibles so that they will not damage the bird while being swallowed) and pulled off and then eaten. After that the gut is pulled out and eaten (or sometimes discarded); the bird then eats the rest of the body from the head end. This sequence of behaviour develops steadily during some six to nine weeks after fledging, although the tendency to discard the gut increases for a longer period – up to about three months after fledging.

The exception is the Long-tailed Tit which apparently cannot hold objects under its feet while perching. However, when eating a large item of food it may hang upside down from the perch by one leg, while holding the food in the other; in this way it is able to break off small bits of food and eat them one at a time[126, 152].

Tits are also adept at obtaining food under unusual conditions such as when problems have been set for them. The simplest example is, perhaps, where the food has been placed on the end of a string and the birds have to reach it by perching at the top of the string and pulling the food up; this is done by pulling up a loop of the string, holding it under one foot while pulling up another loop and so on until the food has been brought within reach[162, 371, 374, 391].

Others have shown that tits can solve quite complicated puzzles in order to get food[38, 39, 40]. There is great variability between individuals but on average Blue and Coal Tits seem to be the best at coping with puzzles (see plate 8). Presumably the Varied Tit, *Parus varius*, of Japan is also good at solving such puzzles since it can be trained to perform small tricks for people[15]. One of the most outstanding achievements reported is that of Blue Tits which reached food by landing on a perch hanging on a string and rotating the perch, thereby rolling up the string round the perch. By so doing they wound the perch up the string until they reached the food; only a very few individual Blue Tits seem able to perform this feat[373].

These activities have been reviewed by Thorpe[372, 373] as possible examples of 'insight learning' (the production of a new, adaptive response as a result of insight or the solution to a problem by the sudden adaptive re-organization of experience). Although some of these activities may not be entirely novel to the bird (for example birds may pull up caterpillars on their threads in nature) nevertheless tits seem to show insight in solving some of the more complex problems set them.

In spite of their apparent adaptability and their tendency to explore new objects the birds do not always recognize a new food source immediately. In the 1940s when peanuts were put out again after a lapse during the war years the food was left untouched for many weeks until a bird made the discovery that there was food available[48]; thereafter several birds started to take nuts and the habit rapidly spread as one bird saw another eating the nuts. A similar form of learning seems to have accompanied the discovery that milk bottles contain a source of food (p. 109); such learning may be one of the advantages of living in flocks.

WINTER FOODS

Since seeds are produced in autumn and few insects breed or grow in winter stocks of food tend to diminish as the winter progresses. Although some insects emerge from their pupae, and so become available to the birds, these do not normally make up for the food consumed. There are few quantitative measurements of such changes but figure 40 gives some information for invertebrates in coniferous woodland during the winter months; these show a decline in food supply until March or April when it starts to improve again, the exact timing being dependent on the earliness or lateness of the spring in each year.

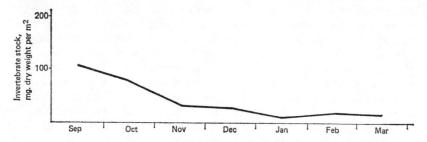

FIG. 40. The supply of invertebrate food during the winter in the Breck 1954–55. The food becomes gradually scarcer until January. In some years the food becomes commoner again from February onwards; this depends on the mildness of the spring (from Gibb 1960).

The numbers of Coal Tits living in the wood tend to decline through the winter and this may be because some die as a result of food shortage (the numbers do not increase again in early spring so the missing birds have not merely gone elsewhere temporarily). The amount of food the tits take has been calculated (from the figures above) and is often a high proportion of the amount by which the food stocks decrease, suggesting that the birds themselves are often responsible for much of the decline in numbers of their prey. The tits sometimes take a quarter or even at times a half of all the available food stocks.

In one particular study Gibb[125] measured the predation by tits on a species of moth which gives an important insight into how the birds feed and so I shall describe it in some detail.

The tiny Eucosmid moth *Ernamonia conicolana* lays its eggs – usually singly – on the outside of young pine cones. The small larvae burrow into the pine cones where they spend their entire larval period, feeding on the developing seeds; each larva eats about seven seeds during its lifetime. When fully grown, the larva makes a small chamber just below the surface of the cone in which it pupates; from this it can break out when it emerges as a moth. Coal Tits and Blue Tits locate the pupae in winter by tapping on the cones; apparently they are able to detect the hollowness of the cone scale. The birds tear open the scale and remove the pupa. Blue Tits with their stouter beaks seem to be better at doing this than Coal Tits, though they are less common than Coal Tits; further most Blue Tits are only winter visitors to the pine-woods[127].

When the moths have hatched and the cones have fallen to the ground, one can count the numbers of larvae that were in them and calculate the predation rates of the tits upon them. An emerging adult moth leaves a neat round hole in the cone scale whereas if the pupa was eaten by a tit there is a ragged hole in the chamber (a very tiny, neat hole signifies that the pupa has been attacked by a parasite so that the rate of parasitism can also be measured). Gibb measured the number of cones that fell (so giving him a measure of the size of the cone crop) as well as the number of pupae per cone and their subsequent fate. Usually only one or two larvae would be found in each cone but sometimes there were as many as eight or more.

The tits tended to take more larvae from the cones when there were higher numbers in the cones (fig. 41) suggesting that they stopped and looked more carefully whenever they found pupae in a group of cones. However this relationship broke down when the numbers of the pupae reached 50 per 100 cones, though in occasional patches of even higher densities the predation rates increased again[128]. Gibb suggested that since the numbers of pupae only rarely reached densities of 50 per 100 cones the birds were hunting by expectation; the birds were not accustomed to densities as high as these and so did not 'expect' to find such large numbers of pupae; they stopped looking as soon as they had done well. However, on the rare occasions when the densities were very high, they could hardly fail to find them and would continue searching. There is a different explanation, namely that the birds are optimizing their feeding rates[321]. Areas of high density of prey are not necessarily the best places to feed; if they are also full of other tits, a bird may do better by going to a place where there are fewer prey but less interference from other birds. Distributions of tits as a result of such manoeuvres could, it is suggested, explain these observations. Whichever explanation is correct it gives a good insight into the working of

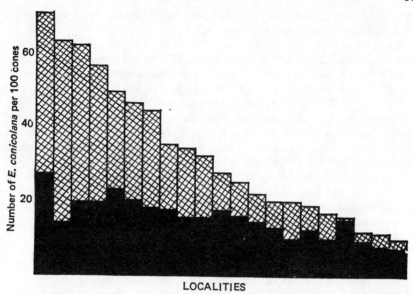

FIG. 41. The number of *E. conicolana* larvae per hundred cones before (full columns) and after (black) predation by tits in the winter 1955–56. Each column represents one locality in Thetford Chase; they are arranged in descending order of the intensity of the larvae. 54% of the total were taken by the tits (from Gibb 1958).

a tit's mind; it is not difficult to imagine a human behaving in either of these ways.

In three different winters in the Breckland pinewoods the tits took between 54% and 60% of the pupae; since they searched most in those areas where the moth was most abundant the effect of their hunting was to tend to level out the densities in different areas. Considering that each cone had to be tapped – in many places – in order to find the pupae, such results also show the very high intensity with which the birds hunt during winter and again demonstrate how much they may reduce a given food supply. In the Breckland forests during winter there were, on average, about 2·1 Blue and Coal Tits together with some 3200 *Ernamonia* per hectare. The birds ate about 1900 of the pupae, hence this source of food could at best only have provided each tit with about ten pupae per day over a six-month winter period, a small proportion of their diet. This is an average figure and hence somewhat misleading. Blue Tits (which are relatively rare) concentrate on this method of feeding to a considerable extent in mid-winter; at this time *Ernamonia* pupae must represent a higher proportion of the Blue Tits' diet. Nevertheless, although the Coal Tits take fewer, all the birds have developed a hunting technique specially for these pupae. They react to changes in the abundance of the moths in the pine cones by hunting more diligently for them where they are more frequent. Presumably the tits must have a whole repertoire of such behaviour patterns associated with the wide variety of different prey that they must find in order to survive.

Since the stocks of food decline during the winter, it is likely that late winter, perhaps February or early March, is the most difficult time for the tits. Although the period for feeding is now appreciably longer (approximately twelve hours each of light and dark), the food supply may be much scarcer. A further difficulty may be that, in milder weather, some of the seeds may start to germinate making them inedible: the time when seeds start to germinate is also difficult for many of the finches[400]. However, this probably only happens at a later stage in spring and so may be accompanied by an emergence of young insects which will counteract the loss.

The suggestion that the most difficult time for the tits is not when the days are shortest, but later in the winter when food is even scarcer, is supported by Gibb's data on insect foods in pinewoods, though these are not the only foods available. Gibb also recorded that the tits found beech seed more easily before than after January. Not only were the seeds scarcer later in the winter, but also the Great and Blue Tits altered their way of searching for them; from January onwards they spent a considerable proportion of the time turning over leaves in their search for seeds that had been covered up. Haftorn[143] also considered that the birds were shortest of food in February in Scandinavia. Such a view is not consistent with the data on feeding intensities in figure 34, p. 123, where the birds spend a higher proportion of the daylight hours available to them hunting in mid-winter than in February. These apparent contradictions may well arise because the measurements were made in different places and in different winters when the food supplies or the weather were different or perhaps because the measurements themselves were not completely accurate.

MIGRATIONS AND IRRUPTIONS

This subject may seem out of context, but is discussed here because many of the movements of tits can be related to feeding conditions. At least three species of European tit – Coal, Great and Blue – undertake long-distance movements at times. The Willow Tit and Lapp Tit may also make some movements, but these are less well documented[160, 164]. Many of these movements are irruptive in nature and some factors associated with them are discussed in the following sections. Irruptions are very similar to true migrations except that they do not take place in every year[365]; in the case of the tits the interval between irruptions is usually two or more years. A complication arises inasmuch as the tit populations tend to be much higher in some years than others so that it is necessary to demonstrate that a higher proportion of tits move in irruption years than in others. This is certainly true (fig. 42).

The evidence for regular, annual migrations of tits is less clear, but in western Europe some tits move almost every year[41, 42]. Movements tend to

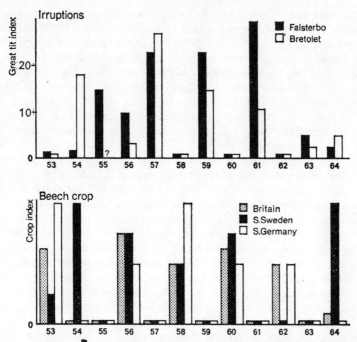

FIG. 42. Irruptions and fluctuations in breeding numbers of Great Tits in relation to the beech crop. Irruptions at the Col de Bretolet, Switzerland, are given in terms of the proportions of Great Tits to all birds other than tits trapped, multiplied by 100. Thus, if 5000 tits were trapped, of which 2000 were Great Tits, and also 10,000 other birds, then the irruption index would be $2000 \times 100 \div 10,000 = 20$. The irruptions at Falsterbo, Sweden, are more subjective; they should be used only to get some idea of relative numbers seen each year. There were no observations at the Col de Bretolet in 1955. Beech crops are all scored differently in the various areas and have been related to similar scales for simplicity. These crops are also subjective – for example, those in Britain are scored from 'nil' to 'abundant' in nine categories – but the increase between one category and the next does not necessarily represent a constant increase in the quantity of seed. The crops are plotted against the autumn of the year in which the seed became available to the birds; for instance, the crop shown for 1960 was eaten by the birds in the winter of 1960/61 (from Perrins 1966).

be in a southerly or south-westerly direction in autumn, towards milder winter climates[35, 89, 353, 390]. Return movements occur in the spring[78, 101], though they are less conspicuous than the autumn movements, presumably because many birds die in winter.

This gives only a rather general picture since the situation varies so much from year to year. Sometimes relatively few adults take part in these movements, but in other years many adults move; this is particularly true in the very large irruptions when both young and old birds are present in large numbers[325]. Some adults may even settle and breed in an area remote from the place where they were believed to have bred the year before. Great Tits do not show strong homing abilities[69, 322]. The proportion of birds in an area that undertake migration has rarely been measured, though it may be low; in Germany the proportion of migrant to resident Great Tits was calculated to be about 16 to 100[87]. The length of the journey also varies greatly. In western Europe, long journeys may be undertaken in irruptive years, but the majority of the birds that move make shorter trips. For example, some German birds spend the winter in Holland and Belgium[78, 89]. Workers in these countries commonly find birds in their winter populations which depart in spring[82, 190]. These are presumably migrants but they may not have come very far. 'Winter visitors' such as these do not regularly arrive in Britain in any numbers.

Regular migration is more common in the more northerly and easterly populations, where it is more necessary to escape the cold winters and very short days, but there is much less information from these areas and many of the recorded movements may have taken place during irruptions. The Coal Tits from eastern Russia may be mainly migratory[138] though some at least of the Great Tits remain at high latitudes for the winter[110, 339]. The latter are often dependent on man during the coldest periods of the year. Birds arriving in Moscow in the autumn depart again – apparently moving farther south almost immediately. It is not known how far south the migrating birds move, though, unless they are looking for good sources of food near man, they have to migrate very long distances to reach milder climates. This is particularly true of Russian birds and, conforming with this, some long-distance ringing recoveries of Russian-ringed birds have been obtained as far south as the Crimea and as far south-west as Portugal.

In some years very large numbers of Coal, Great and Blue Tits may take part in these movements and at such times many of the birds may arrive in Britain[67]. These irruptive movements occur when the food supply for the tits fails and in the autumn and when there are high numbers of tits. Movements of this sort are better known for other seed- or fruit-eating species such as the Crossbill, *Loxia curvirostra*, and the Waxwing, *Bombycilla garrulus*, both of which are seen in Britain in large numbers only when their main food supplies (Spruce, *Picea abies*, and Rowan, *Sorbus aucuparia*, respectively) fail[66, 266].

As with other irruptive species, the tits show a general high level of excitement both prior to and during periods of movement. They fly round a great deal, often rather high and hence are more exposed than usual; they call frequently and often congregate in parties.

Accompanying this excited activity the birds tend to show other unusual behaviour which draws the attention of the general public to them. Perhaps the two activities most commonly observed are the pecking of putty out of window frames and the tearing of paper. Birds frequently enter houses and tear the wallpaper, usually the offender is a Blue Tit; Gilbert White noted that the Blue Tit was 'a great frequenter of houses and a general devourer'. Although he does not enlarge on this, presumably the Blue Tits were being at least an occasional nuisance to house-owners in Selbourne two hundred years ago. Once started on a course of action the tits may show considerable persistence – hence the complaint of Father Imberdis (p. 13). In addition to wallpaper many other objects may be torn or damaged.

The significance of such behaviour has been much discussed[167, 222]. The most likely explanation seems to be that the birds are indulging in a form of food-searching activity. Blue Tits commonly tear bark off trees in their search for food and this behaviour is most prevalent in autumn[119]. The behaviour, already described, by which they find the *Ernarmonia* pupae in the pine cones, shows that at times they search by sound and tear open hollow objects. Tearing away loose putty and wallpaper are not so far removed from these more natural activities.

Logan Home noted that a bird will fly straight from a bird table, where it had fed heavily, into a house and start tearing the wallpaper and thought that the behaviour therefore could not be related to hunger. Hinde disagreed, pointing out that even a well-fed tit ought to be on the watch for where its next meal is to come from and so it would pay birds to continue searching for future supplies. In other species of birds, well-fed individuals continue hunting and it has been shown by behaviourists that the activities of hunting and eating often have different causal mechanisms, so there is no need for surprise when birds leave the bird table and then attack the putty[231, 302].

Logan Home suggested that tit irruptions were in some way connected with unusually dry weather in autumn, but more recent irruptions have not supported this theory[68]. The irruptions are, however, closely related to the seed crops of the beech. These mast crops have such an important effect on the tits that they are dealt with on their own in the following section.

Although irruptions are frequent on the Continent (fig. 42), it is rare for the tits to invade Britain in large numbers. In the autumn of 1957 a large invasion of Britain occurred and this was well documented[67]. Movements into Britain started in mid-September with an influx of Coal, Great and Blue Tits into south-eastern Britain. Possibly a smaller number of Long-tailed Tits were also involved since more than usual were reported on the south and east coasts. The invasion continued for some time, reaching a peak in early October; the invading birds spread widely, some reaching northern England and others as far west as the Isles of Scilly.

Large numbers of tits were reported from many areas during the winter. Some ringers claimed that the birds involved were of Continental origin because of their long wing lengths or slightly different plumage. Together with the high numbers there were many outbreaks of paper-tearing and opening of milk bottles. There was good evidence of return movement in the spring when many birds were again reported on the south and east coasts. Many populations of tits on the Continent were at high levels after a good breeding season in 1957.

In order for such an irruptive habit to evolve, some of the birds that undertake the movements must survive to leave offspring inheriting the

same irruptive tendencies. The movements into Britain in the autumn of
1957 were followed by observations of birds departing in the spring and
there were a number of recoveries of ringed birds that can be associated
with these movements (fig. 43). No individual bird is known to have made
both journeys but, as can be seen, a number of ringed birds moved from
Europe into Britain in the autumn and a number of birds ringed during the
winter in Britain moved to the Continent in the spring. While the place of
birth of the latter birds is not known, there can be little doubt that they
were visitors from the areas to which they subsequently returned. Although
the number of ringed birds involved may seem small, the preceding 50 years
of ringing only yielded 3 Great and 3 Blue Tit recoveries from Europe to
Britain[174].

The return movements in the spring appear to have been on a much
smaller scale than those into Britain the previous autumn. This is to be

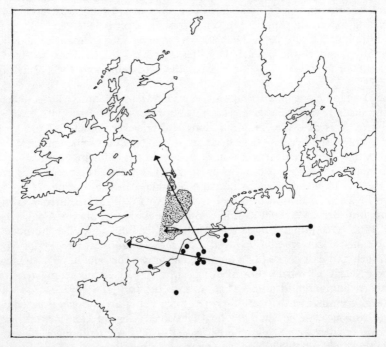

FIG. 43.   Cross-Channel ringing recoveries of Blue and Great Tits relating to the 1957
irruption. The three birds ringed on the Continent and recovered in Britain were ringed as
juveniles in May–July 1957. All those ringed in Britain and recovered on the Continent (shown
as dots on the map) were ringed in eastern areas (hatched on map); they were ringed from
October 1957–April 1958 and are presumed to have been winter visitors from the Continent
which returned. Seven of the 14 were ringed during the period 28.3.58–6.4.58 and an
eighth on 8 March. Five of these eight were ringed in Kent, one in Sussex, one in Suffolk
and one in Yorkshire; in all probability they were already on their way back at this time.

expected since the birds moved into Britain in a year when food was in short supply. What is significant is that at least a proportion of these birds survived by doing this, and presumably more than would have survived in the harsher foodless winter on their breeding grounds.

There is no good evidence that British-born tits have ever been widely involved in any of these movements, even though of course they too suffer food shortages in winter. However a number of British-born birds travelled unusually long distances during the autumn of 1957 and these may have become caught up with parties of invaders on the move. The most likely explanation for this difference between British and Continental tits would seem to lie with the reason for irrupting in the first place. Presumably natural selection would favour a bird's departure from an area for the winter only if it stood a better chance of surviving by so doing than if it stayed where it was; in this way the habit has evolved.

In Europe the winter weather becomes milder both as one moves south and as one moves west (because of the warming effect of the Atlantic Gulf Stream). Hence the birds from northern Scandinavia or Russia stand to gain by moving south and west into areas where, compared with their birthplace, the winter weather is milder and the mid-winter days are longer; both factors are to their advantage. While the advantage of such movement may be marked for the northernmost populations, this cannot apply to the British tits to nearly the same extent. British birds cannot go much farther west and would have to go a long way south in order to get any noticeable benefit from milder weather. Hence it is hardly surprising that, when faced with food shortages, the British tits have evolved the tendency to remain where they are while those in the more northerly populations have tended to move.

At least one other puzzle remains unsolved, and this is that although irruptions occur not infrequently on the Continent, it is unusual for large numbers of the birds to reach Britain. Why they should get as far as Britain in some years and not in others is not known. This may in part be an effect of the numbers of birds involved, but this suggestion does not seem to hold for two of the recent years 1957 and 1959, when large numbers of birds were reported on the move. Many tits reached Britain in the first year but, if anything, there seem to have been larger numbers of birds moving on the Continent in 1959. It seems as if the birds moved in different directions in the two years, though the reasons for this are unknown[68].

Recently it has been calculated that irrupting Coal Tits passing through the Alps may travel at a rate of some 70–80 km. per day[325]. However, this speed is highly variable since the birds may stop and rest on some days and move on more quickly on others. Further, birds with larger fat reserves tend to fly for longer than those with fewer reserves; the latter stop sooner in order to feed. Irruptive movements of tits only occur during the daylight and mostly only for a few hours in the morning after which they stop to feed.

Beech trees produce seed in some years and not others, a typical sequence being as follows: the trees flower heavily in May and if there are no late frosts, many flowers are pollinated and a good seed crop is produced in the autumn. When fruiting, the trees put much of their energy into producing the seeds and, although leaf buds are formed for the following year, the trees do not form more flowering buds; hence there are usually no flowers the following spring and no crop of seeds that autumn. If the trees fare well in the second summer, they may lay down both leaf and flower buds for the following spring and so the sequence is repeated. A beech tree cannot therefore produce heavy crops of seeds in two successive years (p. 137). They may crop every second year, but more often there seems to be an interval of more than two years between good crops of mast.

Late spring frosts may kill the flowers and prevent fruiting in which case the trees may form flower buds for the next year. Since the weather is often similar over wide areas, the individual trees tend to become synchronized with one another and so the seed crops may occur or 'fail' over wide areas of Europe in the same year. In consequence the tits over the same wide area face winters of feast or famine.

The size of the beech crop in southern Sweden has an important effect on the tits[387]; if the crop is good, the birds remain in the vicinity all winter whereas if it is poor, many birds leave the woodland and observers at Falsterbo (a bird observatory on the southern tip of Sweden) report many tits heading southwards out over the sea towards Denmark. In the autumn of 1960 I realized that the presence or absence of beechmast also had a major effect on the tit populations in Wytham with larger numbers breeding after a winter of good seed crops, lower numbers after a winter with poor crops.

Subsequent to Ulfstrand's study[387] it was possible to collect other records of beech crops from Germany and to plot them, together with the Swedish and the British crops, against the numbers of tits observed migrating through not only Falsterbo, but also the Col de Bretolet, a mountain pass between Switzerland and France where migration had been recorded by the Swiss workers. These data showed some remarkable correlations (fig. 42). Movements could be correlated with the beech crops over wide areas of Europe. Only in one year, 1954, was the seed crop markedly different in two areas, and in that year also the irruptions were not synchronized but matched the crops in their own areas. The close correlation between the crops in these two areas does not seem to hold for western and eastern Europe. The numbers of birds migrating at Bretolet is not well correlated with the numbers seen on the move in Finland and Poland[325]; in all probability these birds are on the move from still farther east in Russia where the weather and hence the seed crops are not in phase with those in western Europe.

There has been much discussion as to whether or not the birds that undertake the irruptions in autumn do so because they in some way 'know' that there will be a food shortage in winter. Theoretically they could make such a judgement if the foods that they take in autumn vary in parallel with the winter seed crops, and are already in short supply. Alternatively the birds might have a natural tendency to move when their numbers are high and so avoid over-populated areas. It is usually difficult to separate the effects of these two factors, food and numbers, because the beech crops and numbers of tits go hand-in-hand. As mentioned, large numbers of birds survive to breed following a good supply of beech seed in winter, but this is always followed by a winter without a good beech crop. Hence high numbers – resulting from a large breeding population – tend to occur in autumns when there is no crop and low numbers in autumns when there is a crop. Thus it is difficult to obtain information on years when there are high numbers of birds and also a rich supply of food (p. 244). Nevertheless it is clear that at high latitudes irruptions occur at high densities and, as a result, low numbers spend the winter in these areas[365].

Since the crops of seeds tend to be synchronized over wide areas of Europe, a tit's chance of finding food more plentiful elsewhere is not good; it is more probable that the bird will move from one area of scarcity to another. Nevertheless as can be seen from figure 42 there are years (1954) when some areas have good seed crops while others have none and this coupled with the likelihood of reaching places with a mild winter must make it worthwhile to take the risk of moving, especially since food will certainly be scarce in the immediate vicinity of the bird's birthplace.

FOOD STORAGE

In winter when the food requirements are high and the day is short, the birds may need to feed for most of the day (chapter 11). When the days are shortest, the birds rise earliest and go to bed latest in relation to sunrise and sunset. At such times bad weather makes them particularly susceptible to starvation.

To help them survive under these adverse conditions, many tits store food. In Britain both Coal and Marsh Tits regularly do this. The Willow Tit has also been recorded storing food but since this is a scarce species it is not clear how commonly it does so; the habit appears to be regular in the Breckland pine plantation[127]. Richards[305, 306] has reviewed the storage of food by the British tits. The habit is commoner in Scandinavia where winters are colder and the days even shorter. Haftorn has made detailed studies of food storage by tits in Norway[144] *et seq*.

The foods most commonly stored are seeds of various kinds – or small pieces of peanut from bird tables. Pine seeds are collected in spring and spruce seeds in autumn – the times when they are shed. Gibb records Willow Tits as storing many seeds of dead-nettles *Galeopsis* spp. Naturally, these items keep well throughout the winter. Animal foods are also stored. Both Coal Tits and Marsh Tits have been recorded collecting and storing small slugs[276, 349]. In Norway the Crested Tit stores a considerable amount of insect food, as much as 20% of the total food stored by this species may be animal matter[144]. Caterpillars are usually immobilized prior to being stored but are rarely killed. They may stay alive for several weeks after collection – presumably they keep fresh longer alive than dead. Coal Tits store aphids as well as lepidopterous and dipterous larvae[145, 148, 230]. Larvae are stored singly, whereas the aphids are stored in little pellets, mixed with the birds' saliva, each pellet containing some 20–50 aphids[127]. At least some of these food items are found and eaten much later in the winter, long after live specimens have disappeared from the trees.

All the conifer-dwelling tits in Norway – Coal, Crested, Lapp and Willow – store food, though only one of the deciduous woodland species, the Marsh Tit, does so. Several of the Norwegian species base their whole winter 'economy' on spruce seeds that they have stored, yet only remove about 1% of the available seed[149]. In Britain, the birds may store the food in almost any place, often behind the bark of trees, but also under moss, in grass tussocks and a variety of other places on the ground. In Norway the different species store food in different places (p. 93), but they do not normally store food on the ground, usually they put it in crevices in the bark or amongst the needles. Since thick snow regularly lies on the ground for several months in Scandinavia, food stored there would be inaccessible to the birds at the most crucial time. In the Breck the large majority of the seed was stored behind bark at heights of between 1 and 8 metres above the ground, even though they were collected at all heights. By doing this, the birds reduce the area over which they have to search for the stored food and this too must be a help. In the American Plain Titmouse, the birds only store the larger seeds, eating the smaller ones, this being the most efficient use of time[75].

The subsequent use of the stored seeds has been studied by Haftorn in an area where the tits were colour-ringed. A high proportion of the seeds are found again, though not necessarily by the individuals who stored them; an individual stores seed over such a wide area of the forest that these may be found by many different birds. Nevertheless the fact that all birds store food results in a general raising of the level of available food for all the birds. Crested Tits may move the food from one place to another during the winter. In the Breck, Coal Tits store food all the year round except during the breeding season and in mid-winter, when presumably they do not have time to do so. At other times, they spend up to 25% of the day storing food[127].

For some reason neither Great nor Blue Tits regularly store food. The more resident a bird the more it stands to gain from storing food, since it is the more likely to benefit from it at a later stage[165]. Since both Great and Blue Tits cover largish areas in winter, this may explain why they store food less than the other species. In garden areas in Britain, however, the Great Tit is a major nuisance to the other tits, particularly the Coal Tits, since it will follow them, watch them store food and then collect it. This behaviour may be more than a passing nuisance since, by doing this, the Great Tit may learn the sort of places where the other species hide food and so continue to rob their supplies throughout the winter.

FEEDING HABITS IN SUMMER

After the rigours of winter, the birds may be in poor condition and may need milder weather and better food supplies for some considerable period in order to fully recover. The members of a pair need plentiful supplies of food both before and during breeding since they have additional calls on their time which prevent them from spending the whole day feeding themselves. The male spends much of his day in territorial defence and in accompanying the female as she builds. The female spends a proportion of her day collecting nesting material; in addition she needs extra food to that required for normal body maintenance because her sexual organs – oviduct and ovaries – have to grow to breeding size from the size to which they regress outside the breeding season. Such changes result in her body weight increasing by 10–15% and at this time of year she is heavier than the male (fig. 37). When she actually starts to form eggs the female needs still more food and the male may help by feeding her (p. 172). During laying she is even heavier since she carries a number of eggs in various stages of formation; the largest of them is the one that she will lay the following morning – this is normally fully-formed by dusk the night before. At such times a female Blue Tit may weigh as much as 15 grams compared with about 10 grams at the beginning and the end of the breeding season.

The details of the timing of the breeding season will be discussed later (chapter 14), but clearly the female – and to some extent the male – needs rich food supplies in order to be able to commence breeding. As the breeding season approaches the birds may be seen feeding very busily, often among the opening leaf buds on the trees where newly hatched caterpillars are having their first meal. Blue Tits commonly take small insects off the flowers of 'pussy willow' *Salix* spp. at this time. These flowers are rich in pollen and it is possible that the birds may also eat the pollen, which is a rich source of protein, as well as the insects. In early spring in Japan, the Great Tit concentrates on feeding on the wild cherry, *Prunus* spp., where, at this time, large numbers of very tiny caterpillars are to be found[317].

Typically, once the young caterpillars have hatched, the food supply for the birds steadily increases as the days go by. There may, however, be occasional set-backs as a result of particularly bad weather; when this happens the birds that are building may stop work and no new clutches may be started until after the weather has started to improve again (p. 176).

Once the female has managed to get sufficient food to start laying, she should be able to continue since food becomes progressively more plentiful. However, after she has completed laying she must incubate the eggs for much of the day and so has even less time to spend searching for food; again the male may help her. Normally the female initiates the assistance by following

the male, begging for food; he responds and later starts to bring food without
such stimulation[318].

By the time the young hatch, small caterpillars are fairly plentiful and,
judging by the feeding rates of the parent birds, they must be easy to collect.
The young are fed on a wide variety of different prey though insects are the
main diet and caterpillars predominate in early broods. In Wytham caterpillars of a large variety of species are collected from the oak trees; Winter
Moth larvae form a large part of the diet of small young in early broods (fig.
44).

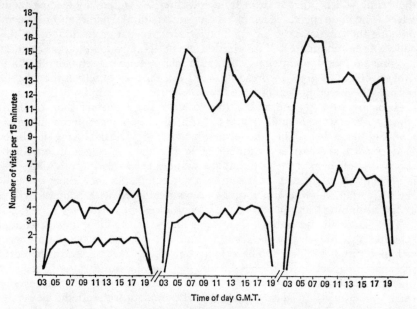

FIG. 44.   The feeding rates of Great Tits to their nestlings. The graphs show the number of
visits made per fifteen minute period to broods in Wytham. The nestling period is divided into
three periods and the feeding rates to large broods (upper graphs) are compared with those to
small broods to give some idea of the range (from Gibb 1950).

The above description of feeding applies mainly to Coal, Great and Blue
Tits feeding in oakwoods. The feeding behaviour in pinewoods also has been
much studied and there is a marked difference from the situation in oakwoods. Different species of caterpillars are of course involved. Except during
rare outbreaks, caterpillars are scarcer in pine than in oakwoods; they
increase more slowly at the beginning of the season and reach their highest
levels long after the first broods have left the nest.

The breeding season of the tits in pinewoods is basically the same as that
in oak, except that there are many more second broods in pine, especially in
the case of Coal and Great Tits (p. 183). The success of the birds is de-

pendent on the food supply. Mortality in the nest tends to be higher in first than in second broods and may reach quite high levels if caterpillars are scarce.

In the Breck young in first broods received about 4·7 grams of food per day compared with 7·3 grams per chick in later broods (though since the later broods are slightly smaller, the total amounts of food brought to the nest are not quite as different as these figures suggest)[129]. The number of caterpillars in pinewoods may be so low as to affect the feeding rates, weights and survival rates of the young tits[18]. Further, the growth rates of young in pinewoods are lower than those of young in oak even when the young are receiving equivalent weights of food; presumably the nutritive value of caterpillars in pinewoods is lower than that of those in oak[18].

In oakwood the food supply for the young increases rapidly during the early part of the breeding season. Nevertheless it is only abundant for a very short period, sometimes as little as two weeks, and then rapidly decreases again. Later in the season when the caterpillars have gone, other insects are present though they are more scattered. Apparently they are less easily gathered than the oak caterpillars since the young in late broods are less well nourished and lighter in weight than those in early ones (but see p. 259).

THE CHOICE OF FOOD

A great deal of information has been collected on the food brought into the nests of Coal, Blue and Great Tits[27, 320, 378]; in particular research workers have been interested in the choice of prey – what is brought in to the young in relation to what is known to be available near to the nest. Individual prey species tend to become more common and then disappear again, so that regular measurements of what insects are feeding on the leaves are usually also necessary.

An interesting pattern emerges from these observations (fig. 45). When caterpillars first become available for food, the birds take relatively few of them. However, as the species becomes more common the birds may, quite abruptly, start to take them in much greater numbers. Often the two members of a pair may collect similar prey and change their choices at the same time, though this is not always so. If the particular caterpillar becomes the commonest available, the birds may concentrate on them to a very high degree. However, they never take any one species to the exclusion of all others and no species ever seems to represent more than about 90% of the diet even though it may represent 99% or more of the caterpillars available to the birds. No such pattern was noted during the predation of the adult moths of *Bupalus piniarius* which were only available for a few hours each day when they had just hatched and were drying their wings[245].

Two main interpretations have been put forward to explain these observations. It was suggested that the birds formed a 'searching image' for a particular type of caterpillar[378]. The tits might learn to recognize a few

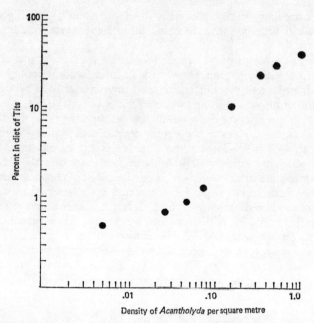

FIG. 45. Relationship between density of a larva (*Acantholyda*) and the percentage of the larvae in the food of nestling Great Tits. Note that the birds do not start taking many of the larvae until they have become quite common, and how the proportion in the diet levels off at about 80% (based on Tinbergen *et al* 1960).

common species and spend most of their time looking especially for them. As another species appeared and became more common the tits, although not looking for it, would 'bump into' it on occasions. At such times they would take relatively few. However, if this species became progressively more numerous, the tits would come across it more and more frequently and so might start looking particularly for it; they would have developed a searching image for this species. From then on the proportion taken would rapidly rise as birds started to hunt for it specifically.

The fact that when a caterpillar species becomes particularly abundant the tits take it relatively less frequently, requires a different explanation. Tinbergen suggested that there might be different food value in different species of caterpillar and hence one species is never taken to the exclusion of all others in order that the young should receive a 'mixed diet'.

A different explanation has been proposed for these observations[320]. This supposes that each species of caterpillar lives in a slightly different way, probably living in different places on the leaves or on the tree (in the same way that each species of tit has a different ecology – chapter 9). The parent tits look into many of these different places and concentrate on those sites which they find to be the most profitable. However, they also spend some time looking in other sites and hence soon notice if a different species becomes abundant. If it becomes more profitable than their other prey, then they concentrate upon it. This suggestion assumes that, however easily they may collect one species of prey, the tits can never be certain that another one might not be still easier to find, so they always spend a proportion of their time looking into the other likely sites. This explains why the proportion of a very abundant prey in the diet is lower than its relative abundance in the field; the birds always spend some time looking in other places where they do not come across it. By sacrificing a little time feeding on the most profitable species, the birds have an insurance policy in that they know where to go for food when the main species of the moment becomes less common. Although differences in 'microhabitats' between the caterpillar species have not been demonstrated, they probably exist; typically the tits take a 'run' of one species of prey, then switch to other prey species which may also be taken in runs. On such occasions, it certainly seems as if the birds know where to go to get the different species.

Whatever explanation is correct, the pattern shown in figure 45 seems to be widespread. It has been recorded in oakwoods and in pinewoods in Britain, Holland and Japan where the birds have been feeding on a wide variety of insects. Further, as with their winter food (p. 134), either explanation requires a complex series of responses and adjustments on behalf of the birds. They are using a series of strategies that result in the collection of considerable quantities of food. Once again it is not difficult to imagine a human being following the same course of action.

Various other relationships between the birds and their prey have been shown. In some cases the numbers of prey species have been known and so it has been possible to measure the proportion of the larvae taken by the tits. In most cases they are taking only a very small proportion of the total prey available. Even though a pair of Blue Tits may take 10,000 caterpillars to their broods during the course of the nestling period, in a good year, there may be over a hundred thousand caterpillars in a single large oak and usually there are several or even many trees in a single territory. All the evidence suggests that in oakwoods the birds are having virtually no effect at all on the populations of their prey at this time.

Hence, although nesting boxes were erected in certain areas (such as the Forest of Dean) originally in order to try to control the numbers of defoliating caterpillars, the beneficial effects of these attempts have been doubted. (However, see p. 255.) While the tits may not have any effect on the numbers of caterpillars, the effect of the caterpillars on the tits is another story altogether; in order to successfully raise their broods the tits must have their young in the nest when the caterpillars are abundant (chapter 14).

Under many conditions the birds may appear to take whatever they come across in woodland – though they may be hunting in places where they are particularly likely to find certain species; it is most unlikely that parent birds, which are so busy feeding young, would leave good food alone. However, they do not indiscriminately pick up anything they find. Some species of insects have irritating hairs or a noxious taste. The tits have a good power of taste discrimination and can recognize and therefore choose the food they take[402]. Tinbergen and his co-workers[378] have shown that size of prey, its conspicuousness, palatability and density all affect the chances of an insect being taken. A tit learns to select its prey by picking up the distasteful insects, trying them, and rejecting them; rejection is often accompanied by every sign of discomfort ranging from gaping to vigorous wiping of the beak. Such distasteful objects are remembered and it has been shown that Great Tits have good memories for them, often avoiding them when they are encountered as much as a year later[59, 315]. Marsh Tits have been shown to remember individual people for at least eleven months[248]. Obviously the tits should be able to remember prey species for at least a year since many of the prey which they encounter are strictly seasonal and so only present at certain times of the year. The outcome of such experience of unpalatable items is that the birds may avoid certain quite common insects or take them only relatively rarely[378]. However, it is not correct to imagine that such insects are totally avoided. While only a low proportion may be taken, the tits' discrimination is far from absolute.

For obvious reasons, most measurements of food are based on food quantity; though the quality of the diet is equally important, it is much harder to study. Nevertheless there are occasions when the birds are being selective in a way which suggests that they are selecting the food by its quality rather than its availability. A good example is the way spiders are fed to the young tits. Usually spiders form only a small proportion of the food fed to the young, less than 5% of the total diet. However, the proportion of spiders in the diet increases during the period when the young are about 5–8 days old, when they may constitute up to 10% of the diet. This change of diet occurs in late broods as well as early ones. It occurs in broods in pinewoods as well as in oakwoods in Britain, Holland and Japan[18, 129, 320]. The reason for the increase of spiders in the diet at this one stage in the nestling period is not known, but in view of the frequency with which it occurs, presumably it reflects some subtle need; spiders must contain something that caterpillars do not, and which is essential to the growing young at this stage.

PROFITABILITY OF DIFFERENT PREY SIZES

Some workers have studied the profitability of different prey. Tits, except the Long-tailed Tit, usually bring back only a single item at any one visit to the nest; if the larvae are small, the parents may bring two to three items per visit. Only if the items are very small do they regularly bring many items; for example a Blue Tit may gather a whole beakful of greenfly at one time. It may seem wasteful to make the journey to the nest with only one or two prey items but there are good reasons for doing so. Large caterpillars can inflict a serious bite on a young tit and if they hold on to the side of the throat of the young bird they may choke and kill it. In order to avoid this, the parent tits take the larva to a perch, put it under a foot and beat it hard. Usually they break the head with a series of sharp blows. This takes but a few moments but it would be difficult to do if they were carrying several large caterpillars at a time.

If the birds are only bringing back a single prey at a time then obviously they will maximize their feeding of the young by bringing large prey wherever possible; the tits rarely bring caterpillars of less than one centimetre in length to their young[378]. However, this might result in their leaving untouched the smaller ones they come across, which would be wasteful. The tits have solved this problem by eating the small prey themselves and bringing the larger ones to the nest. Hence nothing is wasted and the birds spend their time in the most efficient way[320].

It seems likely that the male who feeds the incubating female behaves in a similar manner. At this stage in the season the caterpillars are mostly small. However, the male appears to bring his mate larvae that are larger than average[200], so he is probably eating the smaller ones himself. Taking the largest food items to the nest may further benefit the birds. In addition to maximizing the feeding efficiency the birds minimize the number of visits to the nest; this may well reduce the chances of a predator locating the brood.

The situation changes once the young have fledged – these now accompany the foraging adults so the latter do not have to make journeys with the prey; accordingly the young are fed small as well as large caterpillars at this time.

CALCIUM AND GRIT

The essential nutrients for a balanced diet are not easily studied. They are many and varied and not well known for the domestic hen – let alone for the tits. One element that is needed in considerable quantity for egg formation and chick growth is calcium and a little is known about how this is obtained. The shell of a Blue Tit egg weighs about 0·1 gram and hence the shells of a clutch of 10 eggs 1·0 gram. Egg shell is composed mainly of calcium carbonate and almost half of this (by weight) is calcium. Hence about 0·5 grams of calcium is required for the production of the one gram of calcium carbonate used in a clutch of 10 eggs. In the domestic hen some of the calcium used in the production of egg shells is stored in advance in the skeleton of the birds[311]. However, in the case of the Blue Tit the whole skeleton weighs only a little more than the calcium in the egg shells (about 0·6 grams) so clearly relatively little calcium is stored. Therefore, during the course of the egg-laying period, the birds must be getting sufficient calcium to form the egg shells. Roughly speaking they must get about enough each day to form the shell of one egg.

During the laying period the females go to roost at night with their gizzards full of snail shell. Since this is a good source of calcium, it looks as if the female must collect snail shell specially for this purpose; if so, she must stop her normal feeding in time to allow her to spend the last part of the day collecting the snail shell, and so the time for normal feeding is reduced.

The situation is complicated in that the female goes to roost with an almost completely formed egg in her oviduct; at this time the egg is already pigmented so that it is unlikely that any more calcium will be added to it. Hence the snail shell that the bird takes to roost in its gizzard cannot be for the egg that the bird will lay the following morning but must be for the egg that will be laid the day after – 36 hours after the snail shell was collected.

Some birds have snail shell in the gizzard even if no more eggs are being formed in the ovary and the one already in the oviduct will be the last of the clutch. Hence some of the calcium could be used to replace some taken from the skeleton. Relatively little is known about the collection of calcium for egg shell. The Red-billed Quelea, *Quelea quelea*, collects calcareous grit when it is laying[180]. In this species too the female often collects the grit on the evening prior to laying the last egg. However, unlike the Blue Tit, she often goes to roost without having completed the last egg and therefore she could use the calcium for this.

This description of Blue Tits taking snail shell is based on birds that have been collected during the laying period and dissected. I know of no records where female tits have been actually observed collecting snail shells during the laying period, although one report describes a male Blue Tit calling its incubating mate out of the nest to feed her snail shell[386]. However, it seems as if this method of collecting calcium must be a regular feature and it is slightly curious that it has been overlooked.

The rapidly growing young also need large quantities of calcium for their skeletons and it is not known how easily they can get this from their diets. However, from time to time one finds in a tit's nest bits of egg shell from Song Thrush or Blackbird eggs, as well as small snail shells. Apparently the parent birds may bring these in order to supplement the calcium supplies for the young. However they could also be used as roughage; since birds do not have teeth they need grit in their gizzards to enable them to grind up food. The parent tits bring in quantities of sand for this purpose[18, 320]. Young Blackbirds, *Turdus merula*, are unable to get enough calcium for their needs from earthworms unless these have soil in their guts[31]. The worms' tissues contain little calcium but the soil in their digestive systems contains sufficient calcium for the growing birds. There are a few scattered reports of poorly-developed young tits in pinewoods. Since these are in general acid areas where snails are rare, possibly the parents are not always able to get sufficient calcium for their young.

This is but a brief review of some of the feeding behaviours of the tits. They show such a wide range of different feeding patterns that many biologists have made detailed studies of them and the interpretation of these observations is still far from complete. Nevertheless these birds show themselves to be amazingly versatile. Whether they are struggling in winter to get enough food to survive the next cold night or in summer to rear a large number of young they are clearly responding to what food they come across in such a way as to make the best possible use of the resources. In addition, they collect certain special foods at particular times – snail shells when forming eggs, spiders for small young. We have a long way to go before we understand why or how they do all these things. One thing seems certain and that is that the more we learn the more we realize how superbly adapted the tits are for their way of life.

CHAPTER 13

BREEDING BIOLOGY

AN understanding of the nesting behaviour of the tits will be useful for the following chapters which deal with the timing of breeding, clutch-size and the survival of the young. Once again workers have tended to concentrate on Great and Blue Tits and hence more is known about them than about other species. Nevertheless the nesting behaviour of all British species is fairly well known.

In many ways the true tits (Paridae) are a very stereotyped group, all showing the same basic pattern. Thus what has been found out about Great and Blue Tits is largely true of the other species also. Some of the more marked differences have been given in the chapters on species (2–8) but even these are relatively small. The greatest differences are shown by the Willow Tit and Crested Tit, both of which excavate a new cavity for themselves every year, and by the less closely related Long-tailed Tit, which builds an entirely different sort of nest out of feathers and lichens.

SITE SELECTION

The birds may roost, throughout the winter, in natural holes or artificial nesting boxes. As described earlier, they seem to prefer a smaller hole for roosting than the one they use for nesting in. Only when there is a great shortage of holes (as in a young plantation) do they commonly roost in nesting boxes during the winter. Since they tend to defaecate in the roosting site, they may avoid roosting in good nesting sites in order to keep them clean. The majority of the birds that roost in nest-boxes in mid-winter are males, but females roost increasingly in boxes as spring approaches; often they subsequently breed in the site they choose for roosting. In Kluijver's study area in Holland, the Great Tits ideally need a territory with three suitable nest-holes in it – one for the male to roost in and the other two for the two broods. However, in Wytham not only are there many small natural holes for the males to roost in but also, as two broods are very unusual, one nest-box seems sufficient as a rule.

Normally the pair does not roost together. Tree Sparrows, *Passer montanus*, may roost in the nest-boxes in pairs and Wrens, *Troglodytes troglodytes*, in small groups but the tits almost invariably roost singly. However, Howard's tame Great Tits occasionally roosted in pairs in a rather densely populated area. The female tried to prevent her mate from joining her but on occasions his persistence prevailed.

Since the female often breeds in the site in which she roosts it seems that

154

she is usually responsible for making the final decision over the choice of nesting sites, possibly some months before breeding. In all species the pairs explore together, the male showing sites to the female; in both the Crested and Willow Tits, special 'prospecting' calls have been described[263]. The period of searching for and selecting nest-sites may be accompanied in the males by a distinctive 'butterfly' flight of jerky, shallow wing beats[359]. When the male finds a possible site he attracts the female to it by displaying near by, entering it and calling her to follow; she may then accept or reject the site. The male commonly shows his mate several sites before she accepts one[173]. Howard cites a case where the female never really settled to nest-building although the male tried very hard to get her to accept a variety of sites. In the Long-tailed Tit the male may indicate a site by starting to build there, though again the female appears to make the final decision, accepting or rejecting the male's choice[260].

It is not known what makes the birds finally select a particular site. Each species has a basic preference for a different type of position of nest-site (p. 97) and this clearly affects the decision. In many studies of tits the nesting boxes are cleaned out by observers at the end of the season – often while the observer examines the lining of the nest for unhatched eggs, dead young or other items such as parasites. In nature obviously this would not happen; the nest material would slowly decompose within the chamber and presumably over a series of years the site might become filled with old nests.

Removal of the nests also results in the removal of many parasites which live there from one season to another. In early spring a box that has not been cleaned out may have a ring of fleas sitting around the hole waiting to leap on to the first bird to investigate the site. Study populations of birds may therefore be less infested by parasites than other populations of tits. I suggested earlier that the reason the Willow Tit makes a new hole each year may be linked with gaining freedom from parasites, but if this is the case, why do not all tits make their own sites? In this connection it is noticeable that tits often select new nesting boxes in preference to old when both are available. Every year some of the nesting boxes in Wytham deteriorate to the point where they cannot be repaired and have to be replaced and several workers have noticed that the birds appear to occupy the new nest-boxes preferentially; possibly under natural conditions the birds also select clean sites in order to reduce the hazards from parasites. Curiously, however, they do not appear to remove old nests themselves. Further, the birds seem to choose a different nest-site for their second brood if one is available to them so that the infestations of parasites may be important to the birds in natural situations. There is one Russian reference to second broods being less successful when raised in the same box as the first, apparently as a result of parasites[45]. In Germany also, second or third broods may sometimes fail completely as a result of infestations of fleas[407].

NEST-BUILDING

The female may spend long periods in the hole before she actually starts to build a nest. She is dominant to the male at the nest and he seldom enters at this stage. While in the box, she pecks at the nest entrance, possibly trying to enlarge it or see how firm the wood is. She also spends a lot of time pecking round the inside of the nest-site, removing any soft wood. In an observation box lined on one side with cardboard the female Blue Tit pecked at and removed all the cardboard along the whole side from floor level to about three inches up the wall – about as far as she could reach. Such behaviour presumably serves to check that the nest-site is not so rotten that it may fall apart or be opened easily by a predator. The loosened material is removed from the nesting chamber; this may help to reduce any parasites that are hidden there. Exceptionally in the Blue Tit both birds may excavate and remove wood chippings[11] or excavate a complete nest chamber[307].

In addition to pecking at the nest, the female may spend some time rubbing herself along the bottom of the nest-hole. She rubs her breast against the floor, pushing outwards to the edges of the nesting space. It is not clear why she does this at this stage though later, when she has brought in nesting material, she forms the cup of the nest with an identical action.

In the true tits the female alone builds the nest, though the male frequently accompanies her while she is fetching the material and may look in to see how the nest is progressing. With the exception of the Willow Tit, tits build their nests predominantly of moss; Blue Tits build a foundation including more grass, small twigs and bast (thin grass-like strips of the inner bark from dead trees) than other species. The Willow Tit uses less nesting material than the other species and so moss is a much rarer constituent than in other species. The male Long-tailed Tit does a lot of the nest-building with his mate.

Initially the female may find it difficult to bring twigs into the nest since she often brings them cross-wise in her beak and cannot pass the entrance to the nest. However, usually she soon learns to carry twigs by the end and to pull them through the nest hole after her. Moss is often brought to the nest in such large quantities that one wonders how the female can see where she is going; initially the moss is just dropped on to the floor of the nest hole and pushed towards the edges by the rubbing action described above. The steady accumulation of nest material confines the rubbing action to a progressively smaller space on the nest floor; eventually by turning and rubbing the bird forms a small circular depression – the nest cup. If space allows, the cup is not situated in the middle of the floor, but towards the side farthest from the entrance; possibly this enables the female to have a better – though still somewhat limited – view of the outside world, or perhaps a slightly better chance of escaping a predator. These are rather weak suggestions, but such positioning of the nest is very regular.

Having formed the basic shape of the cup, the female then lines it by

weaving in other materials. In Blue, Marsh and, to a lesser extent, Willow
Tits the final cup is usually lined with feathers whereas in Coal, Crested
and Great Tits feathers are rarely used, the lining being mainly of hair or
fur. Most of the nesting material is gathered nearby and if one finds a
number of adjacent nests lined with the same distinctive material, as for
example the feathers of a Tawny Owl, it is usually easy to find the source of
these by looking for a dead bird somewhere between the nests. Sometimes,
however, presumably when material is scarce, the birds may travel considerable distances to get lining for the nest; they may go to the edge of the
wood and gather wool from gardens or horsehair from a barbed-wire fence
along a field. A well-known way of finding nests of Long-tailed Tits is to
put out small piles of chicken feathers and then return at a later date and
follow the birds as they make sorties to and fro between the piles and the
nests that they are building. This can also be done with other species that use
feathers, but it is more difficult since they use far fewer feathers and collect
them for a much shorter period.

The final shape of the cup is made by the bird turning round and round
while pulling the material up to herself with her beak. In this way she builds
not only a circular nest cup, but also one that fits her snugly, enabling her to
keep the eggs close to her and warm. Occasionally birds build a nest lacking
a base. Sometimes when a laying bird loses a nest to a predator, it will build
another one very quickly in order to continue laying. Such nests are usually
poor affairs and easily recognizable as being rushed; the birds may have
been building for less than a day. In many of these hurried nests the birds
continue building during the first few days of laying until an adequate nest
is completed. Hatching success in such nests is usually low because there is
nothing to prevent the eggs from getting pushed under the moss sides where
they do not then receive adequate incubation. In a well-built nest where a
properly-lined cup is woven into the side walls the eggs tend to roll inwards
and to stay together. Nest building may be spread over several weeks,
especially if periods of cold weather interrupt the birds' activities. On the
other hand, an adequate nest can be completed in as little as three or four
days. Nest lining may be added for several days after laying has started
even in unhurried nests[11].

THE LAYING PERIOD

The female roosts in the nest overnight and usually lays her eggs early in
the morning – at around 0600 hours. Normally she does this before leaving
the nest, but she may leave the nest and return to lay a little later[301].

Once a bird has started to lay she usually lays an egg each day until she
completes the clutch: only very severe weather or some major interference
breaks this routine. Occasionally Blue Tits lay more than seven in a week,
but Great Tits practically never do this. This habit of laying one egg each
day is very useful to the observer since, because the tits usually lay more than

seven, a weekly visit to each box is sufficient to establish the date on which a clutch was started.

During the laying period the female covers the eggs with a wad of nesting material prior to leaving the nest. Presumably when they are covered the nest seems empty to a casual glance and so this behaviour saves some nests from predation. The observer should always remember this habit since it is easy to break eggs if one does not realize that these may be buried in the nesting material. Once incubation has started this habit is discontinued; covering and uncovering the eggs each time the female left the nest would take up too much time. At night when the female goes to roost in the box she uncovers the eggs and sits on them. However, since almost all the eggs hatch within a day or so of one another, she cannot actually be incubating properly. Presumably her body feathers lie between her and the eggs and the latter receive little heat.

INCUBATION

Towards the end of the laying period the brood patch becomes well developed. The feathers on the belly are shed and the brood patch becomes highly vascularized; the extra flow of blood near the surface of the body facilitates the warming of the eggs. In order to reduce unnecessary heat loss the brood patch is covered by the flank feathers when the bird is off the eggs but when incubating the hen moves these aside so as to apply the brood patch directly to them.

In most nests full incubation does not start until the clutch is complete, or nearly so. There is some variation in the timing of the start of incubation in relation to the end of laying; some birds delay incubation until several days after the clutch has been completed but most commonly the female starts incubating when all but one of the eggs have been laid. Females that lay clutches late in the season tend to start incubating some days before the clutch is complete with the result that the young hatch over a period of several days. The significance of this is discussed later (p. 203).

One tends to think of an incubating bird as just sitting on the eggs. In fact, it is often not like this. Firstly the female does not stay on them for long periods; she leaves at frequent intervals in order to get food either from her mate or by searching for it herself. Secondly when the female is actually sitting on the eggs she is seldom still, but perpetually moves around and fidgets with them. There may be good reasons for such activity; a female with a large clutch may not be able to warm all the eggs equally unless she moves them around and in addition, most birds' eggs need turning occasionally if the embryos are to develop properly (perhaps so that an even flow of nutrient and waste matter is maintained around the growing embryo); by moving all frequently she can be certain to have moved each one. Female Blackbirds are also very restless while incubating during the day, though they tend to be quieter at night[141]. The period on the eggs varies markedly; a female Blue Tit may spend an average of 15 minutes on followed by 5 minutes off[301]. The main factor affecting her behaviour is usually the weather, the eggs needing more heat in cold than in warm weather; female House Sparrows spend a greater proportion of the day incubating in cold than in warm weather[76].

The tits are unable to recognize their own eggs and will sit on those of other tits with equal attentiveness. A tit does not need to be able to recognize her eggs or young in the way that gulls or other colonial species do; the chances of one individual's getting confused with those of another are very slight and hence they do not seem to have evolved the ability to recognize their own eggs – or even their young – while these are in the nest. However, especially in years with high breeding populations, more than one tit may lay in the same nest. There are a number of records of such mixed broods[10, 12, 399]. Apart from Long-tailed Tits where two females may occasionally lay complete clutches, usually only one of the females lays a normal clutch. The other lays only a small number of eggs before, presumably, being driven off[7]. As a result in Wytham we have not infrequently had young Blue Tits raised in the nests of Great Tits and the reverse. In addition we have once found a young Coal Tit and once a young Marsh Tit in a brood of Blue Tits and once young Great Tits in a brood of Nuthatches. If there is a marked difference in size between the two species, the young of the smaller species do not fare well, for example young Great Tits in a brood of Blue Tits are more likely to be raised than Blue Tits in a brood of Great Tits. Clutches laid by more than one female Blue or Great Tit are more frequent and doubtless some go unrecognized as such. Although the parent birds do not seem to react to strange eggs in the nest, several observers have noticed that if eggs are marked with pencil-numbers (so as to record the order in which they were laid) the incubating female tends to turn all the eggs so that the numbers face downwards[130]; perhaps out of sight is out of mind!

Since the eggs, except perhaps the last one, all start receiving proper incubation at the same time most of the young hatch within a short period of one another. Within this period there is a tendency for the eggs to hatch in the order in which they were laid, suggesting that they receive sufficient warmth from the roosting bird for a small amount of development to take place before full incubation starts. However, the young in a healthy brood tend to be fairly even in size with only the last one or two to hatch being a little smaller than the rest. In those late nests where incubation starts well before the clutch is complete, the young hatch over a longer period than is the case with normal broods and there may be a wider range of sizes.

The start of incubation is not clear-cut but a gradual process when the female spends progressively longer and longer in the nest. There is considerable variation in the interval between the start of incubation and the time at which the eggs hatch. Some of this variation results from different incubation rhythms of the female during the day; some birds spent more time incubating than others. There is less variation in incubation if one counts not the interval between the start and finish of incubation but the number of hours for which the female incubates; those females which incubate their eggs more attentively hatch them sooner[317].

The length of the incubation period is much the same in all species, being about thirteen to fourteen days (period measured is interval between date of laying of an egg and the date at which it hatches). Since the birds most frequently start incubation about the time of laying of the penultimate egg, in practice the interval between completion of the clutch and the start of hatching is often about one day less than this. The young do not appear to hatch at any particular point in the day. At hatching, the yolk has not usually been fully consumed; the remainder is drawn into the young bird prior to hatching and acts as a reserve of food during the first few hours of the nestling's life. Provided they are kept warm, they can safely hatch at night.

THE NESTLING PERIOD

Each time the female finds a chick hatched she removes the egg shell. This she accomplishes either by eating it or by flying out of the box with the shell and dropping it at some distance from the nest.

Feeding starts soon after the young hatch with the bringing of very small caterpillars. If the weather is cold, the female may have to remain on the nest most of the time in order to keep the young warm. Under these conditions the male collects most of the food – often he passes it to the female for her to give to the chicks. When cold weather is prolonged, the male may have to collect most of the food for the family for several days; the outcome of this is that the young suffer a food shortage and some may die (p. 203).

The weather can thus have a considerable effect on the growth of the young especially if food is rather scarce. They are poikilothermic (unable to maintain their own body temperature) until they have a covering of feathers, which is usually when they are a little over a week old (p. 218). During this first week they need considerable amounts of brooding from their mother; even in warm weather they would die if she did not brood them overnight.

If the parent birds lose their brood, they may occasionally switch to feeding young in another nest. It has been suggested that this may explain the behaviour of some of the auxiliary birds at Long-tailed Tits' nests (p. 80). However, the feeding may be of an entirely different species e.g. Blue Tit feeding Blackbirds[218], Long-tailed Tit feeding Great Tits[329]. Equally it may be the other species which feeds the tits e.g. Blackbird feeding Blue Tits[60], Wren feeding Coal Tits[30]. Occasionally this may occur even though the bird's own brood is near by and the bird's mate is left to raise the brood alone, as happened when a male Blue Tit left his own brood and helped to raise a brood of Treecreepers nearby[8].

The faeces are covered by a gelatinous bag which enables the parents to remove them easily from the nest and so keep the nest clean. To further

PLATE 9. Tits are hole-nesters and will use a wide variety of sites. Here a Great Tit, *left*, nests in a letter box and a Blue Tit, *below*, in an old kettle. The latter is an unusual choice since the birds normally choose a site with a restricted entrance hole, giving themselves the maximum protection from predators.

PLATE 10. Breeding I. *Above left*, Blue Tits often use large strips of material as a foundation for their nests; *right*, the space for the nest cup is formed by the female rubbing herself along the bottom of the nest site, working outwards from the centre. *Below left*, the nest-cup is designed to fit snugly round the female in order to conserve heat. The incubating bird turns the eggs. Note the large, bare, heavily-vascularized brood-patch. *Right*, the incubating female has little time to feed and much of her food is supplied by the male.

facilitate such cleanliness, the young only defaecate immediately after they have been fed. The parent brings in a caterpillar and gives it to a chick – but instead of quickly flying out again, it pauses and watches the chick which, if ready to defaecate, raises the rear end of its abdomen clear of the other young and produces a faecal sac; the parent immediately removes this. In the early stages this is usually eaten, but later, when the sacs are larger, the bird flies out of the nest with them and drops them some distance away. The ability to produce faecal sacs with gelatinous coverings ceases at about the point of fledging and the last few young may defaecate into the nest without such sanitation; the presence of a few such faeces in the nest is therefore usually a good indication that the young have left the nest successfully.

In addition to the parents keeping the nest free of droppings, they have another means of keeping the nest tidy. Several observers have reported that the females lean down under the chicks, lift the nest lining a little way and shake it. In this way possibly the scaly 'dandruff' from the growing feathers and also some of the parasites are shaken through the lining and out of the way into the bottom of the nest cavity. Additionally, this may serve to shake up the 'bedding', preventing the air from being pressed out of it and so maintaining its insulative properties.

The parents may remove dead young if they are small enough to be easily carried; large dead young get trampled underfoot. The birds do not normally remove eggs which fail to hatch though this has been recorded; apparently the birds cannot get their beaks round the eggs and do not attempt to break them in order to remove them. Unhatched eggs seem remarkably strong in the presence of a brood of young and tend to remain unbroken, gradually getting pushed into the nest lining as the young grow. Obviously there is less need to remove an egg than a chick because it does not decompose in the same way as a dead chick. Since the parent can remove small dead young, but not eggs, it is usually possible to guess the fate of any eggs that disappear between one visit to the nest and the next. If an egg failed to hatch it is likely to be still there, buried in the lining, whereas if it is missing, in all probability it hatched and the young bird quickly died.

The nest cup which, initially, held the eggs so comfortably will not hold the growing young. The sides of the cup are forced outwards as the young grow; later the young trample it flat. When they leave the nest, all that remains is a flattened wad on the bottom of the chamber. Even then, in some nest-sites, the young may be very crowded. This description of the nest does not of course apply to the Long-tailed Tit whose rather pliable nest seems to expand to accommodate the growing brood.

Once the young are about half-grown, they need little brooding and the female can concentrate on feeding them. However, in the early stages of the nestling period, the feeding rate may be higher in the afternoon than in the morning, apparently because the female has to spend more time brooding the young in the morning when it is cooler than in the afternoon[29, 121]. In the later stages the female normally feeds the young rather more often than the male who, having started by doing more of the feeding, slows down towards the end. Under good conditions, with not too large a brood, the parents may successfully keep the young well-fed and quiet, but most broods are hungry enough to call noisily for food at some time or other. It appears necessary for the young to call in order to signal to the parents that they are hungry, but calling is dangerous and incessant calls may lead predators to the nest (chapter 18). If one of the pair dies or disappears, the other may continue to feed the brood, though in one case the male, having done this for some time, apparently became overworked and gave up[11]. With a large brood even the pair may be hard-pressed to feed them and the parents of large broods may slow down their feeding rates during the later part of the day, suggesting that they are tired or need to feed themselves[121]. The male cannot raise the brood alone if the female disappears at an early stage since he never broods the young, and small young, without the female's care, would die of cold during the night.

The bigger young keep themselves warm and, though the female will stay with the young in the nest at night, she no longer broods them, nor indeed could she do this effectively with so large a number of young. The female Blue Tit ceases to roost with the young after they are about ten days old, whereas the female Great Tit usually continues to spend the night with the young until they are at least 15 days old[26].

Unless food is scarce the young may get more or less equal shares of food. The parent bird comes to the nest and offers its caterpillar to the nestling whose gape reaches highest or who begs most persistently; if the food is not quickly swallowed the tit takes it away and offers it to another nestling[228, 300]. A large or hungry young may get two or more feeds in quick succession but then will be replete and want no more until it has digested this meal. While this nestling settles down to 'sleep it off', the next hungriest can get fed and so on. Only when food is sufficiently scarce for the largest to be hungry again before the smallest has been satisfied is the food not shared out equally; then the smallest may starve. As the young grow they are fed progressively larger larvae, though this in part at least results from the fact that the larvae are also growing rapidly[379].

When the young are very large the parents do not always come into the nest to feed them but merely poke their head in to give the caterpillar to the first young that jumps up to the hole (see also p. 264). Before the young are ready to leave the nest, they start to exercise their wings and to jump up to the nest entrance and so get their first views of the outside world. When ready to fly, young often leave the nest in the early part of the day, possibly in order to learn their way about before dark. As each young flies from the nest it may be accompanied by an adult to a perch in a bush or tree. If the adult does not see it fly, the young persistently gives a contact call until it is found. Thereafter it may give the begging call. The adults do not seem to like having young both in and out of the nest and appear to try to encourage the remaining young to fly, sometimes by appearing at the box and calling them[11], sometimes by bringing food and then flying away with it. A Great Tit has even been recorded coming to the nest and trying to pull the last young out[396]. In addition, they try to keep the young together once they have fledged.

The nestling period shows considerable variation. The Great Tit, being the largest, takes about three weeks to fly, while the others take two to four days less; poorly nourished young may stay longer in the nest than well-fed birds. Normally, if the young are not disturbed, they will remain in the nest until they are able to fly freely. In such a case, the young should be able to maintain itself at least in level flight or, better still, fly upwards. Although somewhat unco-ordinated at first, they can usually flutter to a perch.

Near the end of the nestling period the nest should be visited with great caution since the appearance of an observer may cause the young to fly prematurely. As soon as they can flutter reasonably (about fifteen days old for the Great Tit, younger for other species) any disturbance may result in premature departure from the nest. If the birds flutter to the ground it is likely that they would not normally have left the nest for a few more days. The reason for this habit of 'exploding' is fairly clear. If a predator finds the nest any young that remain will almost certainly be eaten. If there is any chance of surviving by leaving the nest – however prematurely – this is obviously preferable to certain death and so the habit has evolved. Such premature departure can be advantageous because, on several occasions in Wytham, we have visited nests before the ringed young should have been ready to leave, only to find that most of the brood had been eaten by a predator. However, subsequently we have recaptured one or more young from these broods; although too small to fly, the young must have managed to jump from the nest and so avoid the predator and then have been found and cared for by their parents until they were large enough to fly.

On some occasions where broods have been observed from a distance, the young have stayed in the nest for longer periods than those given above. Hence the nestling periods recorded from visits to the nests may be un-naturally short. In our recent studies we have not attempted to obtain information on this point in order to avoid the risk of disturbing the young when they are about to leave the nest; broods of large young have been left alone and their nests not visited again until several days after they should have left.

THE POST-FLEDGING PERIOD

Once the last young have left the nest the family party is then mobile and can move around as a unit. However, the young leave the nest before their flight feathers are fully grown and so for the first few days – until they are fully capable of flying – they do not wander far. During these few days further growth is largely completed and the young become better practised at flying.

As the young get better at flying the party start to wander farther afield; the old territorial boundaries are ignored. To start with the young stay in the same place and wander only slowly and the parents still have to bring food to them. Later they follow after the parents, keeping close to them while begging for food. During this time they start to look for food themselves and gradually learn how to find it. Over the ensuing weeks the family party slowly breaks up. The young birds may occasionally be seen with their parents for a month or so, but many start to wander away within this period[137]. Families of Coal and Crested Tits may keep together until respectively about two weeks and three to four weeks after the young have left the nest[77]. In the Great Tit the length of the post-fledging care varies in relation to whether it is a first or second brood, being only about six to eight days for the first broods, but twice as long for second broods[190]. I once caught a female Great Tit and four of her young together in November suggesting that, exceptionally, parties may stay together for much longer periods. Normally the pair of birds stay with the party, but at times it appears as if the female stays longest with the brood. In the Crested Tit one of the pair may leave the vicinity almost immediately after the young have flown, leaving the other bird to look after the young; the missing bird often re-appears much later, so it cannot have died[77]. Normally, within about a fortnight of leaving the nest, the young are on their own and must try to fend for themselves; as we shall see, this is far from easy.

SECOND BROODS

When the brood leaves the nest, the parents must decide whether or not to have a second brood. As already mentioned, these are scarce in most species of tits though they do occur under certain circumstances (chapter 14). When a second brood is produced it is usually started within a few days of the first brood leaving the nest. In Wytham it may often be laid in the same nest as the first brood, though in Holland they are more often in another site[190]. Laying of the second clutch may even start before the first brood has fledged[281]. Soon after the first brood have left the nest, there is a recurrence of the female's begging behaviour[135, 173]. Presumably the female needs the male's help again in order to get enough food to form the eggs for the second clutch. The recurrence of begging seems more frequent than the occurrence of second broods. Possibly the females are testing the support that they will get from their mates before 'deciding' whether or not to attempt a second brood. This is not as far-fetched as it may sound since female Common Terns *Sterna hirundo* vary their clutch-size and some other aspects of their breeding in relation to the amount of food brought to them by their mates[269].

We have occasionally noted a single fresh egg in a nest after the brood has left the nest. Presumably, these are laid by females which almost 'decided' to have a second brood but did not go through with it. Often, however, by this stage, the birds are plainly not going to have a further brood. In some cases the adults have shed the first one or two primary feathers (the innermost ones) heralding the start of their moult. In such cases it would be most unlikely that the birds would go on and breed again. Few British song-birds breed while in heavy moult. The birds are now preparing to engage in the battle to survive the winter so that they may breed again in the following season.

CHAPTER 14

THE BREEDING SEASON AND MOULT

ALL individual birds have periods when they nest and raise young separated by periods when they do not. During the non-breeding season they recover from the strain of raising young and moult; some migrate. In the tropics the breeding seasons may be very extended and in some species birds may be found breeding at any time of the year, but each individual still has a period when it does not breed; though more varied in its timing, moult still usually occurs outside the breeding season[175, 282]. In the temperate areas of the world, however, the seasons are clearly defined and all the individuals of any species are normally synchronized with one another.

As a group, the European tits have relatively short breeding seasons; in any one area the majority of the birds of one species lay within a fortnight of one another and, apart from a few that lose clutches and replace them, there is little laying outside this period; only the Great Tit and to a lesser extent the Coal Tit have second broods at all frequently and even these are regular only in certain habitats.

TIMING OF BREEDING

The timing of each species' laying season has been much studied, but there is still room for debate as to how the birds start laying when they do. I have chosen to give the 'classic' explanation first and add some modifications to it afterwards.

The most important factor about the timing of the breeding season is that the tits have their young in the nest at about the time when their caterpillar food is most abundant (fig. 46). As can be seen the peak of the caterpillar season occurs at different times in different years; nevertheless, the tits' season shifts to match. How do they do it? In order to have their young in the nest when the caterpillars are present, the birds must start to breed some time before this and so, somehow, they must 'know' well in advance of the peak of the caterpillars roughly when it will occur. Even if one assumes that the birds build their nest during the period of egg formation, it takes about four days to form the first egg, another nine days to lay ten eggs and about a further eleven to twelve days to hatch them from when the last egg was laid. Hence a tit cannot have young in the nest until some twenty-four days after it has taken the 'decision' to start breeding. In practice the interval between starting to build and having young in the nest is likely to be a few days longer than this. The tits therefore have to get into a state to start breeding about four weeks before the caterpillars are present in abundance.

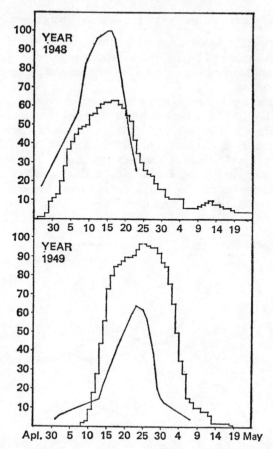

FIG. 46. Numbers of tit-broods and abundance of food-caterpillars (1948 and 1949). Stepped graphs show daily combined total of Great and Blue Tit broods in nestboxes. Smoothed graphs show percentage abundance of caterpillars estimated from volume of faecal pellets. Figures on vertical axis indicate percentage abundance of caterpillars and actual numbers of broods. Note that the caterpillars are only available for a very short time and that the timing of their availability varies from year to year (from Gibb 1950).

Since they appear to match the nestling period to the peak food supply, they must respond to some factor which varies in parallel with the caterpillar season; response to a trigger that caused them to breed at the same date in each year would be disastrous in many years.

By convention, we describe the timing of a given breeding season in any area by its 'mean date of laying'. This is the average of the dates on which each female laid her first egg. Repeat and second clutches are not included in such calculations.

Several factors are known to affect the timing of laying. One obvious one is that birds lay later the farther north they are[20]. Figure 47 gives the spread of laying in Holland and in Fenno-Scandia (Norway, Sweden, Finland) over a series of years. The timing of spring is related to the geography; on the west coast of America the season is retarded by about four days for each increasing degree of latitude, for each five degree shift of longitude eastwards and for each 100–125 metres increase in altitude[172]. The data on the breeding of the tits in Fenno-Scandia were collected over

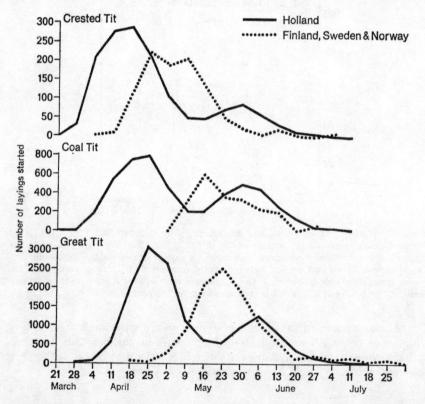

FIG. 47. Laying dates of three species of tit in Holland and Finland, Sweden and Norway. The second peaks in Holland refer to second broods which are more numerous there than in Scandinavia (from Lack 1954b).

a wide range of latitude, but the differences in laying date between these and the tits in Holland are roughly in accord with the calculations for America, with peaks some 20–27 days later some six to seven degrees farther north. Within Norway, breeding is about three days later for each degree farther north one goes[333].

Another point emerges from this figure and that is that the different species have different laying seasons. Here – largely from studies in coniferous woodland – the Crested Tit breeds first, followed by the Coal and then the Great Tit. Within oakwoods in Britain, the commonest species breed in the order Long-tailed, Coal, Marsh, Blue and Great Tit[90]. The first named is usually markedly ahead of the others while the Coal Tit is almost always ahead of the Great and Blue Tits. In both these habitats the order of breeding is related to the body-size of the birds, with the exception that the Crested Tit is heavier than the Coal Tit. In the case of the Marsh and Blue Tits, the weights and laying dates are very close. In Germany the tits breed in the order Crested, Coal, Blue, Great and Willow[407].

Within any given area, there are large variations in the timing of laying in different years and these can be related to spring weather. In Wytham over 26 years the earliest mean date of laying was 10 April in 1948, the latest 10 May in 1951. Similar orders of difference have been recorded in other woods.

There are differences in the timing of breeding between different habitats. Great Tits, but not Blue Tits, in gardens lay a few days earlier than those in nearby woodland (table 15) and tits breed earlier in Scots Pine than in adjacent areas of Corsican Pine – the latter having the poorer insect fauna[129]. Perhaps surprisingly, there does not seem to be a consistent difference between the laying dates of Great Tits breeding in coniferous and deciduous

Table 15. Mean date of laying in gardens and woodland near Oxford. Dates are counted from April 1st = 1 (i.e. 33 = May 3rd) (from Perrins 1963).

	Marley, Wytham		Oxford Gardens	
	No. of birds	*Mean date of first egg*	*No. of birds*	*Mean date of first egg*
Great Tit				
1958	27	35·1	14	31·6
1959	40	23·9	19	17·6
1960	51	27·1	23	23·0
1961	78	21·0	31	15·7
Blue Tit				
1958	15	34·3	5	32·0
1959	20	21·8	15	22·5
1960	22	19·9	17	20·8
1961	46	18·7	13	17·8

woodland[190], although the Coal Tit may breed slightly earlier in conifer, its preferred habitat, than in deciduous woods[90].

Even within Wytham there are consistent differences in the start of breeding between different areas. The birds in the Bean Wood, a low-lying south-facing area, usually start a day or two before the birds in Marley. There are other consistent differences between areas and even within areas though reasons for them are not clear. The birds on the woodland edge often start breeding a little earlier. Hedges often seem to come into leaf before bushes in the central areas of the wood; possibly the plants in more exposed sites get more light and warmth and so come into leaf more quickly than those in more shady places. The differences between areas of woodland and garden could be related to this since gardens are more open than woodland, though, in addition, the heating of houses makes large urban areas a little warmer than the surrounding countryside.

There are sometimes marked differences between the times of start of laying in different areas even though these are not far apart[209]. Unlike the differences just given, these are often not consistent over a series of years – sometimes the birds in one area breed earlier, sometimes those in another. Such differences have not been explained but may be due to small local variations in weather or in food supply.

The date of laying of the individual females is affected by their age. Young birds (breeding for the first time) tend to lay a few days later than those birds which have bred before (table 16). The older birds are known

Table 16. Mean date of laying of female Great Tits in relation to age. Dates are counted from April 1st = 1 (i.e. 33=May 3rd) (from Perrins 1965).

	Age of bird (years)	No. of birds	Mean date of first egg (April)
1961	1	122	22·4
	2	19	17·7
	3	15	17·8
1962	1	52	33·2
	2	40	32·3
	3	12	30·2
1963	1	54	30·0
	2	32	26·7
	3	28	26·4
	4	8	26·1

to take up territories at an earlier point in spring and their general experience of the wood and of feeding sites may enable them to start before the inexperienced young birds.

PEAK DEMAND FOR FOOD FOR THE YOUNG

The data in figure 46 show the periods when the young were in the nest. In order to relate the success of the young birds to the food supply more closely it would be necessary to know at which point in the nesting cycle the young require the largest amounts of food. Unfortunately, there are so many variables concerned that the most crucial times have not been determined. There are a number of points during the breeding season when the availability of food might be particularly critical and we do not know which of these is the most important. The female needs plentiful food both while laying and while incubating and three other times have been suggested as being particularly important. Firstly it might be difficult to feed the very small young at hatching. Young Great Tits weigh about 1·2–1·4 grams, the young of all other species less than 1 gram. It might be essential for there to be a plentiful supply of tiny caterpillars at this time so that the parents could feed such small chicks, particularly since the female has to spend so much of her time brooding that she often cannot search for food. Later it might be easier to find a larger amount of food for larger young, especially since both parents can forage then.

Secondly, the point at which the young are growing fastest and need the greatest amounts of food may impose the greatest strain on the parents. The nestlings grow fastest when around seven to nine days old (depending slightly on the species) and need less food both before and after this stage. Lastly the period in the nest may be less critical than that just after fledging[319]. In the nest, the young are not taking a great deal of exercise and, as discussed later (p. 196), they help to keep each other warm so that in spite of their rapid growth their energy requirements may be lower than when they are out of the nest; then they are much more active and no longer keep each other warm. Royama[319] calculated that the newly-fledged young might need three to four times the food that they needed as growing nestlings. The only factor that offsets this increased demand for food is that the fledglings can follow their parents and thereby reduce the time the adults have to spend flying back to the nest and so increase the time available for collecting food.

A further aspect of the post-fledging period, which may be critical but which has not been examined, is that the young must learn to feed themselves. The few days after they have left the nest, or possibly even more important, after they have left their parents, may be critical ones for young birds. They must learn to find food for themselves and the ease with which they can do this could be very important. If these post-fledging periods are the most important times for the young birds then possibly it is this time and not the nestling period which should coincide with the peak period of caterpillar abundance (shown in figure 46). Hence, on this basis, the tits should be breeding much earlier than they do if they are to take the greatest advantage of the caterpillars. This conclusion is in agreement with those measurements made of the survival of the young, where the early broods are much more successful than the later ones (p. 201).

There are two possible reasons for the breeding season being later than the time which would appear to be ideal. Either there could be years when early broods were disastrously unsuccessful, or the female could need a plentiful supply of food in order to form eggs and if this is not available she might have to wait until it was.

Over a long run of years, there has been no evidence that the birds that breed early were very unsuccessful – even in the very cold summer of 1962 the early broods still produced more surviving young than later broods (p. 203). Figure 66 shows that the birds which breed earliest during the season raise many more young than those that breed later – in some way the earlier birds have a great advantage over the later ones. Hence the nestling period, for most broods at least, should be earlier than it is and so the period shown in figure 46 is not in fact the best time of all for breeding.

FOOD FOR THE LAYING FEMALE

I have suggested that it is the scarcity of the food supply for the laying female which dictates the time at which laying can start[289]. There is an alternative suggestion, namely that the food supply is critical at two periods in the breeding cycle, when the female is forming eggs and when the young are out of the nest, so that the breeding season spans the period of food abundance in such a way that both these periods fall as close to it as possible[18].

The earliest breeders tend to be older birds and ones that are more efficient in raising young, but this is only part of the story since there is a seasonal decline in nesting success in each age class (fig. 48). In addition, if these early breeders lose broods and lay a repeat clutch or attempt a second brood, their breeding success with this later brood is similar to those of other birds breeding at that time (fig. 49). Hence, the timing of the brood's presence in the nest is critical and so the success must be related to the food supply in some way.

Even if the earliest breeders are starting their clutch at the best possible time, most birds are not since they should have their young in the nest earlier. The laying females need 40% more food than usual in order to form eggs[318]. Now in order to have the young at the best time they should start laying some weeks earlier than they do; at that date caterpillars are still scarce and rather small (fig. 46). If the female cannot get sufficient food to start laying until these small caterpillars emerge, then her date of breeding is limited by her own need for the caterpillars.

This situation may be best clarified by a pair of diagrams (fig. 50). Line (i) denotes the amount of food a female tit needs to maintain herself, line (ii) the amount of food she must have in order to form eggs, 'X' denotes the length of the period before hatching (including egg formation, laying and incubation) and 'Y' the length of the period before independence

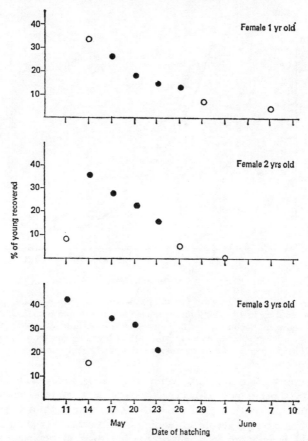

FIG. 48. Survival of young Great Tits in relation to date of hatching and age of female. The term 'recovered' covers all those young birds which are known to have survived to at least three months after leaving the nest. The solid circles are based on more than five recoveries, the open circles are based on fewer than five and are hence less reliable. Note how the proportion of young which survive after fledging decreases with season regardless of the age of the female (from Perrins 1970).

(nestling and post-fledging periods). All are identical in both diagrams. The only difference between the two is the curve denoting the food supply; in (b) the food is abundant for a shorter time than in (a). Given the conditions in (b) a bird could not have finished raising its nestlings (let alone fed them once they had left the nest) before the rich food supply was starting to diminish, but under the conditions in (a) it would be possible. I think that this is the simplest explanation for the situation found in the Great and Blue Tits; only something as overwhelmingly important as the parents' own food supply could prevent the females from breeding as early as would be most productive.

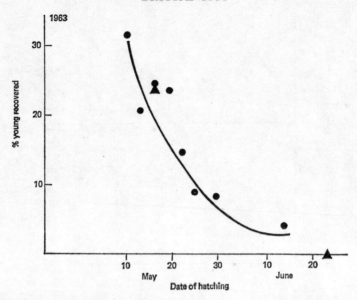

FIG. 49.   Success of second broods of Great Tits in Wytham. In 1963 twelve pairs of birds successfully raised their first broods and went on to attempt second broods. The line (based on the circles) shows the decline of breeding success of all birds in relation to date of hatching. The two triangles show the mean date of laying and of breeding success of the twelve birds that had two broods. See text for further explanation (from Perrins 1970).

This argument is circumstantial, for there is no direct evidence that the laying tits are short of food. However, the argument can be extended further. Smaller females need less food for body maintenance than larger ones so they should be able to get into breeding condition earlier than large ones. They should have more food 'spare' for breeding sooner than the larger birds. At least at times this is the case (fig. 51), but contrary results have also been obtained[182].

Not only does this correlation between body-size and date of laying hold within the Great Tit, but as mentioned earlier (p. 169) it also holds between the common tit species which breed in the order Long-tailed, Coal, Blue and Great Tit – an ascending order of body-size. Perhaps a parallel observation is that the woodland warblers return to Europe in an order inversely related to their body-size, Chiffchaff, *Phylloscopus collybita*, first and Garden Warbler, *Sylvia borin*, last; hence it may be that smaller birds find it easier to get enough food in Europe in early spring than larger ones[113].

Further evidence that laying females may be affected by food availability comes from noting the pattern of laying in relation to the temperature, which just prior to laying may influence the birds considerably. In fine weather the birds build their nests and go on to lay their eggs. However, if the weather suddenly turns cold only the birds that have started to form

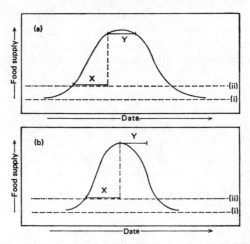

FIG. 50. Hypothetical relationship between food supply, date of laying and date of young becoming independent in two species, (a) and (b). The curve shows level of food abundance against (i) the food required for general body maintenance and (ii) the food required for forming eggs. The straight line X represents the time required for forming and laying eggs and incubating these to the point of hatching. Line Y represents the time taken to raise the young to the point of independence. For further explanation see text (from Perrins 1970).

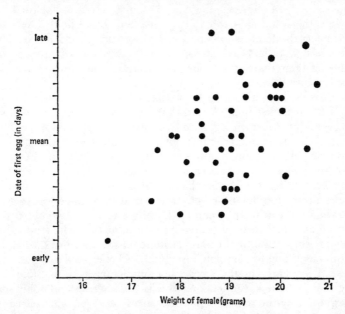

FIG. 51. Relationship between weight of female Great Tits and their dates of starting to lay. The laying date of each female is plotted with regard to the mean for the population. The lighter females are the first to start laying (from Jones 1973).

eggs will continue to lay. No others start until warm weather returns. They take about four days to form their first egg after they have taken the 'decision' to start laying[190]; hence some four days after the weather turns warm again many birds may start to lay (fig. 52). These short spells of

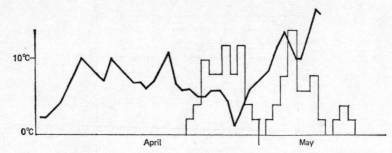

FIG. 52. Air temperatures and start of laying. The figure shows, for a particular year, the mean daily temperature (continuous line) and the number of clutches started by Great Tits (histogram). The dramatic drop in temperature was followed four days later by no new clutches being started. For further explanation see text (from Kluijver 1951).

poor weather do not appear to have any effect on the caterpillar populations (though they do affect their behaviour since, when cool, they are less active and grow more slowly). Hence there is no long-term reason for the birds not to lay when the weather is cold, rather it seems more likely that the cold weather affects the females either directly by making food less easy to find (because the caterpillars are less active) or indirectly because the females need more of their daily intake for body maintenance and so have less to spare for egg formation.

When the weather turns cold birds that have started to lay do not stop laying but finish their clutch. A bird that has already laid one or more eggs carries several part-formed eggs and so does not need as much food to complete its clutch as one that has not yet started to lay though it might have trouble getting enough food to complete the clutch. Further, the weight of an egg can be correlated with the temperature on the days when it is being formed (fig. 53). Again this would be expected if in cold weather the females need more food for body maintenance so have less to spare for egg formation than in warm weather. During an unusually cold period the eggs laid by one bird steadily decreased in weight until she stopped laying after only six eggs. Possibly because of the cold weather the bird just could not get sufficient food to complete her clutch or lay eggs of normal size.

Birds that lay early in the season lay smaller eggs than those that lay later (fig. 54). I have suggested that this is also a result of food shortage at the beginning of the season. The differences between egg sizes cannot be explained wholly by the fact that the smaller birds lay at the beginning of the season and lay smaller eggs; individuals which lose an early clutch lay larger eggs in their repeat clutch. There is no known advantage in having

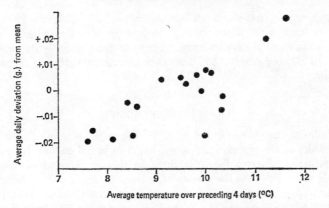

FIG. 53. Egg weight of Great Tits in relation to temperature. The weight of each individual egg (measured against the mean of the other eggs in the same clutch) is plotted against the average temperature for the days during which the egg was being formed (from Jones 1973).

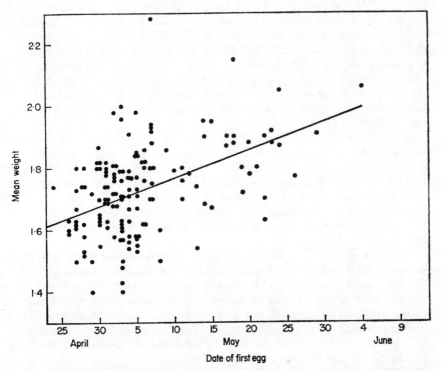

FIG. 54. Variation in mean weight of eggs of Great Tit with date of laying. Each point denotes the mean weight of a single clutch in one year (1966). The regression line is highly significant (from Perrins 1970).

smaller eggs except that the birds laying them need slightly less food to form them. However as we shall see (p. 217) larger eggs often have higher hatching and survival rates than smaller eggs. Hence the most reasonable explanation for the small early eggs seems to be that the birds have difficulty forming eggs at this time.

ARTIFICIAL FEEDING

If the females are unable to breed until food becomes plentiful, then it ought to be possible, as an experiment, to get them to breed earlier by providing larger quantities of extra food for them in spring. Several attempts have been made to do this, but the results have been inconclusive. Kluijver found that in early spring his Great Tits stopped taking the artificial food, switched to natural foods and showed no change as a result. In Wytham, Great Tits fed a diet of sunflower seed showed no difference in the time at which they bred when compared with birds in an area in which they were not fed. Possibly as in Kluijver's attempt, the birds fed mainly on natural foods at this time[179]. However, the situation with the Blue Tits in the same wood was less clear. Initially the birds showed marked signs of breeding earlier than those in the control area; they started building before the latter birds and some nests were well built when a prolonged period of cold weather intervened, during which nest-building ceased. On the resumption of mild weather, the birds in both areas started to breed. Hence it is tempting to think that, had the weather not changed, the birds in the experimental area would have bred earlier – though this was the case only with the Blue and not the Great Tits.

More recently in Sweden Källander has shown that Great Tits tend to lay earlier when supplied with a rich stock of mealworms compared with areas without extra food[182]. The date of laying of old birds was advanced by about three to four days and that of young birds by about six to seven days. It is of interest that the young birds, as a result, bred at a similar date to the older birds instead of being three to four days later; with plenty of food the differences between the age classes (perhaps in experience in hunting for food) disappeared.

As shown earlier, both Blue and Great Tits bred earlier in gardens than in woods (table 15). The difference is slight and it seems more likely that this can be accounted for by the slightly higher temperature in towns than the surrounding countryside or in the slightly more open situations and earlier breaking of the buds (see p. 169) than in the food they get. Much food is put out for birds at this time, but the small difference in the date of laying suggests that either the females are not short of food or they are dependent on finding the right natural foods.

When the female tits have the greatest difficulty obtaining their food, their mates help them. The feeding of the female by the male is usually referred to as 'courtship feeding', but this is a misnomer since it occurs not while the birds are forming pairs, but only much later when the female is laying and incubating.

Courtship feeding has been recorded in all the British tits except the Long-tailed Tit, where if it occurs it does not seem very important. (In Japan the male Long-tailed Tit feeds the female at least during the incubation period[260].) During both the laying and the incubation periods the female needs a plentiful supply of food. While laying she needs up to about 40% more food than at other times in order to form the eggs; the females manage to get about enough food each day to maintain themselves but are dependent on the male to provide the extra food for the egg[318]. During incubation, since she has to spend much of her time incubating the eggs, the female must be able to get her food in the relatively short spells that she is off the nest.

The male Great Tit brings to his mate much larger items of food than the male Blue Tit, but to compensate the male Blue Tit brings the female about eight times as many feeds as the male Great Tit brings his mate. The male Blue Tit feeds his mate at great speed when she is off the nest – at such times she may get as much as two and a half times the food that she could collect alone[200]. In the Pied Flycatcher, which nests in the same areas at about the same time, the male may provide as much as 50% of the incubating female's total food[71].

Two further factors may make the males' assistance even more important. In chapter 12 I discussed the possibility that the female tits may need to spend some time collecting snail shells in order to acquire the calcium for their eggs. In doing this they reduce the time available for finding other food. Secondly when the female Grey-backed Camaroptera *Camaroptera brevicaudata* is laying eggs she is much less active during part of the day than at other times – possibly she is unable to move around much in case the egg is broken; while the shell is being laid down it must be very delicate[107]. In the tits this subject has not been studied, but the egg shell must be laid down some time during the day since it is usually fully-formed by dusk; if the female tits are less active at this time, then their feeding rate will be reduced and the need for help from the male correspondingly increased.

PROXIMATE FACTORS AFFECTING TIMING

The ultimate reason why birds time their breeding as they do is to enable them to raise their young at the most opportune time of year or, as I have suggested here for the tits, as near to this as they can get. In order to do so they need to be able to identify that time of year when they should start

breeding and this they do by use of proximate factors. Such factors may be
of no immediate use to the bird, but are essential if breeding is to be correctly
timed.

The best known proximate factor by which animals time their annual
cycle is day-length. Since early pioneer studies[316] it has been known that
birds can use certain aspects of the change of day-length to time both
breeding and migratory behaviour. Little work has been done with tits, but
in Finland day-length affects the date at which the reproductive organs of
Great Tits developed in spring. This was shown by taking male Great Tits
in January, keeping two groups in a relatively warm indoor area and two in
cold outside aviaries. One group in each place was maintained under normal
daylight while the other was subjected to artificial illumination for the
whole of the 24-hour period. The reproductive organs of both the groups
subjected to increased length of day enlarged rapidly towards their breeding
size while those of the others did not. Hence the birds came into breeding
condition in some way as a result of the change in day-length and temperature
did not affect them[363].

Plainly the length of the day is one of the most reliable guides to the time
of year and would be a good timing device for birds to use. Nevertheless it is
not known in what way it affects the birds; it may simply enable them to
have a longer period feeding and so gives them a greater chance to get into
breeding condition than birds with a short day. Possibly more important
still, birds experiencing longer day-length have a shorter night to go without
food.

The use of day-length alone would not be sufficient to get tits into breeding
condition at the right time when the season varies so much from year to
year. One must be cautious about taking this rather simple explanation; the
timing of breeding is likely to be the result of a complex series of different
factors of which the effect of day-length might be relatively unimportant[239].
In one series of observations day-length changes could not explain the time
at which tits came into breeding condition. Marshall collected tits (as well
as other species) from Wytham at the same date (13–14 March) in two
different years – 1947 and 1948 – and examined the state of their reproductive organs. He was fortunate that these two winters were ones with
very different weather, the former being exceedingly cold, the latter very
mild. At the same date, the reproductive organs of the birds were much
further advanced in the mild winter than in the cold one. The most likely
cause of such a difference is the effects of food supply; although we do not
know the relative availability of food in the two years, the birds would have
needed much more food for body maintenance in the cold than in the mild
winter and would therefore have been much less likely to be able to get into
breeding condition[238].

The general spring temperatures also influence the time of breeding. We
talk of early and late springs, a result of the temperatures at that time.
Such variations in temperature are reflected in the birds' breeding, the

warmer the early spring weather the sooner the birds start breeding (fig. 55). This method of analysis is not wholly satisfactory since in some years (e.g. 1951) the birds did not breed until about two weeks after the end of the period for which the weather was plotted while in 1948 the birds started to breed very early and so the weather at the end of the period could not have affected their breeding date. Nevertheless, the general pattern is clear.

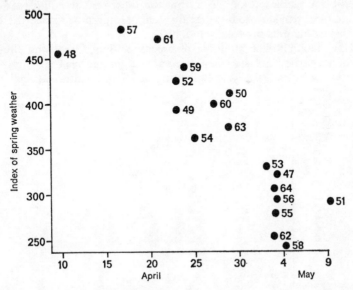

FIG. 55. Average date of breeding of Great Tit in relation to spring weather. The index of spring weather was obtained by adding the average for the maximum and minimum temperatures for each day from 1 March–20 April. The date of laying is the average of the dates on which each female laid its first egg. Years are indicated by numbers against the points, i.e. 57 = 1957 (from Perrins 1965).

There are a variety of possible explanations as to why the tits breed earlier in warm weather. They could use the temperature as a proximate factor 'warning' them that the caterpillar season would be early; there would be more food available earlier so that the females could get into breeding condition earlier, or even if the food supply remained the same, the birds would need less food for body maintenance in warm than in cold weather and hence more of the food that the females ate would be available for breeding purposes. Clearly more than one of these factors could be involved.

One piece of evidence suggests that the actual warmth during the period prior to breeding is not important in itself, but must have its effect through the changes it causes in the environment. There is a similar correlation to that in figure 55 between the spring temperatures and the date of breeding in the Collared Flycatcher *Ficedula albicollis* and also in the Pied Flycatcher breeding in the Forest of Dean[214, 224]. However, both these birds are migrants from Africa and do not return to central Europe until about mid-April. Hence the early spring temperature cannot have any direct effect on the birds and so must affect their breeding date indirectly through some action on the environment.

The correlation between temperature and breeding date is not linear – the later the birds breed the earlier they start in relation to the temperature. One possible explanation for this is that the later the breeding season the earlier the birds can start to breed at any given temperature since the length of day for feeding gets progressively longer.

A further factor affects the date of breeding. Both Great and Blue Tits tend to breed earlier in years when survival over winter has been high – later when it has been low (fig. 56). Chitty suggested the winter survival of the

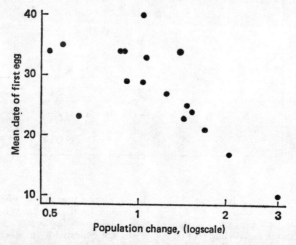

FIG. 56. Relationship between mean date of laying and change in population. Dates are reckoned from 1 April (i.e. 40 = 10 May). Population change is measured by dividing the numbers breeding in one year by the numbers breeding in the previous year. Hence those points below '1' show populations which decreased, those above '1' populations which increased (from Chitty 1967).

birds will be higher in years when food supply is plentiful and that therefore the birds may come through such winters in better condition than those in which survival is poor. Hence, perhaps, they are fitter and more able to start breeding early under these conditions.

In the Long-tailed Tit, the nest may be completed some considerable time before laying starts. Gaston notes that 'it seems likely that the factor holding up the onset of egg-laying concerned the ability of the female to lay, rather than delay in preparing the nest'[116].

SECOND BROODS

I have argued in the previous sections that food for the female is the main underlying factor which influences the timing of laying and have suggested that other factors such as day-length and temperature have their effects largely through the influence they have on the food supply or on the feeding time available. Such points of course only apply to the start of the breeding season; fewer studies have been made of the reasons why the tits have so short a season. Nevertheless the poor success of late broods in Wytham suggests that it may not be worth the tits' while to go on breeding longer even though, at the time when the birds could lay the clutches, there may be sufficient food for the females to form eggs. Further insight into the reasons for the short season can be obtained from an examination of the occasions when the birds have second broods.

Relatively few of the European tits regularly have second broods: only Coal and Great Tits do so often. For Britain at any rate, it seems safe to say that genuine second broods of Blue, Crested, Willow, Marsh and Long-tailed Tits are so rare that precise details of the success of the first brood (to ensure that it did not fail) and the identity of the adults should be available before the record is accepted. Less is known about Azure, Sombre and Siberian Tits but these seem also to be single-brooded as a rule; the northern habitat of the last named species experiences so short a summer that second broods would almost certainly be so late that neither the adults nor the juveniles would have time to moult before the onset of cold weather.

Blue Tits not only have few second broods but also they stop laying repeat clutches at an earlier stage in the season than Great Tits. As can be seen from figure 64, the clutch-size of the Blue Tit declines more swiftly during the season than that of the Great Tit implying that the Blue Tits have relatively more difficulty than the Great Tit in raising broods late in the season, hence it is not surprising to find that they stop breeding earlier.

Enough is known about the second broods of the Great Tit to be able to make some general statements about when they are most likely to be found. They are laid under conditions when it seems most likely that the young could be raised. As might be expected, the earliest pairs to have a first brood are usually the only ones to have a second brood since they alone raise their first broods sufficiently early for a second attempt to be worthwhile. A higher proportion of the older, than of the one-year-old birds, have second broods.

In Wytham second clutches are almost always laid by the older birds; they are the most efficient parents with their first broods. In spite of the success with their first broods, the second broods of these birds are usually very unsuccessful. In Wytham in 1963 12 pairs of Great Tits successfully raised 84 young in their first broods, of which 21 (25%) are known to have survived at least to the winter. These same birds went on to have second broods, but raised only 21 young to fledging and none of these were known to have survived the post-fledging period (fig. 49).

There is much more information on second broods in Holland where they are more common; they occur most frequently in years when breeding density is low (fig. 57); in the early years of the Wytham study (1947, 1948) when the numbers of tits were low and the numbers of caterpillars extremely high there were more second broods than in most years since, suggesting again that the opportunities for having second broods were greatest then. Kluijver even records one case of a third brood and notes

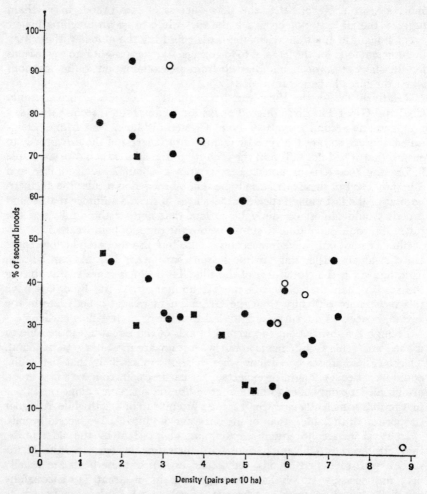

FIG. 57. Correlation between percentage of second broods in Holland and both population density and initial date. Each point denotes a separate year. In years in which the breeding season started unusually early (marked ○) more birds started second broods than in those years when the season started unusually late (marked ■) (from Kluijver 1951).

that it was laid under conditions of effective low density; one pair was breeding alone in a small coniferous wood. Second broods are more likely to be produced in years when breeding starts early – the birds will then be ready to start a second brood early. This effect is also apparent in figure 57 where early, normal and late years are separated.

In a larch *Larix leptolepis* wood in Germany all the Coal Tits had second broods as did 90% of the Great Tits and 58% of the Blue Tits; only one Crested Tit and no Willow Tits had second broods. Even more surprisingly, 29% of the Coal Tits and 4% of the Great Tits had third broods[407].

In more recent years, second broods occurred in Wytham in three years 1960, 1962 and 1963. Reference to figure 65 shows that, in these years, the fifteenth-day weights of young were relatively high over a prolonged period, in fact higher than those of the early broods in some cases. This strongly suggests that for some reason conditions were relatively good for later broods in those years (and this is borne out by the high survival rates of the young subsequently). Indeed in 1960 survival from second broods, though only 40% of that of first broods, was still relatively high. Therefore the parent birds appear more likely to start a second brood when late first broods are doing unusually well; presumably they can respond to the level of the food supply which is still relatively high.

Hence within Wytham, date of laying, age of female, density of breeding pairs and probably the food supply influence the likelihood of the pair having a second brood. Second broods are rare there; usually less than 5% of the Great Tits attempt a second brood. However, there are two situations where Great Tits have second broods more frequently than in British broad-leaved deciduous woodland; these are in pinewoods and on the Continent.

Some 28% of the pairs of Great Tits which breed in Scots Pine in Britain have second broods, many more than those in oakwoods; only about 11% have second broods in Corsican pine. Second broods are also common in larch *Larix leptolepis* in Japan, as well as in Germany, where second and third broods are recorded so commonly. The reason for the more frequent second broods is fairly clearly related to the food supply. In oakwoods the food supply is abundant for only a very brief period whereas in pinewoods, though never so abundant, it is present for a much longer period (fig. 58). The result of this different food supply shows markedly in the breeding success of the tits. In the Scots Pine areas of Breckland, about 38% of the Great Tits and about 29% of the Blue Tits in first broods died (as compared with fewer than 10% in broad-leaved woodland of Wytham). However, those Great Tits that went on to have second broods were more successful with them than with their first broods[129]. Not only were there fewer nestling losses in second broods, but also the weights of the young were higher (19·7 grams compared with 16·6 grams in first broods). Some of the young of the first broods were so retarded that they left the nest after 25–27 days instead of the normal 19–20 days. Survival after fledging was not measured, but the young from the first broods left the nest at a time when in oakwoods the

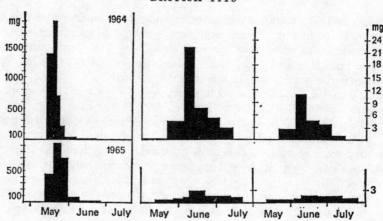

FIG. 58. The abundance of caterpillars in oakwoods (left) and pinewoods (centre and right). Caterpillar abundance is measured by the weight of droppings falling on to trays a quarter of a square metre in size. Note that the scale is different on the pinewood samples and that caterpillars are available throughout June and most of July in pinewoods though not in oakwoods (from van Balen 1973).

caterpillar supply is rapidly diminishing whereas in Scots Pine it was at a steady level or even increasing slightly. Hence possibly these rather light young from the first broods still survived quite well (see p. 203 for survival rates of early, but light, young in Wytham in 1962). Similar results have been obtained in Holland, where in pinewoods there may be lower mortality in second than in first broods; in accord with this, the parents of first broods often fed longer into the evenings than parents in oak woodlands, suggesting that they were having considerable difficulty in obtaining enough food[18]. The breeding success in areas of Corsican Pine, *Pinus nigra*, where the food supply is poorer than in the Scots Pine, was even lower and only about 11% of the Great Tits started second broods[129].

In addition to such differences between broad-leaved and coniferous woodland, the proportion of Great Tits starting second broods is very much higher on the Continent than in Britain and this seems to be true for all habitats. In the broad-leaved woodlands about 36% of the Dutch Great Tits have second broods[190] compared with Wytham's less than 5% and often none. In Dutch pinewoods 76% of the Great Tits start second broods compared with the 28% in the Brecklands of East Anglia – only a little over 200 miles away! The reasons for this large difference have been a mystery for some time, but recently van Balen[18] has shown that the food supply in Holland is not the same as that in Britain and that relatively more food is available for longer in both oak and pinewoods there. In Britain, the isolated nature of our island means that there is a smaller variety of almost all sorts of animals; presumably the richer number of species of caterpillars on the

Continent results in there being more food available for a longer period[246].

Second broods do not occur frequently in gardens, but Len Howard records her birds as having several – these birds were particularly well looked after by her and so probably were more able to raise second broods than those in other garden areas.

The above description applies mainly to the Great Tits. The only other species which has any number of second broods is the Coal Tit. As shown previously, the pinewoods tend to have a richer supply of caterpillars late in the season and the Coal Tit, like the Great Tit under these conditions, has a number of second broods. Curiously, however, although the Coal Tit is thought to be adapted to coniferous woods (chapter 9), it has fewer second broods there than the Great Tits, only about 9% of the pairs raising second broods in Scots Pine and 4% in Corsican Pine where there is a lower supply of caterpillars (by comparison 28% and 11% of the Great Tits had second broods). Unlike the Great and Blue Tit, the clutch of the Coal Tit does not decrease markedly with the time of year, there being only about a one-egg difference between the size of first and second clutches[214]. In marked contrast to the Great Tit, however, the Coal Tit raises almost all the young hatched. Excluding nests taken by predators the nestlings mortality was 2% in first broods and 1% in second broods. In view of the high success of the second broods it is rather surprising that more parent Coal Tits do not attempt second broods in pinewoods.

Coal Tits relatively rarely have second broods in deciduous woodland. In Wytham in 1963, a year when several Great Tits raised second broods, three out of seven pairs attempted second broods. This is a very small sample, but the clutches were markedly smaller than the normal found in first broods in Wytham (average 7·3 compared with 11·0 in the first broods); in addition only about two-thirds (13 out of 22) of the young were raised successfully. Hence in oakwoods the Coal Tits appear to have the same difficulties as the Great Tits in raising second broods, even though in pinewoods they are much more successful.

THE ADVANTAGES AND DISADVANTAGES OF SECOND BROODS

Natural selection will strongly favour those birds which leave most offspring; the young inherit the characteristics of their parents and if many healthy young are produced these will tend to increase in the population in competition with other, less successful, birds. Hence, at first sight, all the tits should have second broods in order to increase their output. However, the situation is not quite as simple as that since second broods do not necessarily increase greatly the number of young produced. There are three main reasons for this.

Firstly, in Britain at least, late first broods do not produce many surviving young (fig. 66) and what information there is on second broods suggests that they would normally be even less successful than late first broods. Hence the gain from second broods may be relatively low. Secondly, in order to start the second brood swiftly, rather less care may be taken of the first brood young than would otherwise be possible. The female must put her efforts into getting the food necessary to form eggs and the male has to help her; this leaves less time and food for looking after the first broods. In Holland, it has been shown that the parents look after second broods for longer than first broods[190]. However, the parents looked after first broods for more or less the same length of time whether or not they went on to have a second brood, the main difference being that females laying second clutches did not feed the fledglings of the first clutch at all. Hence, possibly, the first brood may suffer slightly if the parents have a second brood and this will tend to diminish the advantage of having second broods.

The third factor that will counteract the advantage of having a second brood concerns the survival of the adults themselves. It must be dangerous to breed; the female may be taken by a predator while she is on the nest. Both parents are vulnerable while out of the nest. They have to work very hard and make regular trips to the nest; as a consequence their general alertness may diminish and predators may more easily lay in wait for birds making fixed journeys. At such times Sparrowhawks found it relatively easy to catch the breeding tits in the Breck[129].

Hence, it is not worth the tits' while trying to raise young unless the chances of their surviving are good; it would be better for the adults to cease breeding and try to survive to the next season. It is clear why birds in oakwoods do not often attempt second broods; the slender chances of raising young are outweighed by the dangers to the adult. In some years at least, the survival of the birds is affected by the number of broods they raise; in some years, though not in others, fewer birds raising two broods survive to the next year than those raising only a single brood (Kluijver in. litt.). This further reduces the advantage of trying to raise a second brood. However it is interesting to note that the Great Tit – and to a lesser extent the Coal Tit – shows some plasticity in its breeding season, attempting second broods when it seems that they may be raised successfully.

In coniferous woodland, especially on the Continent, conditions are much more favourable for raising second broods; they seem even more successful than first broods. Why do not all the Great and Coal Tits raise second broods in these habitats? There are two likely reasons for this. Firstly, although the post-fledging survival of birds in coniferous woods in Britain has not been studied, on the Continent the survival of the late as opposed to early young Great Tits is less good, though the seasonal decline in survival rate may not be as striking as that shown in figure 66 for birds in deciduous woodland. Hence second broods may still be relatively less worth having than first broods.

There is so little quantitative data on Crested, Marsh, Willow and Long-tailed Tits that one cannot be certain that a small proportion do not attempt second broods under favourable circumstances. However, one can be reasonably sure that this is not the case with the very common Blue Tit; presumably as discussed earlier this is related to its greater lack of success with late broods than with early ones when compared with the Great Tit.

Finally, the birds have another activity to complete before the onset of winter; they must complete their moult. Since birds do not normally go into heavy moult while raising young (as they would be making yet another demand on their food supplies) the birds should complete breeding in sufficient time to complete their moult before winter.

MOULT

Some adult tits start their wing moult before the young have fledged. There is considerable variation in this but, not surprisingly, the birds raising late broods are more likely to be in moult before the young leave the nest than those raising early ones. Males seem to start to moult slightly before their mates and one-year-old birds before older birds. The latter may well do so because their feathers are the ones grown when a nestling and so these are by now fifteen months old (instead of twelve as in older birds); they are frequently decidedly worn and it may be urgent to replace them. The males, however, continue to moult throughout the period during which the females are moulting and so have a longer moult[83].

The complete moult takes almost four months in adult birds. In Wytham, many are in moult by early June and so do not finish until about the middle of September. This is longer than is found in some other small birds; for example Newton (1972), working in Wytham, showed that many of the different finches take about eight to thirteen weeks to complete their moult[266]. One of the main differences is that while in most small birds the body feathers and those of the wings and tail are moulted concurrently, the moult of the wing and tail in tits occurs before there is much moult of body feathers and the moult of the latter goes on long after the wing and tail moult has been completed.

The fact that the moult takes so long suggests that possibly the birds may have difficulty finding the extra food for it, though this seems improbable in view of the time of year. Nevertheless the early start (when breeding) suggests that there is some urgency to get on with the moult, and, if so, why do they take so long?

The moult of the juveniles does not take so long since, except for the Long-tailed Tit, they do not moult the flight feathers in the wing. They do, however, sometimes moult some or all of the tail feathers. This happens frequently in the case of the Great Tit; 80% of Great Tits may moult the whole tail, and about 15% of the Blue Tits moult the central tail feathers[106]. In Blue Tits, the proportion of birds completing moult of the wing coverts varies with sex and is different in different years. The fledglings usually start to moult some six weeks or so later than the older birds and tend to complete their moult by the end of September. The juvenile Continental

Great Tits show difference from the British ones in that up to half of them moult the bastard wing whereas only very few of the British ones do[83].

Blue and Great Tits in southern England start to moult some two to three weeks earlier than those in northern England and Scotland (presumably as a result of different timing of the breeding season in the different areas, p. 168), but the northern birds apparently moult rather more rapidly so that they complete moult only a little later than the southern birds[106].

CHAPTER 15

CLUTCH-SIZE AND REPRODUCTIVE RATES

As with date of laying there is a great deal of information on clutch-size and on nesting success. In comparison with almost all other birds, tits lay large clutches. The Blue Tits have the largest clutches; in Wytham, the average clutch of this species is about 11 eggs[286]. The Coal Tit is not far behind with an average clutch of about 10[214], that of the Long-tailed Tit is 9–10 eggs[116], and of the Great Tit about 9 eggs. There is less quantitative information about the other three species, but the Marsh Tit lays about 7–9, the Willow Tit about 8–9 and the Crested Tit about 5–7[52, 264, 409].

All these are, of course, average figures and the numbers of eggs laid by different individuals vary markedly. Figure 59 shows the variation in the number of eggs laid by different Blue Tits in Wytham in a single year; while the average was about 11, clutches of from 4 to 21 eggs were recorded, the latter almost certainly by two females. In other years both higher and lower

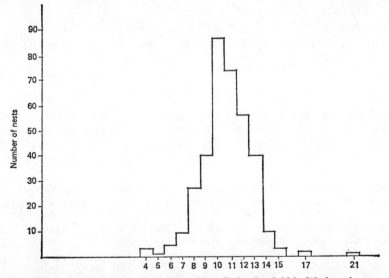

FIG. 59. Distribution of clutch-size in Blue Tit; all clutches laid in Wytham in 1974. The smallest clutches are believed to be repeats laid by birds that had lost an earlier clutch. Clutches of 15 to 17 are laid in almost every year and are usually laid by a single female. Still larger clutches such as that of twenty-one are probably usually the result of two females laying in the same nest; in this case after fourteen eggs were laid, there was a break of several days before the other seven were laid.

clutches have occurred; up to 18 or even 19 have been laid by a single individual.

In the first part of this chapter I shall look at the nesting success of these birds and at some of the factors that affect success. Later I shall discuss some of the features that are known to affect clutch-size, together with some of the possible adaptive reasons for such variations, and finally some of the evolutionary implications.

NESTING SUCCESS

In spite of having so many eggs to incubate and hence so many mouths to feed, the tits tend to have a high nesting success. Nesting in holes is relatively safe since so many of the larger predators, including virtually all the bird predators, are unable to reach the eggs or young (see chapter 17). In consequence only some 20–30% of the tit nests in Wytham are lost to predators, while as many as 80–90% of the nesting attempts of Blackbirds and Song Thrushes may be taken[345].

In good conditions some 90–95% of the eggs hatch (table 17). As can be

Table 17. Number of Great Tit eggs failing to hatch in Wytham in the four years 1958–61. These figures exclude clutches taken by predators (from Perrins 1963).

Clutch-size	2	3	4	5	6	7	8	9	10	11	12
No. clutches	1	—	2	12	23	73	126	116	59	19	3
No. eggs	2	—	8	60	138	511	1008	1004	590	209	36
No. lost	0	—	1	6	5	19	59	36	28	7	2
% lost		10·0			5·8	3·7	5·9	3·5	4·7	3·7	

seen, there is no significant difference in hatching success between clutches of different sizes except that abnormally small clutches may have a lower hatching success than larger ones. The hatching rate varies slightly in relation to habitat. I know of no simple explanation since hatching success is not always lower in those habitats which appear, on other grounds, to be poorer for tits (table 18) so that food supply does not seem to be implicated. The tits also sometimes have a lower hatching success in cold weather. Possibly

Table 18. Number of eggs failing to hatch in Marley (mixed woodland) and areas of Wytham that were richer oakwood (from Perrins 1963).

	Marley			Other areas of Wytham		
	No. eggs	No. lost	% lost	No. eggs	No. lost	% lost
Blue Tit	348	18	5·2	1085	86	7·9
Great Tit	420	13	3·1	999	82	8·2

PLATE 11. Breeding II. *Top*, the young are blind for several days after hatching. At this stage they reach straight upwards to be fed, the chick which stretches the highest being the most likely to receive the food. *Centre*, once their eyes are open, they beg towards the female and when larger still, *bottom*, will grab the food from her. Note the worn tips of her flight feathers, a result of flying in and out of the nest. The bird will moult the worn feathers shortly after the young have become independent.

PLATE 12. Sanitation. As soon as the chick has been fed, the parent waits in case it needs to defaecate. *Above*, the chick raises itself above the others and turns upside down, so presenting the parent with the faecal sac. This the parent removes, *below*, and drops some distance from the nest.

since they need more food then, they have to spend more time searching with the result that they incubate the eggs less effectively. Late clutches also have a lower hatching success; again this is a result of less efficient incubation, but the reason for this is different. The females of late broods start to incubate before the clutch is complete (p. 203) and so the young hatch asynchronously over a longer period than is the case in early broods. The female has to feed some young several days before the last eggs are due to hatch which, as a result, receive less adequate incubation and so have a lower hatching success.

Once the young have hatched they must be fed and raised to the point of independence which occurs a week or more after leaving the nest. In nests that escape predation, survival of nestlings is very high; in good habitats most of the young that hatch leave the nest successfully (table 19); some exceptions to this general statement are discussed later in this chapter. However,

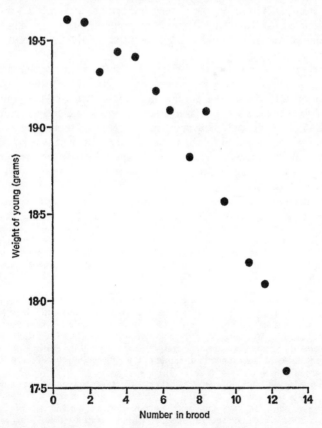

FIG. 60. The average weight of nestling Great Tits in relation to the number of young in the brood (from Perrins 1965).

G

Table 19. Chick losses in different habitats, Great Wood (Oak), Marley (mixed wood) and gardens (from Perrins 1963).

| | Great Tit | | Blue Tit | |
	No. young	*% lost*	*No. young*	*% lost*
Great Wood	888	5·9	1639	4·6
Marley	1705	11·3	1316	7·0
Oxford Gardens	522	44·4	391	30·8

detailed measurements show that, although most young leave the nest successfully, there are some important differences between them, especially in their weight. When weighed on the fifteenth day – a few days before leaving the nest – Great Tits in large broods are lighter than those in smaller ones (fig. 60). The weight of the young is very important since it is an indication of how well nourished they have been. By trapping in late autumn and winter we have shown that many more of the heavy than of the light young survive (fig. 61, see also footnote*).

Clearly then, it is important for the young to be heavy when they leave the nest, but what causes these differences in weight? The answer lies mainly in the amount of food that the parents are able to bring to the young. The larger the brood the harder the parents have to work and the more food they bring to the nest (table 20). However, the increase in food brought to the young is not proportional to the increase in the number of young. Although the parents make more visits to large than to small broods they are unable to feed the individual young in large broods as well as those in small broods. Similar results have been obtained from studies of other species[210, 247].

The measurements in table 20 are based on feeding rates, measured by the number of visits to each nest by use of mechanical recording devices[121].

*In order to obtain these figures of survival – and others used later – we have ringed large numbers of nestlings with individually numbered rings (and recorded for each, their brood-size, date of hatching, weight at the fifteenth day etc.). We have then spent much time in winter trying to recapture these ringed birds and it is the percentage recaptured that is shown in figure 61.

We have only included birds which have been recaptured at least three months after they have left the nest; in practice the birds are not easy to trap in numbers until about November and so most birds have left their nests for at least five months before being captured. By this time the young are fully independent of their parents and have completed their first moult. By then we think the young birds are no longer showing effects of the nestling period; hence the recapture rates should give a good indication of the differential rates of survival between different classes of young.

I have assumed (and have no reason to believe otherwise) that those recaptured are a random selection of the birds still alive and so give an indication of how well each class has survived. However, while one may compare the survival rates of a given class of young birds with those of another in the same year, the reader should be cautious about doing so between years. Variations in the amount of trapping done, the ease with which the birds can be recaptured and other factors mean that comparisons between years may not be valid.

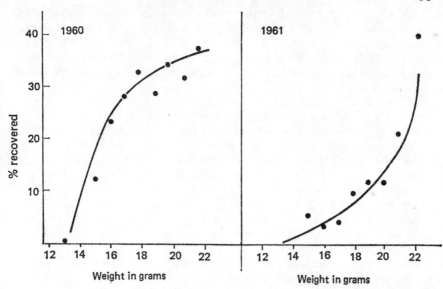

FIG. 61. Survival of young Great Tits after leaving the nest in relation to nestling weight on fifteenth day. The vertical axis shows the percentage of the young of each weight class that are known to have survived at least three months after fledging (from Perrins 1965).

These are not a totally reliable measure of the food brought to the young since the size of the prey brought varies in a rather unexpected way: the food items brought to large broods are on average smaller than those brought to young in smaller broods[319]. Royama, who discovered this, attributed the variation to the pressures on the parent birds. As described in chapter 12, the parent birds maximize their feeding efficiency by eating the small caterpillars themselves and taking the larger ones back to their young; by doing this they make the greatest use of their time and do not waste it by making frequent flights with small items. However, under the stimulus of hungry young that continually beg for food the parents bring back more of the smaller larvae in an effort to appease their hunger. Presumably, as a result of this, they take less food themselves. At any rate compared with young in smaller broods the young in large broods receive relatively less food than

Table 20. Number of visits per day to nests of Great Tits in relation to brood-size (from Gibb 1955).

Brood-size	Feeds per brood per day	Feeds per chick per day
Small broods (av. 5·5)	428	78
Large broods (av. 11·0)	637	58

would be expected from the feeding rates alone. In addition to being less well nourished, the young from large broods suffer another disadvantage compared with those from small broods. Because they are begging more persistently for food, they are noisier and more easily found by predators. As a result larger numbers of large than of small broods are taken by weasels (p. 267).

Measurements of survival rates in relation to weight of young have not been made for other species though the weights of young Blue and Coal Tits also vary in relation to the size of the brood[118, 129]. Hence a correlation similar to that shown in figure 61 for the Great Tits seems likely.

The above description of the survival rates of Great Tits is over-simplified since there is considerable annual variation (fig. 61). For example in 1961 the light young were at a considerable disadvantage compared with the heavy ones whereas in 1960, although the very light young (13–15 grams) survived less well than those that were heavier, there was little difference between the survival rates of young that weighed 16 or 17 grams and those that were much heavier.

The reasons for such marked differences in survival rates between years are not known, but they seem in part to be an effect of the food supplies that are available late in the nestling period, not the oak tree caterpillars which have disappeared by this time. Nevertheless, in occasional years the late broods receive reasonable amounts of food (p. 202) and then even the light young seem to fare well after fledging.

PHYSIOLOGICAL EFFECTS OF BROOD-SIZE

By comparing figure 60 with table 20 the reader will notice that although the individual young in large broods receive less than 80% of the feeds received by individuals in small broods (and the feeds may be smaller because the parents are working harder and being less selective over the size of food brought), they weigh more than 80% of the young in small broods. Similarly Kluijver noted that individual young in broods of seven received one and a half times as much food as those in broods of ten, but they were not one and a half times as heavy at fledging as the young in the larger broods[189].

This apparent anomaly is explained by the amounts of energy that the young birds use to maintain their body temperature. In the early stages young tits receive a considerable amount of warmth from the brooding female, but as they get larger the female must go and collect food for them and then they must keep themselves warm; this they do by 'burning' some of their food supply. One factor which greatly affects the amount of food that the young tit must use in order to keep warm is the number of other young in the brood, the effect of 'huddling'. The rate of heat loss by a young bird (and hence the food it must use to provide that heat) is related to the amount of insulation that it receives. Other young give good insulation since they are warm and in close contact; the larger the number of young present, the less heat each individual loses and consequently the less food it needs to maintain its body temperature.

Such differences have been measured by setting up artificial broods in the laboratory. Young Blue Tits of the same age were brought into the laboratory for a few days (and then replaced in their nests); they were put into artificial broods of three, six and ten in similar artificial nests. In the first experiment each chick in each brood was given as many mealworms as it wanted at each hourly feed: the larger the brood, the fewer mealworms each young took (table 21). In the second experiment each chick was fed a fixed number of mealworms per day, regardless of the number of young in the brood. The young in the larger brood did better on this diet than did those in the smaller brood.

Table 21. Food consumption of nestling Blue Tits in relation to brood-size. The young were kept in the laboratory and given as much food as they would take (from Royama 1966b).

Brood-size	No. mealworms eaten (per chick per day)
3	44·7
6	39·0
10	30·7

The food requirements of young Great Tits have been measured by observing the oxygen consumption of artificial broods of different sizes as they rested overnight. Food must be combined with oxygen in order to be used as fuel and so the oxygen consumption of an animal gives a measure of the amount of energy that it is using. (While roosting the young birds are probably using stored fat as their energy source, but this does not affect the argument.) The measurements again showed that the individual young in larger broods used less food than those in smaller broods, the saving being mainly in the amount they needed to keep themselves warm[243, 426].

From these figures it can be seen why the food requirements of broods are not exactly related to the numbers of young. Figure 62 shows the energy requirements for Blue Tit broods of different sizes. Since the parents have to supply all the energy for the brood, these figures may be taken as a measure of the work required by them. In particular it is interesting to note that chicks in very small broods have high energy requirements. Two points arise from these figures; firstly the parents do not save themselves a great deal of work by having fewer than about six young; much the same amount of food is required since any advantage gained by a reduction in the number of young is off-set by the extra energy that the young in the smaller broods require to keep themselves warm. Tits in temperate areas do not commonly

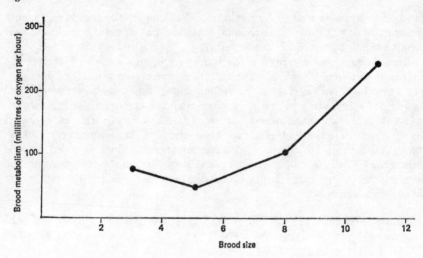

FIG. 62. Oxygen consumption of broods of Blue Tits in relation to brood size. Measurements were made on young of 6–7 days old at 20°C (from O'Connor 1973).

have clutches smaller than about six or seven eggs and perhaps this is the reason for it. Secondly, young in very small broods of only one or two chicks (which normally occur only when most eggs fail to hatch) require very large amounts of food. It has been noted by several observers that young in such small broods are often light in weight; such young may not be able to take enough food to maintain a steady growth when they have to use so much food just in order to keep warm. It is also possible that the young in large broods may occasionally be at a disadvantage from being unable to cool down if they overheat. Some experiments suggest that this may be so but only with brood-sizes and temperatures well above those which are normally found in nature[17]. It seems unlikely that a natural nest-site in a hollow tree in woodland would ever reach the temperature used in these studies, though they might be reached in a nest-box situated in full sun on a garden wall. However, it remains possible that some small deleterious effects of overheating may exist under normal conditions which might affect the weight and subsequent survival of the young in large broods[426].

The results of these laboratory experiments should be borne in mind when variations in clutch-size are discussed; the female does not always save herself as much energy by laying fewer eggs as may, at first, seem likely.

VARIATIONS IN CLUTCH-SIZE

The mean clutch-size may vary markedly; for example, in Marley the mean clutch of Great Tits has been as high as 12·3 and as low as 7·8 in different years. Several factors are known to affect the clutch-size and, as we shall see, the tits' reactions to these factors seem 'sensible'; in each case, a smaller clutch is laid under conditions when the food supply for the growing young is likely to be poorer and a larger one when it is likely to be better. Evolution has favoured those parents which raised healthy young with reasonable chances of survival and hence the birds have evolved the ability to vary the number of eggs they lay adaptively so as to have a brood no larger than they can feed adequately.

Before describing the factors which are known to affect clutch-size it is perhaps worth noting some which do not appear to affect it, although one might have expected them to do so. Firstly there is no evidence that the clutch-size varies with the amount of food available (fig. 63 and footnote*). In view of the huge superabundance of caterpillars during the nestling period (p. 255) fluctuations in the numbers seem unlikely to matter to the tits – unless of course they become much too scarce.

A second possibility that can be excluded is that the female lays as many eggs as she can and stops when she has exhausted her reserves. One cannot exclude the possibility that certain essential nutrients for eggs are stored and used up during laying; however, the majority of the materials for the eggs are not stored (p. 128). If the clutch is lost, say to a predator, the female hurriedly builds a nest in a near-by site and continues laying almost without a break; the combined number of eggs in the two clutches may be considerably larger than the normal clutch. Further, by experimentally removing eggs, the birds can occasionally be induced to go on laying for a prolonged period; a Great Tit may lay as many as 23 eggs under these conditions[190]. Secondly clutch-size is largest at the beginning of the season and decreases thereafter (see below, p. 201) although the food supply is scarcer at the beginning and more plentiful later on. Indeed replacement clutches are usually laid at the time of maximum food availability, yet they are smaller than those laid earlier.

The size of clutch cannot be related to the maximum number of eggs that the female can successfully incubate; the average clutch of Blue Tits in Wytham is about 11 eggs, but almost every year a few birds lay 15 or 16 eggs and these large clutches have a similar hatching success to that of smaller clutches (p. 192); plainly the tits can successfully incubate more eggs than they normally lay. Hence it is more likely that the size of clutch may be related to the numbers of young that the parents can raise.

The following sections cover factors which are known to affect the number of eggs laid by females within local populations. However, there is also a

*This contradicts earlier work which claimed that clutch-size was affected by the density of the caterpillars on the oaks[209]. However, this apparent correlation was largely due to the fact that in 1948 there were large numbers of caterpillars and in 1951 very few; the clutch-size of both Blue and Great Tits was the highest recorded in 1948 and the lowest in 1951. With a longer run of years now available for analysis this correlation does not hold; the variation in clutch-size in 1948 and 1951 can be explained in relation to other factors (largely the unusual dates of laying in these two years, p. 181).

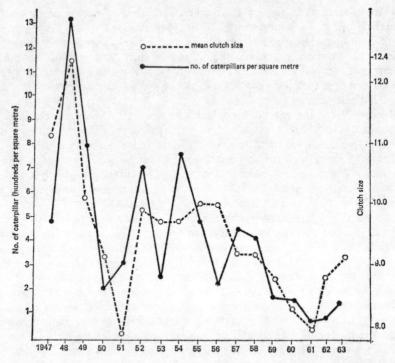

FIG. 63.   Mean clutch-size of the Great Tit in Marley in relation to caterpillar density (measured in hundreds per square metre. For explanation see text) (from Perrins 1963).

considerable amount of geographical variation. Within Europe, clutches tend to be smaller in the south and increase as one goes northwards. This is true for a number of bird species and probably true for several of the tits. For example, the average clutch of the Blue Tit is about 6–7 eggs in the western Mediterranean, but about 11·6 in Britain[343]. However, although for some species the number of eggs in the clutch continues to increase as one goes farther north, for some at least of the tits the clutch-size may start to decline again. Blue Tits lay about 10 eggs in northern Europe and in Crested Tits the clutch-size also apparently declines from central Europe northwards (p. 52).

FACTORS AFFECTING CLUTCH-SIZE

1. *Date of laying*

Many species of birds lay relatively small clutches at the end of the breeding season, but both Blue and Great Tits show reductions in clutch-size from the early part of the breeding season onwards (fig. 64). The seasonal

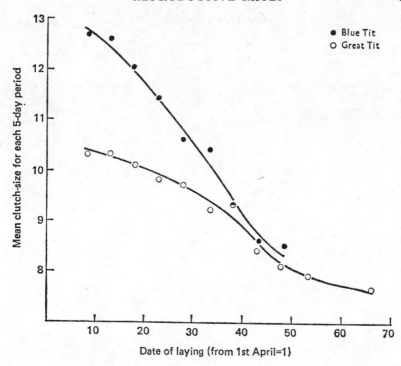

FIG. 64. Seasonal decline in average clutch of Great and Blue Tits in English broad-leaved woods (after Lack 1966).

decline in clutch-size may not be marked in the early part of the season and in some areas in Holland clutch-size may even rise slightly in the early part of the season[18].

The reason for the progressive decrease in the size of clutch is probably associated with the rapid reduction in the number of caterpillars that occurs in deciduous woods late in the season (p. 167). Even the early broods may not be hatched in time for the parents to make full use of the peak period of caterpillar abundance; the later the brood hatches the less food there is for the young, especially towards the end of their nestling period. A further disadvantage of having a late brood is that they are very susceptible to predation, probably because they are hungrier and so noisier than early broods.

The importance of early breeding can be seen in both the weights and survival rates of the young birds. Although the young from early broods are not always the heaviest, they tend to be heavier and to have a much higher chance of subsequent survival than those which hatch late in the season (figs. 65 and 66). At times there is as much as 5% decline in the chance of

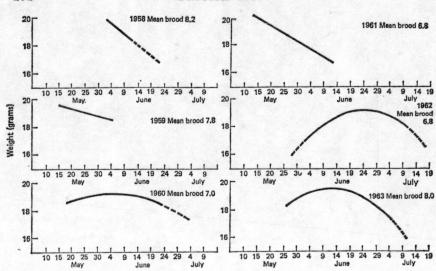

FIG. 65. Average weight of nestling Great Tits (for average brood-size in year in question). Weights are given in grams and date is that on which the broods reached 15 days old (from Perrins 1965).

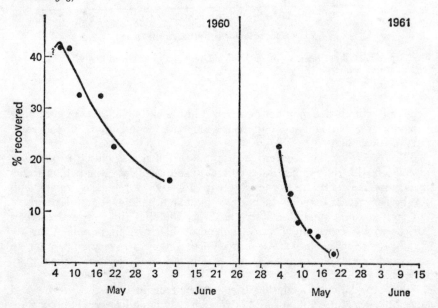

FIG. 66. Survival of young Great Tits in relation to date of hatching. The vertical axis shows the percentage of young that were known to be alive at least three months after fledging. Points surrounded by brackets are based on fewer than 5 recaptures (from Perrins 1965).

subsequent survival for each day's delay in hatching. The effect of hatching date on survival of the young shows a good reason why birds that breed late should not have a large brood. Even with a smaller brood their chances of raising their young are not high. With a larger brood the young would be even lighter in weight and have an even poorer chance of survival. Once again, there is considerable variation in different years. In 1962 the early part of the nestling period was unusually cold and many of the females brooded the young for much of the time and hence could not feed them. As a result not only were the early young light in weight, but unusually large numbers of young died (table 22). Nevertheless although the early young left the nest at lower weights than those which hatched 10–15 days later, they still survived better than the later birds; hence in this year at least it was more important to fledge early than to be heavy.

Table 22. Nestling mortality in Great Tits in relation to date of hatching in 1962. The early part of the season was unusually cold (from Perrins 1965).

Date	13–27 May	28 May–17 June	18–30 June
No. young hatched	916	200	28
No. died	212	18	11
% died	23·1	9·0	39·3

In addition to being smaller, late broods tend to hatch asynchronously (p. 158). Asynchronous hatching is usually held to be an adaptation to a variable food supply[208]. The later-hatched young, being smaller, only receive food when the larger ones are satisfied; if food is scarce, the small young quickly die without having eaten much food that could have been fed to the larger ones, but if there is plenty of food then all the young may be raised.

Food supply is likely to be more variable later in the season. At the beginning of the season there are almost always so many caterpillars that the actual quantity rarely seems to matter to the tits. Later, however, the quantity available seems to matter very much. The condition of the late young seems to be highly variable, as judged by their weights and survival in relation to earlier young (fig. 66). Hence the need for an adjustable brood at this time.

In fact the parent birds gain two advantages by laying smaller clutches. Not only do they have fewer mouths to feed, but by laying a smaller clutch they complete it earlier and so the eggs hatch earlier than if the clutch were larger; this in itself affects the survival of the young. They also gain two advantages by starting to incubate before the clutch is complete; not only do they have a more easily adjustable brood because the young hatch asynchronously, but again the first young hatch earlier than they would have had the female waited until the clutch was complete before she started incubating. These may seem small advantages, but the date of hatching has such a marked effect on survival that they are important.

The Great and Blue Tits show very marked declines in clutch-size during the season but the latter species shows the most marked changes, and also less frequently has late broods; genuine second broods are very rare in Blue Tits. Other evidence suggests that the Blue Tit is more adapted to oakwoods than the Great Tit and its breeding season seems more closely tied to the oak caterpillars than is the case with the Great Tit. In fact the information given in figure 66 masks some of the advantages of an early brood; the overall advantage of early breeding is still greater than that shown, since the early broods are larger than the later ones and so the combination of larger clutches and higher survival rates makes them, relatively, even more successful than is apparent from the figure. In addition, the earlier a bird lays, the greater is its chance of having a second attempt if it loses the first to a predator.

Little is known about seasonal reduction in clutch-size of Marsh or Willow Tits though late clutches seem to be small. The Long-tailed Tit lays smaller clutches later in the season[116, 212]. The Coal Tit shows a slightly different pattern in that there is almost no reduction in clutch-size during the first month or so of the breeding season, but a gradual one thereafter; food is available at higher levels for longer in pinewoods than in broad-leaved woods[18, 129]. In Germany, first and second broods are similar in size, but third broods are smaller. The Crested Tit in Scotland appears to be an exception to this rule since late clutches average 6·2 eggs compared with 5·9 in first clutches[264].

2. *Lateness of season*

The clutch-size not only decreases as the season progresses, it also tends to be smaller in later seasons (fig. 67). There seems to be no correlation between the numbers of caterpillars and the lateness of the season. At one time, it was thought that it might be so important for the birds to lay a small clutch late in the season that they laid a clutch related to the time of year and not to whether they were laying early or late in a given season; this would produce a pattern similar to that in figure 64. In other words the small clutches in later years were thought to be a by-product of the adaptation for a seasonal decline in clutch-size.

However, it is now known that the food available for the tits is affected by the timing of the season. Although the numbers of caterpillars do not vary in relation to the timing of the season, the length of time for which the caterpillars are present in the trees is markedly affected. Caterpillars are cold-blooded and their activity is related to the temperature of the environment at the time; the warmer it is, the faster they feed and develop. Since on average the temperature rises slowly through spring towards summer, late

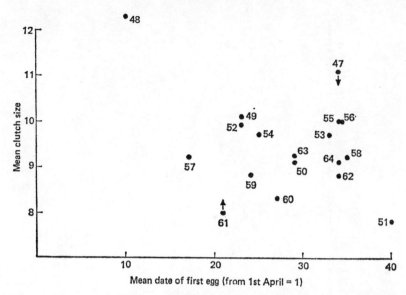

FIG. 67. Mean clutch-size of Great Tits and mean date of first egg. Clutch-size is also greatly affected by the number of breeding pairs and in 1947 was larger than normal owing to low density of breeding pairs and in 1961 was smaller than expected as a result of unusually high numbers of breeding pairs (from Perrins 1965).

breeding seasons tend to be warmer than early ones. As a result the cater-pillars grow more quickly and so finish their development more quickly in late than in early seasons. Hence the length of time for which caterpillars are abundant varies in relation to the earliness or lateness of the season (fig. 68); birds in a late season face a shorter period of food abundance than those breeding in an early year. This may be the reason why the tits lay smaller clutches in late than in early years.

Figure 68 shows, of course, only the average situation. Obviously it is possible for a late season to be particularly cold or for an early one to be unusually warm. Such variation may account for some of the variation in breeding success of the tits; the weather between the end of the laying period and the end of the nestling period will greatly affect the length of time for which the caterpillars are available. There is nothing the tits can do about this – unless they can forecast the weather! However, they can respond to the average situation by laying a smaller clutch in later seasons.

3. Habitat

The clutches of Great and Blue Tits vary in relation to the habitat in which the birds breed. Within deciduous woodland, the clutches of Great Tits do not seem to vary very much though Blue Tits have slightly higher clutches in areas where oak predominates (table 23). Conforming to this in Wytham,

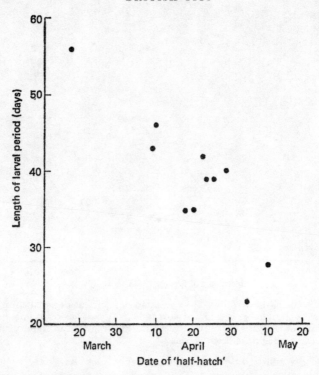

FIG. 68.   The relation between the date at which the larvae of the winter moth, *Operophtera brumata*, hatch and the time taken to develop. Each year an estimate was obtained for the date by which half the larvae had hatched and the date by which half the larvae had fallen to the ground to pupate. Each point represents the means for a different year. Data from G. C. Varley & G. R. Gradwell, personal communication (from Perrins 1973).

the nestling survival of both species seems to be slightly higher in areas where oaks are most plentiful than in areas such as Marley where oaks are less numerous (table 19). These differences are small, but more striking differences are found between woodland habitats and gardens where clutches are smaller (table 23). However, the reduction in numbers of eggs in gardens does not seem sufficient since these areas are very unfavourable habitats for breeding tits. Losses of eggs are not particularly high, but the

Table 23. Clutch-size of Blue Tits near Oxford in relation to habitat (from Perrins 1963).

	Gardens	*Mixed Woodland*	*Oakwood*
Av. clutch	8·8	9·7	10·9
No. clutches	58	168	121

parents have considerable trouble getting enough food for their young, many of which die in the nest. The weights of the young in gardens are very low; Great Tits on the fifteenth day after hatching weigh only about 16·0 grams compared with about 19·0 in Wytham. These are very low, especially when one considers that they are biased; the weights are only from larger young (since some 30–40% of the lighter, weaker chicks have already died). Many young fledge at so light a weight that it seems unlikely that they can survive for long. Reference to fig. 61 shows that woodland young of 16·0 grams usually have little chance of surviving.

The tits in gardens cannot find a food supply as rich as that in woodland. Natural food is almost always preferred by the birds in the breeding season, but it is hard to find. It is not uncommon to see a Blue Tit searching hurriedly through rose bushes picking up greenfly. It has considerable trouble holding

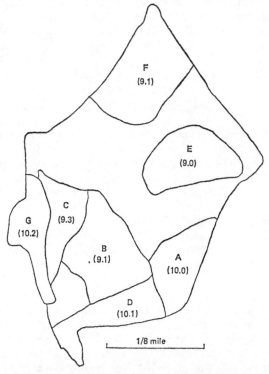

FIG. 69. Variations in clutch-size between small areas of Marley. The figure shows the average clutch for each area over a long series of years. Areas A (5·8) and G (4·4) are predominantly oakwood, D (4·0) is mostly Wych Elm, B (9·2), C (4·1) and E (7·4) are largely hazel with fewer large trees and F (10·0) is mainly a mixture of hawthorn and elder, again with fewer large trees than areas A, D and G. The figures given in brackets after each area above are the size in acres (from Perrins 1963).

a number of these small items in its beak at one time and it needs many to equal the food value of a single caterpillar. At such times one can be reasonably certain that the young are starving; the Blue Tit would not take greenfly if better food was available.

Even if the young are very hungry the parents normally ignore food on bird tables at this time, though it may be fed to the young in the later stages of the nestling period[173]; almost always food on bird tables is of poor quality compared with a natural diet and so a high mortality still occurs. Nevertheless high protein diets such as cheese may be of some value in relation to the poor diet of garden birds, if they would take it.

Even within Marley Wood there are constant differences in the average numbers of eggs laid in different areas (fig. 69). These areas are very small, some as little as about four acres, yet the differences in clutch-size have been apparent throughout the study. The reasons for the differences are not known, but areas (B, C & E) where small clutches are laid are predominantly hazel with relatively few large oaks and other trees and a poor understory, while others (A, D & G) contain more big trees and a richer herb layer. In those areas where birds lay large clutches the survival rate of the young is about 10% higher than in the areas where the birds lay low clutches, but the difference is not statistically significant[199, 286].

4. Density of breeding pairs

Tits lay smaller clutches in years when there are larger numbers of breeding pairs than in years when the breeding density is low (fig. 70). Even in years of high density the food available during the nestling period is far more than the birds would need. However, it is possible that under these conditions there tends to be a shortage of food later when the young have left the nest; Kluijver has shown striking effects of some form of interaction between the young birds after fledging; the survival of the young being markedly affected by the numbers of other young Great Tits present (p. 250)[196]. Under conditions of high density it may be important for the parents to make sure that their young are particularly well nourished, so that they are able to stand up to competition from the many other young; a slightly smaller brood may be better under these circumstances.

In one year in Marley (1961) there was some evidence of food shortage for the nestlings. The caterpillar population in Wytham was the lowest recorded during the study while the Great Tits in Marley were at their highest recorded density; the levels elsewhere in Wytham were high but not as high as in Marley. There was an unusually high nestling mortality in Marley (compared with other years and with other areas of the wood in the same year) and those that fledged in Marley survived less well after they left the nest than those in the rest of Wytham (table 24). Hence the low survival rates of the young Great Tits in Marley may well have been a result of the high density. Under these circumstances it is clearly essential that the young

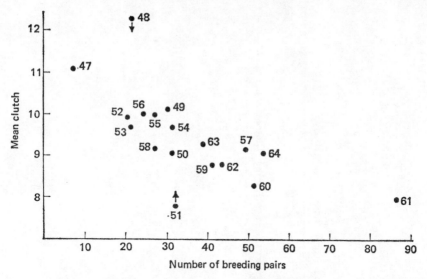

FIG. 70. Relation between mean clutch-size and number of breeding pairs each year of Great Tit in Marley Wood (arrows indicate abnormally early or late seasons).

be as well nourished as possible. One way for the parents to achieve this would be for them to lay smaller clutches.

Table 24. Losses of young in two areas of Wytham in 1961. For explanation see text.

	Marley	Rest of Wytham
Av. weight of young on 15th day	18·0	19·0
Nestlings died (%)	16·4	3·0
Fledged young recovered after 3 months	6·6	12·4

The reduction in clutch-size in response to increasing density is marked, but density has another effect on the reproductive output of the birds which has an even larger effect; the proportion of second broods is markedly affected by the density of breeding pairs (p. 184).

5. *The age of the female*

Older birds lay slightly larger clutches than young birds; the difference between the dates of laying of the two age groups (p. 170) is insufficient to account for the difference in clutch-size. Young parents lose slightly more young in the nest even though they start off with fewer; hence it might be expected that they were not such good parents.

Table 25. Success of fledglings in relation to age of the female which reared them (from Perrins 1965).

	1960		1961 (excluding Marley)		1961 (Marley only)		1962		1963	
	Yearling	Older	Yearling	Older	Yearling	Older	Yearling	Older	Yearling	Older
No. hatched	160	234	489	359	278	194	349	745	476	875
No. broods	23	29	73	48	37	22	45	87	52	94
Mean brood	6·9	8·1	6·7	7·5	7·5	8·8	7·8	8·5	9·1	9·3
No. recovered	40	75	45	45	11	12	55	110	66	163
Recovered (%)	25·0	32·0	9·2	12·5	4·0	6·2	15·8	14·8	13·9	18·6
No. recovered per brood	1·74	2·59	0·62	0·94	0·30	0·55	1·22	1·26	1·27	1·73

The differences given for clutch-size and fledging success between the two age groups are rather small, but once again the post-fledging survival rates show more marked differences; the older birds raise more surviving young than birds which are breeding for the first time (table 25); presumably such rates must be related to the inexperience of the young females. It is perhaps surprising that the young birds do not start off with a markedly smaller clutch than the old ones in view of the differences in survival rates of their young and it would be interesting to know how the young birds increase their success in a later season. Other factors associated with the age of the female are discussed in chapter 16.

6. *Size of nest chamber*

In at least Great, Marsh and Willow Tits, the birds lay smaller clutches in small nest chambers than they do in larger ones[229, 232]. The same may well be true for Blue Tits where one often finds that the nests in very cramped sites contain rather small clutches. In the case of the Great Tit the differences may be quite considerable between the two sites. In one year Löhrl found that Great Tits nesting in holes with an internal diameter of 20 cm. laid an average clutch of 11.4 eggs compared with clutches of only 9·1 eggs in nests with an internal diameter of 9 cm.

The reasons for this modification are not clear. In the smaller sites a large brood would be much more cramped and possibly more likely to overheat (p. 198). In Löhrl's study (even though the clutch-size was smaller to start with) there was a slightly lower nesting success in the smaller chambers (87% of the young fledged, compared with 94·5% in larger chambers) but this was only true in one year, not in another. The nesting boxes of different sizes were moved from one area of the wood to another in different years and most of the birds nested in them so that effects of age and other factors seem unlikely to be important factors for consideration.

7. *Other factors affecting clutch-size*

The six factors discussed (lateness of season, date within season, habitat, breeding density, age of female and size of nest-hole) are not the only ones to affect the size of clutch laid by the tits but they are the only ones to have been quantified. Several studies have shown that these factors account for only a proportion of the variation in clutch-size and that therefore other factors must also affect clutch-size[286, 292, 294].

One further factor is known but cannot be quantified. In a study on the survival rates of young from broods of different sizes (p. 195) we found we were unable to obtain sufficient information on large broods since they were too uncommon. In order to obtain more information we artificially manipulated some of the broods. For example, if on the day of hatching we found two broods of nine young we would remove three from one brood to the other and so obtain broods of six and twelve young respectively, smaller and larger than we commonly met in the field. The parents treated the foster young identically to their own – they fledged at the same weight and had similar survival rates to the original young in the brood. However, overall survival of the young from the artificial large broods was not as good as that from natural broods of the same size.

The most likely explanation is that the birds lay a clutch whose size is related to their ability to raise young. In other words a bird that lays 12 eggs is more likely to be able to raise 12 young than one that lays 9 eggs and has another 3 given to it. This could come about in a variety of ways, the female that lays 12 may be laying in a particularly favourable small area of the wood, or her own abilities at raising young or those of her mate may be particularly good. The female must of course recognize and respond to such signs at the time of laying, varying her clutch accordingly. This may seem rather far-fetched, but there is no reason why it should be. The clutch laid by a female Common Tern *Sterna hirundo* can be related to the feeding efficiency of her mate[269] and the rearing ability of individual birds of other species may vary in parallel with the clutch-size[74, 76, 279].

I have suggested that some of the variations in clutch-size are adaptive inasmuch as higher clutches are laid at times when larger broods can be raised and the reverse. However, if this is so, it is perhaps surprising that some of the variations in clutch-size are not larger. Why, for example, do the birds not lay still smaller clutches in gardens since breeding success is so low there?

It is also worth remembering that while some reasons for the adaptive nature of these variations may be put forward, we still do not understand by what mechanism the birds vary their clutch in relation to the changing environment. Yet these small birds in some way modify their clutch in response to a wide variety of environmental changes; in most cases the direction of the change – to larger or smaller clutch – seems adaptive.

THE EVOLUTION OF CLUTCH-SIZE

From the evolutionary point of view, the tits which leave the largest number of surviving offspring should become the commonest in later generations, provided that their young inherit the tendency to lay a clutch similar to that of their mother.

Analysis of the inheritance of clutch-size is not easy. One major problem is that the same bird may lay a clutch of quite different sizes in two successive years. Hence plainly, an individual tit does not lay a clutch of a fixed size, but varies it in relation to the environmental conditions at the time of laying; this is true both within and between years. Nevertheless the clutches of a given individual show a constant relation to the average clutch; for example a bird might lay 12 eggs in a year when the average was 11, or 9 when the average was 8. Similarly, the clutch-size of a daughter can be related to that of the mother; if the latter laid clutches that were larger or smaller than the average, the daughter's clutch tends to show the same variation[292]. In other words, part of the variation in the clutch-size of an individual is inherited, part the response to environmental changes. If, as I have suggested, the latter responses are also adaptive, then the ability to vary the clutch in response to such a wide variety of factors is also likely to be inherited, but this has not been shown.

In some of the earlier sections of this chapter we have seen that the percentage of young that survived varied under different conditions. While this measure is useful for many comparative purposes, it does not tell us which is the most productive brood-size, since this will be the one that produces the greatest number of young which survive to breed. Table 26

Table 26. Hypothetical relationship between brood-size and survival. Note that the broods which produce the largest *number* of surviving young do not have the young which have, individually, the highest chances of survival. On these figures the birds should have evolved the tendency to lay clutches of 5 or 6 eggs.

Brood-size	1	2	3	4	5	6	7	8	9	10
% survival	100	90	80	70	60	50	40	30	20	10
No. surviving	1·0	1·8	2·4	2·8	3·0	3·0	2·8	2·4	1·8	1·0

shows an imaginary range of brood-sizes with varying survival rates; although the individual young in smaller broods survive better than those in large broods, there are too few of them for there to be as many survivors as from broods of 5 and 6, while the declining survival rates of the larger broods outweigh the advantage of the extra number of young. It may seem grim, but natural selection acts on those that live and not on those that die: by having more young – each with less chance of survival – the parents may raise a larger number of surviving young than if they start with fewer but raise a higher proportion of them.

The actual figures for Wytham Great Tits in which the effects of date have been allowed for, are plotted in figure 71; the largest broods produce fewer surviving young than those of slightly smaller size. Nevertheless the most productive brood has been, on average, slightly larger than that most commonly found in Wytham; in some years the most productive brood-size has been considerably larger than that found in nature. Since it would be so important to raise as many young as possible, how can one account for this discrepancy? There are a number of possible explanations. The most important is that, as described earlier (p. 212), the birds that lay large clutches are better at raising large broods than are those which lay smaller clutches and are given larger numbers of young. Hence, in some way the females are making a judgement of their own that we cannot allow for. However, when we swap the young around, the most successful brood-size is closer to that most commonly found in nature.

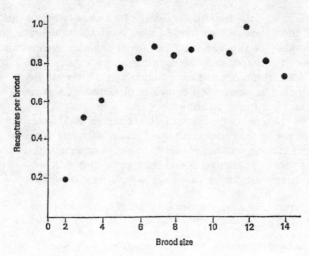

FIG. 71. Survival of young Great Tits in relation to brood-size. See text for explanation (from Perrins and Moss 1975).

The other factor that would have a large effect on the optimum brood-size is the survival of the females.

ADULT SURVIVAL IN RELATION TO BROOD-SIZE

If the parents of larger broods suffer higher mortality this would modify the effect of natural selection acting in favour of such broods. The parents have a much higher chance than the young of surviving to the next season (p. 220) and it is important that they do not overwork themselves to the stage that their chances of survival deteriorate.

Pressures of work may occasionally result in harm to the adult birds; especially if they take less food themselves, the parents of large broods can become severely overtaxed. Blue Tits (p. 129) have lower fat reserves towards the end of the nestling period than at any other time in the breeding season. Great Tits may lose condition while raising their young[173]. On occasions adult birds speed up their rate of feeding but seem unable to maintain the new level of work (p. 195); eventually they slow down again[121]. Similar results have been obtained with the Starling *Sturnus vulgaris*; here the birds were induced (by the noise of extra, hungry young) to go on feeding as fast as possible for long periods but eventually they gave up, apparently from exhaustion.

There is no good evidence that such pressures regularly result in adult tits getting into such poor condition that they die. However, in 1961 the density of caterpillars on the oaks was the lowest recorded during our study. In this year the young Great Tits were not only very light in weight but also unusually large numbers of them died (16·5%). Associated with these observations that parents could not, in that year, obtain enough food for large broods, there was some evidence that they themselves might have suffered. Although the samples are not large, 32% of the females raising broods of 12 or more young were seen again after the breeding season compared with 47% of those with smaller broods.

One would not expect to make such observations very often. From the evolutionary viewpoint it is probably usually better for the female to desert her brood rather than to risk becoming weakened and dying while trying to raise her young. If the broods were likely to survive, it might be a different matter, but under conditions when the female cannot collect enough food for the young, it is hardly likely that the young will survive. Further, if the female died before the young had been raised, they would have virtually no chance at all. Hence it can seldom be worth a female's while to overwork herself for the sake of her brood; she is more likely to leave surviving offspring if she deserts her brood in the hope that she will survive to breed again.

On the island of Vlieland the survival of the adult birds is affected by the numbers of young that they raised[196]. In part this results from the fact that the birds which had large numbers of young were those which successfully raised second broods; it is not known whether it was the work of raising many young or whether it was the prolonged period of looking after young which adversely affected the parents. Their survival may be affected through the timing of their moult; Bullfinches which moult later in the summer are less likely to survive than those which moult earlier[265]; the same sort of situation could affect the survival rates of the adult Great Tits.

Plainly there are fewer advantages of having a second brood if the survival rates of the adults are reduced by so doing. Second broods in Holland (most common in pinewoods) are more successful than those in Britain, but less successful than first broods. Hence the advantage of having second broods – from which relatively few young are likely to survive – may be slender. Such a suggestion might help to explain the marked differences in the proportion of Great Tits raising second broods in Britain and the Continent. The advantages of so doing are rather finely balanced and unless the chances of raising young from them are good, the disadvantages in terms of adult mortality outweigh the advantages.

In conclusion one may say that the tits show a remarkable ability to vary their clutch in response to a wide variety of environmental conditions. Such variations seem adaptive in that they reflect the difficulty or ease with which the birds may expect to be able to raise their young. The birds inherit a tendency to lay a clutch of a certain size and the size laid approximates to that which yields the greatest number of surviving young. The mechanisms by which the birds adjust their clutch-size are not known at all.

CHAPTER 16

GROWING UP AND GROWING OLD

COMPARED with open-nesting birds such as the Blackbird, hole-nesting birds, such as the tits, tend to have large clutches and long incubation and fledging periods. These factors are believed to be associated with the greater safety of nests in holes since these sites are safe from many predators. It is therefore more practicable to 'put all one's eggs into one basket' than is the case with the birds that nest in more vulnerable sites. The length of time the nest is in use is much longer in a tit than in a Blackbird (about 41 days and 29 days respectively). The tits take longer because they have more eggs to lay and because the eggs and young develop slowly compared to those of Blackbirds; such slow development is presumably associated with the large brood-size; with so many mouths to feed the parents cannot rely on bringing enough food to the young to enable them to achieve a faster rate of growth. This is not a situation which can be altered easily if food becomes abundant but rather an evolutionary 'choice' of a rate of development whereby a larger number of young that grow a little more slowly, has proved more successful than a smaller number of faster-growing young. In order to increase the size of the brood, the tits have had to 'economize' somewhere, in this case through slower growth even though this carries the accompanying risk that the nest is vulnerable to predation for a longer period; the increased production has outweighed the increase in losses.

EGG-SIZE

The eggs of the tits vary markedly in size; for example the average weight of fresh eggs in different clutches of the Great Tit may vary in a single season from about 1·3 to 2·1 grams – a difference of more than 50%. Two reasons for this variation are known. Firstly, as discussed in chapter 14, the birds that lay at the beginning of the season tend to have smaller eggs, probably because it is harder to find the necessary food for egg formation then than later. Secondly, larger birds tend to lay larger eggs than smaller birds; part of this variation in egg-size is inherited[179]. However, the seasonal variation is not just a result of the larger birds laying later and laying larger eggs (p. 176); individual birds tend to lay larger eggs in repeat clutches than in their first clutches.

The size of the egg from which it hatches has an effect on the future of the young bird. The larger the egg, the larger the chick that hatches from it (fig. 72). Larger chicks have a faster growth rate than smaller ones so that, comparing two young from eggs of different sizes, the chick from the larger

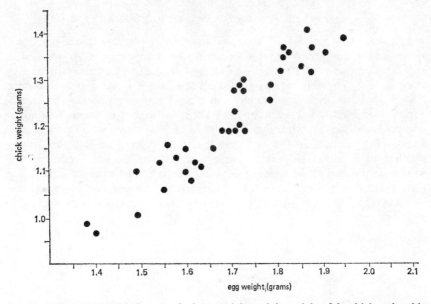

FIG. 72.   The relationship between fresh egg weight and the weight of the chicks at hatching in Great Tits. All chicks were hatched in an incubator and weighed before being fed (from Jones 1973).

egg will grow steadily larger in relation to the chick from the smaller one. Such differences are noticeable throughout the first eight days of the nestling period; thereafter the growth rate of the largest birds starts to slow down (see below); the gap between the two young begins to narrow in the latter part of the nestling period[327]. A further factor is involved in that the chicks from the large eggs may have a greater chance of surviving than those from small eggs if the conditions are poor enough for nestling mortality to occur (table 27).

Table 27. Survival in relation to egg-size in late broods of Great Tits. The table shows the percentage of eggs which produced fledged young. Such effects are not normally noticeable in the early part of the season; feeding conditions have to be bad for such an effect to show (from Schifferli 1973).

Egg-size (fresh weight)	*Success* (%)
Less than 1·4 grams	64·3
More than 2·0 grams	86·5

NESTLING GROWTH AND DEVELOPMENT

When the young hatch they are blind, helpless, with only sparse patches of down and are unable to maintain their body temperature. As with other small nidicolous young (those that remain in the nest until ready to fly), they have a relatively large head and gape and a large digestive system. They are basically a food-conversion factory and are able to grow quite rapidly provided the parents can keep them warm and well-fed. The young compete with one another for food – the one that can reach up farthest is usually the one which gets the food. Since the young need to be able to reach as high as possible it is not surprising that the legs grow relatively fast in the early stages of the nestling period. Compared with the legs, the wings grow more slowly; they are of no use to the small nestling and so growth can be delayed in favour of structures of more immediate importance (fig. 73).

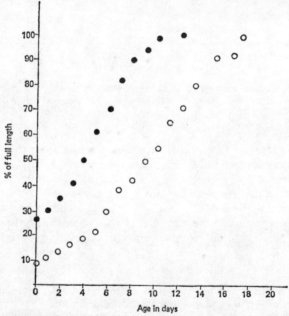

FIG. 73.   Relative growth rates of legs (●) and wings (○) in Blue Tits. Both are plotted as a percentage of full-length to make them comparable. Note how much sooner the legs are fully grown than the wings (from O'Connor 1973).

The eyes open when the young are about a week old and feathers start to appear about the seventh to eighth day in the Great Tit, a little earlier in the other species. Gradually the body becomes covered with feathers; the wing feathers start to develop at about the same time but, being large, take a considerable time to become fully grown. Normally they are not fully grown even by the time the young bird leaves the nest. As the young nestlings feather up they become progressively better insulated until they can be more or less independent of their parents for warmth; they begin to maintain their own body temperature. Since at this time the young are approaching their maximum rate of growth the female needs to be able to brood them less so that she can devote more of her time to collecting the necessary food. It is particularly important that the female be free to collect as much food as possible since, after the first week, the need for food is greatest and it is at this time that, in poorly nourished broods, starvation starts to show[18, 118].

Figure 74 shows the growth of young Great and Blue Tit nestlings in typical early broods in Wytham. The young grow rapidly during the first half of the nestling period and reach their maximum rates at about the

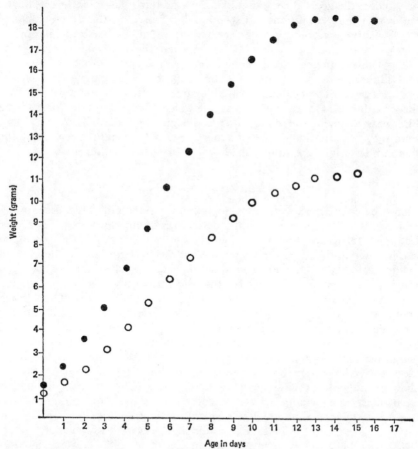

FIG. 74. Growth rates of Great Tits (●) and Blue Tits (○). Day of hatching is called day 0 (from Gibb 1950).

eighth or ninth day after hatching. Thereafter growth slows down and well-fed young reach a peak in weight about the thirteenth or fourteenth day in the Great Tit, earlier in the other species. Thereafter the weight drops slightly until fledging. Less-well nourished young may grow more slowly, reach a peak weight at a later stage and even sometimes spend several days longer than usual in the nest.

This observation poses one problem. In chapter 15 I showed that survival of the young was dependent to a large extent on their weight on the fifteenth day. If, however, the young that were lighter on the fifteenth day reach the same weights as the heavier young, but at a later date, the observations on weights and survival rates (fig. 61) become more complicated. Possibly weights on the fifteenth day not only indicate actual weight, but also in some way reflect the general condition of the young bird that will affect its future survival. Under conditions of exceptionally poor diet, the development of the few surviving young may be severely retarded; in Corsican Pine in the Breck, three broods of young Great Tits left the nest on the 25th, 26th and 27th days after hatching, compared with the normal 19–20 days[129].

Relatively little is known about the young birds after they have left the nest. However, the evidence available suggests that the young birds find life very difficult while they are learning to fend for themselves. Most young birds caught during the immediate post-fledging period are lighter in weight than they were in the nest. Fitness must be very important; presumably the more underweight the young, the lower their chances of survival.

SURVIVAL RATES

Simple calculations show that if a population is to remain stable, the number of birds that die each year must equal the number that are born. For example, if a pair of tits raise 10 young (i.e. 12 birds in all) then only two can be alive in the following year; 10 must die. Emigration can be ignored in such calculations though it may be important on a local scale (p. 239). Usually the large majority of birds that die are the juveniles.

In Wytham we have studied the survival rates of Great Tits. On average about 50% of the adults (or one of each pair) survive from one season to the next (fig. 75) and correspondingly one young bird per pair survives and 'replaces' the dying adult; the data are shown in table 28. Hence only about one in ten of the eggs laid or one in four or five of the young birds that leave the nest live long enough to breed. Once the birds are one year old further changes in death rates are small (fig. 76), though the sparse data suggest an increase in mortality after the age of five or six. However, birds that breed for the first time are less successful than the older birds and their survival rates are not quite as high as those of birds aged two or more. Adult Great Tits have an average annual survival rate of about 50%, but this varies somewhat from year to year, the extremes in our Wytham study being about 40% and 70% surviving. Similarly Dutch Great Tits have

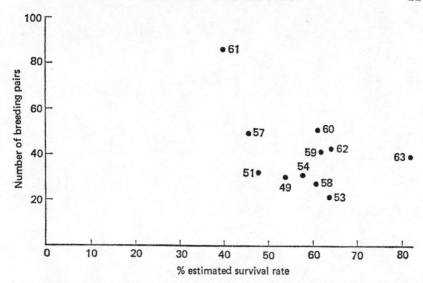

FIG. 75. Estimated survival rate of adult Great Tits from one breeding season to the next as a percentage of number present in first season. The numbers by the points denote the year in which the birds bred. Note the relatively small differences in survival rate between years compared with that for the young in fig. 82. There is no apparent connection between the survival rate and the breeding density, but all the years with lower survival were ones without a crop of beechmast (from Lack 1966).

an average survival of 51% [190]. Survival of other species seems likely to be similar to this, though there are few detailed studies. In the case of the Blue Tit, with a slightly higher clutch-size, obviously more birds must die each year. In this case, the adults also seem to have a higher mortality with up to 70% dying each year [343].

As with most birds, there is no evidence that many tits die of old age. Possibly a few birds die of old age, but in order to demonstrate this it is

Table 28. Life table for Great Tits in Wytham. Based on Bulmer and Perrins (1973).

Mean clutch	8·6
Losses of eggs or young	17%
Mean brood at fledging (per successful nest)	7·16
But one-third of nests lost to predators so mean brood at fledging for all pairs	4·8
Survival of young to next season	22%
No. surviving (per brood) to next season	1·05

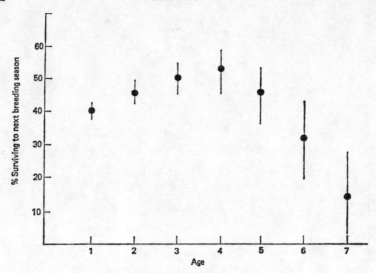

FIG. 76. Annual survival rates of Great Tits in Wytham in relation to their age. There is a very slight increase in chances of survival each year for the first few years, after which survival rates decline. Vertical bars = 95% confidence limits (from Webber 1975).

necessary to show that, once a certain age has been reached, the death rate increases sharply: research has failed to demonstrate this. At least one can safely say that the large majority do not die of old age. Most die before the age of five or six but in Wytham one Great Tit has been known to reach its ninth year and one or two Blue Tits have reached a similar age. On a national scale, where many more birds have been ringed, there are records of older ones, but these are not very much older (table 29). A few still older have been recorded on the Continent.

Table 29. Oldest known British Tits. The list is supplied by the Ringing Office of the British Trust for Ornithology. The ages given are based on the period of time between ringing and last recapture; most of the birds would have lived longer than this.

Great Tit	9 years 4 months
Blue Tit	11 years 5 months
Coal Tit	7 years 4 months
Marsh Tit	9 years 0 months
Willow Tit	8 years 11 months
Long-tailed Tit	8 years 0 months

REGIONAL DIFFERENCES

The survival rates given above do not hold true everywhere. The different species show regional differences in clutch-size and in the proportion of birds having second broods. Hence from place to place there are marked differences in the numbers of young produced with consequent differences in the subsequent survival rates.

The most detailed study of this sort has been made with the Blue Tit. In this species the proportion of young to old birds can easily be determined from museum specimens and so the age structure of the population in different areas can be determined and, from this, the survival rates of the birds can be calculated. These differ in relation to the clutch-size in the different areas; where the clutch-size is lower the survival rate of the adults is higher (table 30).

Table 30. Numbers of old and young Blue Tits (*Parus caeruleus*) in the breeding population, and clutch-size. Note that the more southerly the population the lower the clutch-size and the higher the proportion of old birds. Northern Europe includes Scandinavia, European Russia, the Baltic States and Poland (from Snow 1956).

	Adult	First-year	% adult	Clutch
Britain	36	84	30	11·6
Northern Europe	20	37	35	9·9
North Africa	25	34	42	7·5
Iberian peninsula	26	21	55	6·0
Canary Islands	22	18	55	4·3

In the areas where many Great Tits have second broods, the number of young raised per year may be markedly greater than is the case in Wytham. The highest numbers recorded are those for Vlieland, Holland, where the average number of young fledged per pair may be as high as 11 (compared with 7 per pair, or 4·8 after predation has been allowed for, in Wytham – table 28). This situation is discussed in more detail in the following chapter; under conditions where so many young are produced survival of both young and adults seems unusually low. On the mainland of Holland, where second broods are also common, though not quite as common as on Vlieland, the estimated survival rate from fledging to breeding is 13·2% though, as in Wytham, the adult survival rate is about 50%.

In addition to variation in mortality in different areas as a result of regional differences in clutch-size, there may be differences within an area as a result of differences in habitat, but this has not been investigated in detail. Nonetheless there do seem to be more records of ringed Blue Tits reaching ages of nine or ten in gardens than there are in woodlands. The information cannot easily be examined on a quantitative basis, but it may be that once a bird has survived the very poor nestling period in gardens, a more reliable winter food supply results in the birds having a better chance of reaching a greater age than is the case in woodland. Possibly also survival of Great Tits in pinewoods is not as high as that in oakwoods, since the average winter weights of birds may be lower in the former than in the latter[16].

The survival rates of the two sexes are often different. The average annual figures for the Wytham Great Tits are: males 56%, females 48%. Hence females have lower survival rates than males. The most important reason for this is predation during the nesting season, though deaths as a result of egg-laying and other features associated with breeding may also play a part. Every year in Wytham a number of females are taken by weasels and it seems likely that we under-record the actual number. Although we normally recapture about 50% of the breeding females from one year to the next year, we find that a lower proportion of females whose broods are lost are subsequently recaptured; presumably therefore some of these females are taken with their broods though we fail to notice any trace of this. Females tend to be slightly less faithful to their nesting site than males, but the observed differences in survival rates are unlikely to be caused by more females than males moving outside the study areas[190].

With the survival rates given above, an average of 1·04 birds per pair survive to breed again the following season. This is slightly higher than needed if the population is to remain stable since rather more than one young per pair survive to breed (Table 28). At least part of the discrepancy is explained by the fact that some males do not breed at age one.

In Wytham the average age of the females was 1.91 years compared with 2.47 years for the males. These figures are about average for tits; once they have reached the age of one they may expect to live another one to one and a half years. There are similar figures for other species; Marsh Tit 16 months (males 19, females 13)[347]; about 24 months for the Black-capped Chickadee[272]. As mentioned, the Blue Tit with its higher birth-rate has a slightly lower survival rate.

The different survival rates of the two sexes need not all result from differences in the breeding season – the females may also suffer a higher winter mortality. Males are known to be dominant to females (p. 115) and tend to feed more frequently at food put out for them by man and, by doing so, may keep the subordinate females away. Even under conditions where the food supply is dispersed, such as in pinewoods, there is some evidence that some of the females were light in weight in winter and hence probably short of food – even though such a situation was not observed in the males[16].

As a result of differential mortality, the adult sex ratio tends to be unequal with a higher proportion of males than females and some consequences of this will be discussed in a later section. There is no evidence to suggest that the sex ratio is unequal at hatching, but more females than males may die during the nestling period so that the sex ratio may be already unequal at fledging[80]. Female Great Tits are slightly smaller than their brothers and such differences are already evident in the nest. At fledging male Great Tits weigh about one gram more than females but it has been shown by dissection that females are lighter than males at a much earlier stage than this[179, 285].

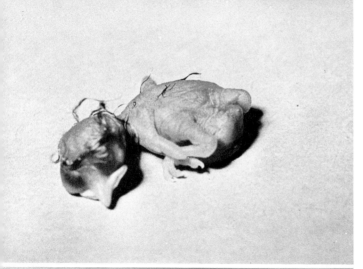

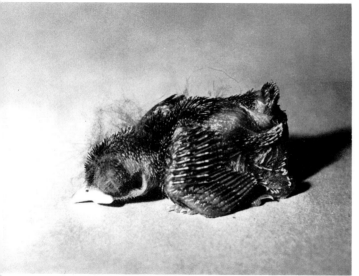

PLATE 13. Development of the young. *Top*, the young tits hatch blind and naked except for a few wisps of down (still wet in the photograph). This young Coal Tit weighs slightly less than a gram. *Centre*, by seven days old the young Coal Tit is well over half its eventual weight of about nine grams and the feathers are in quill; the down is still attached to the tips of the growing feathers. *Bottom*, by the time the young Blue Tits are two weeks old they can fly weakly, though they would not normally depart for another four or five days.

PLATE 14. Predation. Several species of animals are predators of nesting tits, taking eggs, young or adults. Nests in both natural sites and in nest boxes are taken and the predator may leave clues to identity. *Above left*, the Grey Squirrel enlarges the hole so that it can enter. *Above right*, the Great Spotted Woodpecker makes a hole at the level of the calling young and drags them out. Another serious predator, the weasel, can enter without enlarging the hole. *Below*, this German box, made of cement and sawdust, is virtually woodpecker-proof and the smooth plastic top greatly reduces predation by weasels.

If food is scarce during the nestling period the smaller females may suffer in competition with their larger brothers. One might predict that the sex ratio at fledging would be more skewed (in favour of males) in areas with higher nestling mortality, but this has not been examined.

TIMING AND CAUSES OF DEATH

Wild birds, especially small ones such as tits, are rarely found dead in woodland. Being small they are rapidly consumed by other occupants of the wood and hence it is difficult to establish the timing and causes of death. Recoveries of ringed birds do not give a good estimate; they tend to exaggerate the proportions of birds killed as a result of their association with man. More corpses are recorded from places where man is likely to find them (flying into windows, run over by car, killed by cat etc.) than from other forms of death such as those where birds have been killed and eaten by wild predators. Mostly estimates have to be made by noting the times of year at which the birds are last seen; if it seems unlikely that they emigrated at that time, then presumably they died and one may sometimes infer what was the cause of death, but rarely can one be certain.

The nestling period is the only one when the timing and causes of death can be quantified with any confidence. As we have seen, a proportion of nests are lost to predators – mainly weasels in British woodland, but also a variety of other predators – at times (chapter 18). Most of the rest of the nestling deaths are attributable to starvation and they occur most frequently in large broods, or in poor habitats or in late nests in good habitats.

We believe that very large numbers of the young birds die within a short period of leaving the nest (p. 238), presumably from lack of food which in the case of the lighter young is exacerbated by their lack of reserves. However many must also be taken by predators at this time (chapter 18). Clearly, even though much differential mortality has occurred by the autumn (chapter 15) not all the young birds that die do so then, many must die later on in the year. In Holland the mortality of young birds between December and May was estimated at about 43% compared with 25% for old birds; however this figure was very variable and the young birds seemed to suffer much more in years of very cold winters than did the adults[190]. This fits well with the Wytham observations during the very cold winter of 1962–63; although large numbers of young were present in the autumn there were many fewer the following spring even though the survival of the adults was, if anything, a little better than average[214].

Estimates have also been made in Holland of the losses at different times of year; only the adult birds were used so that problems arising from movement or emigration are likely to be minimal. Over a series of years an average of about 32% of the adults died in the seven months of May to December compared with about 25% during the five months December to May – an almost identical rate of loss in both periods[190]. These measurements show that the dangers of breeding and moult during the milder period of the year are about the same as those of the winter, which one tends to think of as being the more difficult for small birds.

During the winter period, starvation is an obvious cause of death and several people have shown that the losses appeared to be higher in cold winters[190]. Such losses may well be modified by the presence of the beech crop or by other sources of food available to the birds during the winter[142]. Apart from the increased demands for food resulting from the low temperatures, bad weather may make the food harder to obtain as is the case with Great Tits when there is thick snow cover. Glazed frosts on the branches of the trees are another likely cause of death[24]. Predators will also take their toll, but few quantitative measurements of their importance are available; sparrowhawks attack foraging tit parties during the winter[253], take their toll of territorial, singing birds in spring (p. 273)[377], and of the adults feeding young in the summer months[129].

Observations on causes of deaths in urban areas reveal a high number resulting from tits being caught by cats, killed by cars or flying into windows. A high proportion of these are young birds or birds that have had to move into such unfamiliar areas in their search for food; once familiar with an area the birds are much less likely to be vulnerable.

Practically nothing is known about the effect of disease on wild birds, epidemics are only rarely observed and these are usually in the more gregarious species where transmission of the disease is easier, rather than in more dispersed species such as the tits. However, there was apparently an epidemic of some form in the Oxford area in the spring of 1949 when a number of birds were found dead in the nesting boxes in which they were roosting[165]. Since dead birds would remain for a long period under such conditions and since there are a large number of areas where nest-boxes are regularly inspected, it is clear that outbreaks of this kind are very rare.

The effect of parasites is also poorly known; virtually nothing is known of the internal parasites of adult tits. However, the nest parasites of tits are better known. The two most common ones are fleas and the parasitic fly *Protocalliphora azurea*. The fleas may at times cause heavy infestations of the nests, but their effect on the health and survival of the birds is not known. *Protocalliphora* is a fly about the size of a blow-fly which lays its eggs in the nest of birds. The larvae suck blood from the young tits and, having become full grown, pupate in the nest lining. They are not often seen since they live in the nest lining and only come up to feed; in addition they probably retire rapidly from the light as soon as the lid of the nest-box is opened. However, they are not uncommon and their presence may often be recognized from spots of blood on the legs or bare undersides of the nestlings. The pupae are easily found in the empty nest.

The effect of *Protocalliphora* on the tits is not known. I found them to be more common in the larger broods. Some of these large broods were ones that had been artificially increased by me (p. 211) and so implies that either the flies lay a number of eggs related to the number of young in the nest or, more probably, that the survival of the larvae is related to the numbers of tits; this finding needs checking. In Holland it is believed that many of the young attacked by the flies may be so weakened that they are more likely to die soon after leaving the nest than are unparasitized young[196].

NON-BREEDING MALES AND AGE OF PAIRS

As a result of the higher mortality of females (and possibly of the slightly smaller proportion of young females than young males coming into the breeding population) there are more males than females amongst the potential breeders. There are two reasons for thinking there may be a number of non-breeding males in the population. Firstly, compared with females, a relatively high number of males are found breeding for the first time at the age of two; they were not apparently breeding at one. Secondly, many of these males were reared (and ringed) in Wytham and have presumably been there all the time; they have just not been able to find mates. Our guess is that about one-third of the first-year birds fail to obtain a mate or about one-seventh of all males do not pair.

The birds that fail to find a mate are in fact probably mostly one year old since the composition of the breeding pairs is not random. There is a tendency for the old females to mate with old males. Since there are more old males than old females the rest of the old males mate with young females which in turn leaves a shortage of young females for the young males. No work has been done on the selection of a mate in the tits, but the above observations suggest that some form of choice goes on, with many of the older females who lose their mates managing to find another old bird with whom to pair. If the age of both male and female affects breeding success (p. 209) then there would be selection for choosing an older mate, but it is not known how this would come about. The older birds may tend to come together because they are those that first get ready to breed. They also tend to be the ones that indulge in territorial activity in the autumn so could have an opportunity to pair then. It is not clear what the males that fail to get a mate do during the breeding season, but they do not maintain a regular territory (p. 113).

FIDELITY TO MATE AND NEST-SITE

Since about half the adult birds die each year, in only about 25% of cases do both members of a pair survive from one year to the next (in 25% the female dies, in 25% the male and in 25% both die). Of these, the majority breed together again the following year; only about a quarter of the birds 'divorce'[190]. This may imply that the birds live together or remember each other throughout the year. However, once they have bred, both sexes tend to be faithful to their nesting place; while they may not nest in the same hole in successive years, they are likely to breed close by. Hence they are also likely to pair again purely by chance.

In Holland, where second broods are common, the pair usually breeds together again for the second time. Perhaps this is again because of the proximity to one another, but in addition the breeding cycle of a pair will be closely synchronized, and this may not be the case with adjacent pairs. Where the female took a new mate for her second brood there was sometimes evidence that the first mate might have died and the new mate may have been one that was previously unmated[190]. However, the female may also take a new mate when her first is still alive; there is a record of a female Great Tit leaving her mate to care for the fledglings while she went and started a second nest with another male[22].

Females are slightly less faithful to their previous nesting sites than males. This tendency for the females to wander more than males is also apparent in the distance between the birds' places of birth and the places where they settle to breed. In Wytham the average distance between the two points is 864 metres for females and 702 metres for males, though of course these figures are only for the birds that settled within the wood; many others will have moved outside[46].

Although such dispersal is relatively small, it results in the birds settling at some distance from their natal site and reduces the chance that they will breed with either one of their parents or with a sibling; it is even possible that the birds tend to avoid the area within about 200 metres of their birthplace for this very reason[190]. There is some slight evidence that such 'incest' may be disadvantageous. Of eight nests where the parents were close relatives, only 42 of the 68 eggs hatched and fledged: the 38% mortality compares very unfavourably with the average of 17·5%. Further, none of the 42 young that fledged was subsequently recovered, although from this number we would normally expect to recapture about three[46]. Recent work confirms high nestling mortality, but post-fledging survival may be normal[419].

EFFECTS OF AGE ON BIRDS

The age of a tit affects it in a variety of ways; again most of these have been calculated for the Great Tit, but are likely to affect the other species similarly. Firstly, size varies with age; young birds have slightly shorter wings than older ones[188] though this was not apparent in a study in Sweden[33]. Older Blue Tits also tend to have longer wings than first year birds as possibly do Coal Tits[358].

In a much more detailed study, wing length of both sexes increased slowly up until the age of three or four after which it declined slightly[16]. To my eye, the males of both Blue and Great Tits get steadily brighter in colour during their first few years so that there may be some improvement in the colour of the plumage as well as the wing length. It has also been shown that the weights of Great Tits increase with age up to about three or four years old[16]. However, this varies in different habitats to some extent, being less clear in pinewoods where some of the birds may have been short of food.

Age also affects the size of the territory; the male Great Tits defend larger territories each year until about the age of four[79, 82]. In this study there were one or two older birds which had smaller territories suggesting the possibility of a decline in territory size in old age.

The breeding success of Great Tits is markedly affected by the female's age[293]. Success increases steadily with age until the female is about three years old. The four-year-old birds have a breeding success similar to that of the three-year-olds, but thereafter breeding success steadily declines (fig. 77). The low breeding success of the first year birds results from two causes.

The first-year birds tend to breed a little later (so reducing their success, p. 210), but even when this is allowed for their breeding success is still lower than that of two-year-old birds. Hence they must be genuinely less efficient parents, as well as starting late. It is worth noting that the older females do not lay smaller clutches; the lower breeding success is a result of higher nesting losses.

The above data were obtained from an analysis of the breeding success in

FIG. 77. Survival of young Great Tits in relation to the age of the female. The figure shows the percentage of young recaptured at least three months after leaving the nest. Vertical bars show the 95% confidence limits. The right hand solid circle shows the average for birds of five, six and seven years old; the three open circles show the data for these three age classes separately, but the differences are not statistically significant (from Perrins and Moss 1974).

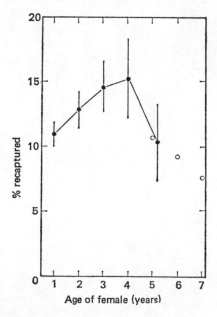

relation to the age of the female; since the females are more easily caught at the nest than the males there is more information available for them. Nevertheless since old females tend to mate with old males some increase of breeding success with age may be due to the abilities of the male. However, the breeding success of young females with old males is lower than that of old females with old males so the effect seems to be largely due to the age of the female[179].

Two biases could affect such findings. Firstly, the more successful breeders among the young birds could be those which also have the highest survival rates; in this way an apparent increase in the breeding success would be observed. Secondly, if birds worked less hard at raising their young they might survive better; this could produce the apparent decline in nesting success in the later years of life. Neither of these possibilities seem to occur, but they should be checked further.

The reduction in wing length, weight, territory size and breeding success after the age of four suggests that birds of this age are no longer as fit as they were hitherto. This suggestion fits with the figures shown earlier in the chapter where annual survival rose after the first year, but declined again after the birds reached four years of age. Hence we may consider the tits as reaching their peak of fitness in the period when they are aged from two to four years old.

CHAPTER 17

POPULATION STUDIES

DENSITIES OF BIRDS AND THE EFFECT OF NESTING BOXES

In chapters 2–7 I gave a range of breeding densities for the different species. Few studies have been made of changes in numbers of Crested, Marsh or Willow Tits largely because of their low densities, and likewise few people have undertaken population studies of Long-tailed Tits because they do not breed in nesting boxes; however, a recent series of papers from Japan describes such a study of this species[258].

Detailed population studies have been made only on the three common species Coal, Great and Blue Tit. The Great Tit has received the lion's share of the attention since most – usually 100% – of the birds nest in boxes if these are available, whereas some Blue Tits select natural holes even when a surplus of boxes is available. In five years in Marley, no Great Tits were found nesting outside boxes whereas as many as one-third of the Blue Tits used natural sites[120]. In some areas Coal Tits may nest in the ground. Hence both Blue and Coal Tits are less suitable for studies of populations than is the Great Tit. In many pine plantations, in Holland and in the Brecks of East Anglia there are few natural holes and the Great Tits may roost as well as nest in the boxes and so can easily be caught outside the breeding season; in other less intensely forested areas, with more dead timber, they tend to roost in small natural sites. Little is known of the situation in wholly mature woodland since there is so little of it. However, such woods have so much dead or dying timber that it seems unlikely that the tits would be without holes of some sort. This view is supported by two series of observations of apparently suitable natural sites in Germany where only 36% (out of 89) and 17% (of 69) holes were used for nesting by small birds[326]. In these areas, one would assume, the birds must have had sufficient natural sites for their needs.

The effect of providing nesting boxes for the tits has already been touched on (chapter 1). In most areas of woodland in western Europe there are relatively few old, dead and dying trees, this being particularly true in well-managed forestry plantations. There is no doubt that the provision of nesting boxes in such woods enables more tits to breed there (p. 255); the numbers normally leap up immediately the boxes are provided[296]. However, the continued increase of nesting boxes above a certain level, seems to have no noticeable effect on the numbers of tits, though other, more colonial species may continue to increase[45]. Most tit populations studied have been provided with a comfortable surplus of nest-boxes so are unlikely to have been limited by shortage of nesting sites. This is particularly true for the Great Tit since it can usually obtain boxes from either Coal or Blue Tits if nesting sites are scarce; if these species occupy boxes in any numbers the Great Tits cannot be short of them.

Another possibility is that the provision of nesting boxes may increase the individual's breeding success. Since there are almost no records of the breeding success of birds out of nesting boxes there is very little evidence to show whether or not this is so[268]. In one analysis of Great Tits in Wytham, I divided the adult females into two groups, those known to have bred in the boxes and those that had not been found breeding; if the latter birds bred at all they must have bred outside the boxes. Similarly I divided the first-year birds as to whether they had or had not been raised in boxes (i.e. whether or not they were ringed as nestlings). The ratio of young raised in boxes to females known to have bred in the boxes was higher than the ratio for young to adults that had not been in the nest-boxes. There are a large number of possible biases in such a calculation, but if they could be corrected for, most of these would have the effect of decreasing the young: adult ratio for those that did not breed in boxes. Hence it seems likely that the females that do not breed in boxes are less successful than those that do; either they do not breed at all or they lost more young because their nest-sites were less suitable or were in less suitable habitats, perhaps, for example, being more liable to predation. Other evidence suggests that there are more male Great Tits than females in the population (p. 224) and that most females breed; therefore one might guess that those not found in boxes were less successful breeding elsewhere rather than that they did not breed at all.

Hence in the context of the population studies discussed in this chapter we can safely assume that whatever may limit the numbers of Great Tits it is not the availability of nesting sites nor is it likely that the other species are short of them. It does not, of course, follow that this is true in woods outside the study areas.

FLUCTUATIONS IN NUMBERS

The longest series of population data for the tits is that for the Great Tits in Holland studied by Wolda and Kluijver (fig. 78). The slight upwards rise in numbers noted there is apparently the result of young woodland growing older during the 30 years; the more mature woodland may contain more food for the birds now than it did formerly. Support for this suggestion comes from the fact that in the Dutch studies the changes occurred in the young mixed wood, not in the older mature pinewoods which comprised part of the area (fig. 79).

A number of points arise from these population data, the main one being that the changes in numbers are very small compared with what is theoretically possible; the birds never became extinct locally (as can happen in cold weather with the Long-tailed Tit) nor did they increase by much more

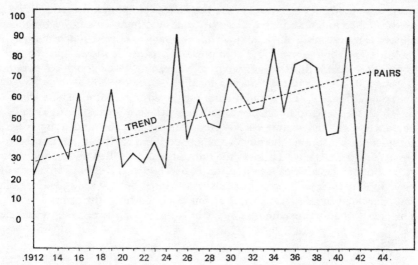

FIG. 78. Number of breeding pairs of Great Tits in Oranje Nassau's Oord, Holland in 1912–44. Note upward trend in breeding numbers (from Kluijver 1951).

than two-fold except in one year (1924–25). Hence, as previously discussed, although each pair may raise eight or more young in a single season, relatively few of these survive to breed the following year.

Similar observations hold for other populations of the Great Tit and also for those of Coal and Blue Tits (figure 80 and figure 4). Two points arise

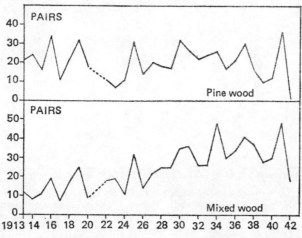

FIG. 79. Numbers of breeding pairs of Great Tits in two parts of Oranje Nassau's Oord, Holland 1913–42. *Upper:* mature conifer, *Lower:* maturing deciduous woodland. Note increase in breeding pairs in the latter area (from Kluijver 1951).

from this second set of figures. First the Great Tit populations in different areas tend to fluctuate in parallel with one another. This is by no means always true but most of the major changes have occurred synchronously in the different study areas. This is important because it shows that the study populations are indicative of what is happening over much of western Europe and are not just fluctuating locally.

Second, the Blue Tit populations (and possibly to some extent those of the Coal Tit) tend to fluctuate in parallel with the Great Tit. Again this is not always so; the changes in Wytham between 1962 and 1963 were a conspicuous exception: the Blue Tits increased markedly but the numbers of Great Tits fell slightly. This was the hardest winter in Britain for about 200 years, but coincided with a rich supply of beech seed. The Blue Tits were able to get most of their food from the seeds on the trees, but the less agile Great Tit was prevented by deep snow from getting the seed from the ground (p. 96). This was probably the main reason for the differences between the two species

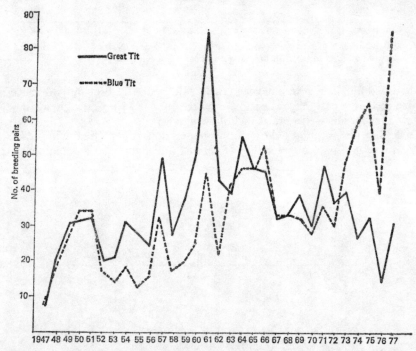

FIG. 80. *Above*, the numbers of breeding pairs of Great Tits (solid line) and Blue Tits (dashed line) in Marley Wood, 1947–76. Note the tendency for both species to fluctuate in parallel. The relative rise in Blue Tits since 1973 is partly due to the provision of a new type of nest-box (see Plate 14). *Opposite*, the numbers of breeding pairs of Great Tits in four different areas. The two areas of higher density are broad-leaved woodland, the other two are conifer. Note an overall tendency for the populations to show similar changes in numbers (from Lack 1966).

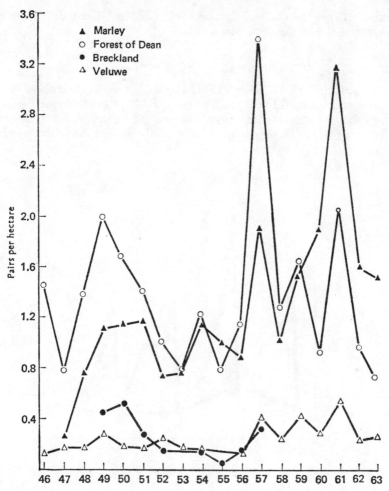

in this year. A similar situation may have occurred in Holland following the very cold weather in the early part of 1942: the numbers of breeding Great Tits in Kluijver's study area dropped from 93 pairs in 1941 to 18 in the following season, while the comparable figures for the Blue Tits were 13 and 15; in Britain at least there was a good beech crop in that winter. Since most of the changes in numbers – especially the larger ones – in the different species seem synchronized the different species may at times be similarly affected by the environment, as is indeed to be expected. However, as outlined above for the Great and Blue Tits there may be occasions when this is not so. Kluijver found much less tendency for the different species to fluctuate in parallel than is apparent from figure 80. In particular he found no correlation between the changes of numbers in Coal and Crested Tits, though these species live in the same pinewoods.

Figures 78, 79 and 80 show the changes in breeding numbers of tits from one year to the next. Such figures tend to make one forget the large changes that take place within each year. Figure 81 shows such changes in the Wytham Great Tit population. There is a large increase in the numbers

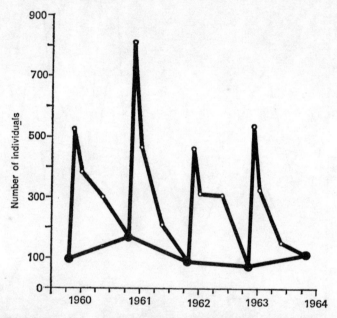

FIG. 81. The changes in numbers of Great Tits within a year. The line joining the solid circles is that representing the numbers of breeding adults from year to year. The three open circles for each year show, respectively, the total of adults plus eggs, the total of adults plus young that have left the nest, and the estimated autumn population.

of birds when eggs and young are produced, followed by a sharp fall in numbers between fledging and the autumn and a more gradual decline thereafter.

As discussed in the previous chapter the annual survival rates of adults are fairly constant compared with those of the young. The survival of the young to the autumn or winter is most easily estimated from the ratio of adults to first-year birds present in the population; fortunately in both Great and Blue Tits it is possible to separate first-year from older birds by their plumage. In Wytham in different winters there have been as few as one first-year bird to every six older birds and as many as two young to each older bird – a twelve-fold difference. In common with many other species of animals this highly variable survival of the young is of major importance in determining the annual changes of numbers. If many young survive, the breeding population the following year will be high, and vice versa. In practice the ratio of first-year birds to adults in the autumn has often been a good guide to the level of the breeding population in the next spring (fig. 82).

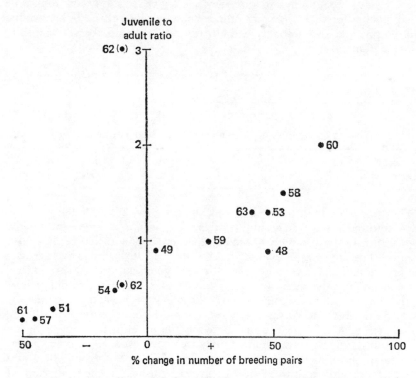

FIG. 82. Ratio of juvenile to adult Great Tits in winter in Wytham Wood in relation to change in breeding population in following year. In 1962–3, unlike other years, the ratio was high at the start but low at the end of the winter (presumably due to juvenile mortality during the exceptionally cold weather), so both points are shown in brackets (from Perrins 1965).

TIMING AND CAUSE OF JUVENILE MORTALITY

This subject has already been discussed in chapter 16, but certain aspects are more relevant here. Regular counts in woodland showed that the numbers of birds dropped very rapidly shortly after fledging (fig. 81) suggesting that this period is critical for the young birds and that many may die then[120]. In the Dutch populations mortality is also high during the first few weeks after fledging[18]. Young Great Tits lose weight during the post-fledging period, again suggesting that they may have difficulty feeding themselves soon after independence[404].

In figure 61 I showed that more of the lighter young died than did the heavier young. The information in these graphs was drawn from recapturing the nestling birds during the ensuing winter. In 1963 and 1964 I put colour rings on the young birds in relation to their weights on the fifteenth day and in early July – about a month after they had left the nest – I went round the wood looking for them; already proportionately more of the lighter young had disappeared and probably had already died – within about a month of fledging (table 31).

Table 31. Proportion of young Great Tits of different weights seen in July (from Perrins 1963).

	Weight class (grams)					
	<15·9	16·0–17·9	18·0–18·9	19·0–19·9	20·0–20·9	21·0+
No. fledged	39	182	269	405	268	89
% seen	0	2·7	4·8	8·1	11·2	10·1

The tits are difficult to catch during the summer, but over the years we have captured and ringed a number of young Blue Tits and these have had a high survival rate to the next breeding season, similar to that of the adults from one breeding season to another. Hence once young birds have survived the first month of life they appear to have a good chance of living longer, again suggesting that it is the first month or so of life that is so dangerous; by the time that autumn comes most of the heavy mortality of the young has already occurred. In Wytham the ratio of old birds to young ones during the winter seldom changes much between the autumn and the following summer suggesting that the young birds survive almost as well as the adults from then onwards. However, evidence for other areas for both Blue and Great Tits suggests that there may be a steady decline in the proportion of young birds throughout the autumn and early winter and even possibly thereafter[423, 425]. We know very little about the causes of this highly variable mortality. The main clue may be (p. 203) that in Britain survival of the young after fledging seems to be in some way correlated with the weight of late broods and with the occurrence of second broods. In those years when the late broods are doing well and some parents are even attempting to have second broods it seems reasonable to assume that feeding conditions should also be unusually favourable for fledged, independent young; indeed this seems to be the case.

Variable feeding conditions need not be the only cause of losses during the summer. Continental workers have stressed the importance of aggressive and territorial behaviour in early autumn as having an important effect on regulating density, arguing that such behaviour results in large-scale emigration at times of high density.

Dutch and Belgian workers have shown that a higher proportion of young from late, than from early, broods are recovered at some distance from the nest[81, 196] and have suggested that the young from these late broods have difficulty in establishing themselves in competition with the young from earlier broods. The young from late broods will settle near their birth-place in the absence of the young from early broods; in an experiment (p. 250) Kluijver removed most of the young from early broods and high numbers of young from late broods settled in the area.

It is not clear how comparable this situation is with the British one. Most of the broods whose young emigrate on the Continent are from second broods and, as we have seen, these are rare in Britain. Further, in Wytham there is no evidence that the young from early broods settle nearer to their birth-place than the young from late broods.

It is clear from all these studies that very large numbers of young tits 'disappear' between fledging and early autumn but since it is almost impossible to find dead birds in woodland, we cannot establish how many of them have died locally and how many have emigrated. Nevertheless, one must be cautious about ascribing the losses to emigration. Since the fluctuations in many tit populations appear to be synchronized, emigration from an area of high density does not necessarily solve a young bird's problems; in all likelihood it will merely move into another area of high density. Plainly some birds will move into areas where nesting success has been low and others into areas of marginal habitats where breeding success is always low but, on average, decreases in the numbers of young birds must mean that most of these young birds have died, either within the study area or elsewhere after emigration. In Wytham there is a considerable 'shuffling' of the young birds about a month after fledging; many of the ringed birds move out of the study area while numbers of other unringed birds move in, resulting in a mixing of the populations[120, 137].

Emigration is usually considered to occur as a result of a bird's failure to establish itself in competition with more aggressive neighbours, though it could equally be because of its inability to find plentiful food in competition with more efficient rivals. A number of observers have noted that young tits are aggressive at an early stage, long before they are involved in territorial disputes. Hinde recorded aggressive behaviour in young Great Tits within about eight days of leaving the nest and young Marsh Tits are aggressive to one another in early autumn even though they may not be maintaining a territory[165]. Such behaviour could result in the movements of some young birds away from the area in which they were born, especially under conditions of high density. In the American Black-capped Chickadee the older young are dominant to the later-hatched ones[133].

Aggression reaches its peak in the spring and autumn, when the birds defend their territories.

The territorial behaviour of some species is believed to limit the number of breeding birds. Since it is presumably harder for a bird to establish itself in an area when the numbers of residents are high than when the numbers are low, such behaviour could have an important effect on the numbers of birds settling in an area. However, in tits there is no completely convincing evidence that this is so. There is no doubt that territorial behaviour results in spacing out of the birds over all the available habitat, forcing some birds into less favourable areas (p. 112), but evidence that birds are prevented from breeding at all is lacking. We can, however, eliminate the possibility that there is a fixed territory size since the breeding population in an area varies so much from year to year.

There are two main periods of territorial behaviour, in autumn and in spring, and these are the most obvious times when one might expect birds to be driven out of an area. However, there is no good evidence that spring territorial behaviour has this effect; it does not seem to lead to a marked reduction in numbers in most cases and removal experiments have not demonstrated a surplus of non-breeding birds, but only that some had settled in rather less suitable habitats (p. 112), a factor which would have a considerable effect on the numbers of young raised. Occasionally birds have been reported moving out of the study area in spring but at least some of these birds could have been temporary winter visitors returning to their breeding grounds in spring[82, 335]. Hence spring territorial behaviour could be regulatory if (as is likely) the birds that breed in poorer habitats have lowered breeding success, but may not prevent birds from breeding.

Kluijver considered territorial behaviour in autumn to be more important in regulating the population and certainly this behaviour occurs before many of the young birds on the Continent emigrate. However, in Britain many of the young birds do not indulge in autumn territorial behaviour. As far as can be seen they move through the wood in small parties and are not noticeably affected by the territorial adults. Nevertheless, young birds could still respond to the numbers of adult territory holders present.

Similar results have been reported by Southern and Morley in their study of the Marsh Tit; clashes between the territory-holding adult birds and the flocking juveniles were not common at any time of year[347]. Indeed the territory-holders might join the flocks of non-territorial birds and feed with them while they were in the territory – though they would leave the flock to chase off an intruding neighbouring territory-holder. However, the

Plain Titmouse of North America, like the Marsh Tit, is territorial the whole year round but the territory-holders, unlike the Marsh Tit, do not tolerate the non-territorial flocks within their territories and so the latter are confined to marginal habitats. In the case of the Marsh Tit, when an adult dies it may be replaced at almost any time of year, suggesting that there is a small surplus of non-territorial birds. Nevertheless, the interval between the death of a territory-holder and its replacement is sometimes considerable, suggesting that non-territorial birds are by no means plentiful.

There are few good counts of numbers of tits around the time of autumn territorial behaviour, but about 50% of the Coal Tits present in the Breckland pinewoods at the end of June had disappeared by the end of September and it was thought that aggressive behaviour was the cause of their departure[127]; the birds that departed did not return at a later date. This reduction in numbers in late summer was far greater than any changes in spring, which were usually negligible. Nevertheless, the reduction in numbers in late summer apparently did not result in each remaining bird securing sufficient food for itself for the whole of the following winter since there was a progressive reduction in numbers throughout the winter, which Gibb attributed to starvation (p. 133). Possibly more birds survived than would have been the case had all the birds remained in the wood in autumn; under those conditions the food supply would have been depleted far faster and even greater mortality might have resulted.

Observations such as those given in this section should not be taken as meaning that territorial behaviour does not have a regulatory effect on tit populations, but rather that this has not been conclusively shown. As mentioned previously it could be extremely difficult to demonstrate a relationship between population size and territorial behaviour when much larger changes are taking place for other reasons in the survival rates of young in late summer. Nevertheless the effects of territorial behaviour might be important, though, in view of variations in numbers of birds settling to breed in different years, they are clearly not very precise. Are the numbers settling a reflection of the fact that in different years the birds adjust their territorial requirements differently? If so, we do not know how they do it; the birds cannot normally know in autumn exactly what their winter food supply is going to be like, especially since the weather may influence this greatly. However, there are occasions when they could gauge, well in advance of winter, whether or not food would be relatively plentiful; this would be the case with a heavy beech crop.

The tits spend a lot of time defending their territories and thereby consume a lot of energy that, at least in spring, could profitably be spent on other activities. Such an elaborate behaviour would not have been evolved were it not advantageous to the individuals who thereby gained a territory. So what is its function? Krebs has suggested that the function of territory is to ensure as much space as possible around the pair[202]. Not only does this enable them to court and feed with minimum disturbance from adjacent pairs, but it has the important survival value of spacing the nests as far apart as possible thereby minimizing the chance of predation (p. 263).

Gibb made a similar point in suggesting that if the birds need a large area in order to rear their young successfully, meeting this need could be the function of territorial behaviour[122]. However, avoiding predation seems the most likely function; all the studies of the feeding of the parents during the nesting season have shown that most birds use only a small proportion of their territory for collecting food for their young, while those with small territories trespass with impunity. Nevertheless, earlier spacing as a result of territorial behaviour could still have beneficial effects at this stage.

A similar function could be ascribed to territorial behaviour in autumn. By evicting other birds from the woodland, the remaining individuals would gain a greater food supply for the winter months, thereby increasing their chances of surviving. Even though they do not necessarily confine themselves to their territory during the winter and may wander widely, there would still be fewer birds within a given area of woodland. Although preserving the food supply might be the reason for territorial behaviour in the Breckland Coal Tits, it seems unlikely to be the same for either Great or Marsh Tits. The former wander widely during winter and the juveniles remain in the woodland during the period of territorial activity in autumn while the latter, although the pair remain steadfastly in the territory, permit parties of non-territorial birds to wander through. It seems more likely that the acquisition of an autumn territory somehow enables the birds to have that space in spring.

Hence territorial activity results in the spacing out of the birds and this may be its sole function in spring. Again, we do not know what is gained by territorial behaviour in autumn; in particular, its value as a regulatory mechanism is uncertain.

POPULATION REGULATION IN THE TITS

Two major questions are raised by data such as those in figures 78 and 80. First, why are the birds found in the numbers that they are; why are they not more common or more rare? Secondly, what causes the year to year changes in numbers? It is important to realize that these two questions may be largely independent of one another.

The first of these questions, concerning the 'carrying capacity' of a particular area, has not received much attention in the tits, partly because it is so difficult to study. For most of the tit species, however, large differences in breeding density have been recorded between different habitats; higher densities occur where breeding is most successful. For example Blue Tits are most common in pure oakwoods, less common in mixed broad-leaved woods and rare in conifer. Great Tits are also rarer in conifer than in deciduous woods though their density in broad-leaved woods seems less dependent on the presence of oak than does that of the Blue Tit. The Coal

Tit is much commoner in conifer than broad-leaved woods though in this case the nesting success is no lower in broad-leaved woodland than in conifer.

There is not enough critical evidence to show how it comes about that there are more birds in some habitats than others. It could be because more birds survive in the better habitats because the food supply is better throughout the year. In Holland during the winter female Great Tits in coniferous woodland may be lighter in weight (as a result of lower fat stores) than those in deciduous woodland and this may be the result of food shortage[16]. Hence different survival rates in different habitats could be responsible for some of the observed changes.

Another possibility is that individuals settle preferentially in habitats in which they can breed most successfully[192]. In the case of the Great Tit in Holland, the oakwoods 'filled up' quickly so that late arrivals were faced with the alternative of fighting hard to obtain a small area in the preferred deciduous woodland or of accepting a larger area in the neighbouring, but less desirable pinewood. If this is so, how do the birds know which areas to choose? This again has been little studied though captive (wild-caught) Coal Tits seemed to prefer to hunt in branches of conifer than in those of broad-leaved trees and also showed a preference for Scots Pine compared with Corsican[123]. Recently it has been shown that hand-raised young of both Blue and Coal Tits show different preferences when first offered branches of oak and pine to perch on[280]. The young Blue Tits select the oak branches, the young Coal Tits the pine; hence each species has an inborn preference for the types of foliage which the wild birds select.

Kluijver gives a striking example of how the tree composition of a forest can affect its carrying capacity. On the Friesian Island of Vlieland there were some plantations of small oak trees greatly shaded and retarded by larger Scots Pine. When many of the latter were removed, the small oak 'grew up luxuriously' and the average number of breeding pairs of Great Tits increased from about 20 to about 40 within a space of two years[196].

There has been considerable study of the reasons for the year to year changes in numbers. Populations of animals fluctuate in numbers for two main reasons; they may be affected by external, or exogenous, factors (either favourable or unfavourable) – the so-called density-independent factors, or they may be influenced by endogenous factors, those that are related to their own population density (density-dependent factors). The actions of exogenous factors are not influenced by the density of the birds and though they may result in changes, often large ones, these do not regulate* the population; in contrast density-dependent factors may have less striking effects on the population, but nevertheless may regulate the numbers of animals in the long term.

---

*I am here using the term 'regulation' in the sense that it is usually used by population ecologists. Regulatory factors are compensatory in nature, in that they tend to allow the population to increase when it is low and to produce a reduction in numbers when it is high. Hence they usually have a stabilizing effect.

244

Two density-independent factors are known to have marked effects on the numbers of tits; these are the winter food supply, as indicated by the beech crops or stocks of insects, and the weather. The former has already been discussed in relation to irruptive movements (chapter 11), but also appears to have important effects on changes of numbers. The beech crops occur at irregular intervals and either the crop itself or other factors which occur at the same time have a very important effect on the numbers of tits breeding in the following year (fig. 83).

The importance of beechmast to the tits comes as no surprise to anyone who has watched the birds busily feeding under the beeches in a year when there is a rich supply of mast. However, great caution seems necessary before

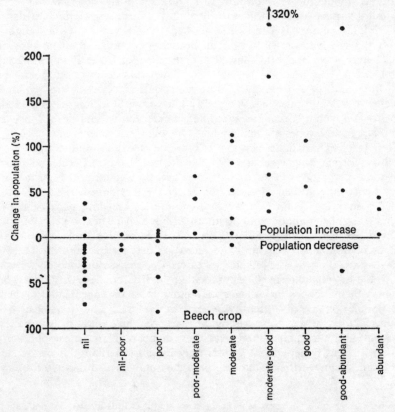

FIG. 83. Changes in breeding numbers of Great Tits in relation to the size of the beech crop. The change between two successive years is calculated as a percentage and plotted against the beech crop in the intervening winter (from Perrins 1965).

we finally accept the whole importance of the beech to the tits. There are two reasons for this. Firstly, the populations of tits in many areas (such as those in parts of Scotland) are in areas of pinewoods with no easy access to beech, yet they frequently fluctuate in parallel with those in Wytham where the birds have access to beech. Secondly, in order for there to be a high population the following year, large numbers of young birds must survive (fig. 82). However, much differential survival of the young appears to occur before the beech is available to the birds as food; hence the high numbers still alive in winter with a good beech crop have already encountered other advantageous conditions which may possibly be more important than the beech. The second of these two objections might be overcome if it could be shown that the young birds reduced their aggressiveness in summers when a beech crop was forming, so allowing higher numbers to settle. However, the fact that synchronous changes in numbers occur in areas where there is no beech is more difficult to explain away. On balance therefore it seems that the beech may be merely one of a series of factors that themselves fluctuate in parallel and of which the beech crop is a reliable indicator; high crops of seeds of other species of tree tend to occur in the same years as those of the beech.

Kluijver has pointed out that numbers of the Great Tit tend to 'see-saw' (fig. 78)[190]. This could imply some regulatory mechanism, but almost every one of these year-to-year changes can be explained in terms of the beech crop or its associated factors (fig. 83 includes the data for the Dutch populations in fig. 78). As pointed out earlier (p. 143) the fluctuations associated with those of the beech crop tend to lead to there being high numbers of tits in the summer prior to a winter without a beech crop and vice versa. Hence it is difficult to exclude the large effects of the beech when examining possible density-dependent factors.

The survival of the Coal Tits in the Breck during the winter can be related to their food supply[127]; the higher the invertebrate stock of the pine trees the better the survival of the birds (fig. 84). In this case the relationship may well be affected by density; it is likely to be a product of both the food supply and the numbers of birds. The tits make such large inroads on some of their foods – taking up to 50% of them – that they affect their own survival in a density-dependent way.

Another factor may be associated with the winter food supply; in those years when breeding starts early (i.e. when the spring is mild) there are usually high numbers of tits (p. 182)[58]. Several workers have suggested that the later part of the winter may be the most difficult period for the birds; by then they have consumed most of the winter food stocks. If spring comes early this period of dearth will be shortened by the appearance of the insects and one might, accordingly, expect over-winter survival to be greater.

Weather affects the birds in a variety of ways. In Britain winter survival is not usually closely correlated with winter weather and hence the latter does not normally seem to have a serious effect on the numbers in the popu-

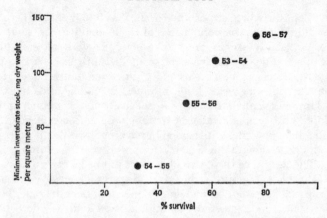

FIG. 84. Correlation between the lowest level to which the invertebrate stock in Scots Pine foliage fell during winter and the survival of Coal Tits from October to April of the same winter. The figures against the points denote the winter concerned (from Gibb 1960).

lation. However, if the winter is very severe, survival may be affected, as happened to the Blue and Great Tits in 1946–47[375]; in this winter there was no beech crop. In 1962–63 there were also large losses of Great Tits, though not Blue Tits; the latter were still able to get at their food (p. 96). Hence severe weather in winter usually results in changes in numbers only when it is both very severe and accompanied by food shortage. The Coal Tits in the Breck survived better in mild than in severe winters[127] and in North Wales about 50% of the birds apparently died in the hard winter of 1962–63[171]. The Long-tailed Tit is by far the most susceptible species of tit to hard weather (p. 68).

On the Continent, however, where the winter tends to be colder than in Britain, the vagaries of the weather may be more important. In Holland the population changes seem to be weakly influenced by the coldness of the winter, though apparently there also the changes in numbers are modified in relation to other factors such as the food supply[190]. Farther north, in Finland, the population changes are more clearly affected by the severity of the winter (fig. 85). Here too the changes are modified by the food supply, though even with more plentiful food the effect of the weather is still apparent.

Weather at other times of year may also affect the tits. Whole broods may be lost in late snow falls[233]. If it is extremely hot during the period from laying onwards the caterpillars develop more swiftly than at other times and so late season food may be poor (p. 204). Very heavy rain during the period when the young are learning to feed for themselves just after leaving the nest may cause widespread losses[317, 335].

Wet or cold weather during the nestling period can result in smaller numbers of young leaving the nest[80, 190]. There are many possible reasons

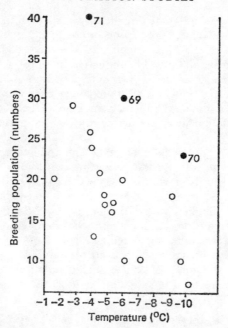

FIG. 85. The breeding population of Great Tits in a study area near Turku, Finland in relation to winter temperatures (measured as the average temperature in the months December–February). The open circles denote normal winters, the solid circles winters in which much food was provided for the birds (from von Haartman 1973).

for this; in cold weather the young need more food, but may also need more brooding which reduces the time the female has available for feeding (p. 160). In addition the caterpillars are less active in cold weather and so may be harder to find; when it is raining or windy the continued movement of the leaves may make searching difficult.

In Wytham a third factor sometimes seriously affects the numbers of fledged young. The weasels occasionally take so many young birds that few fledge; in the four years with the lowest fledging rates (1951, 1957, 1961 and 1970) the first was a combined result of a late breeding season with low clutch-size followed by cold weather, but the other three were primarily the result of heavy predation. It seems likely that predation by weasels is best considered as having both density-independent and density-dependent components (p. 266).

DENSITY-DEPENDENT FACTORS

Several density-dependent factors have been identified. The parent Coal, Great and Blue Tits raise fewer young per pair in years of high than of low breeding density. The main reason for this is that the birds lay smaller clutches at times of high breeding density (fig. 70). In the case of the Great Tit in particular, the production of young is also markedly affected by the proportion of the birds which start second broods and this too is related to the breeding density. The reduction in reproductive output is not proportional to the increase in the breeding population so that in any given area more eggs are always laid (and more young are normally fledged) with a large breeding population than with a small one. Hence it has always been held that this variation in reproductive rate is unimportant in regulating numbers.

This argument is not wholly correct. The reduction in clutch-size is sufficiently large that even without any other density-dependent influences a high population can drop while a low one can rise. This apparent paradox comes about because the survival rates of adult and juvenile birds are so different (p. 220). The best way of demonstrating the differences is to take two examples of 10 and 80 pairs with clutches derived from figure 70 and survival rates (to the following breeding season) of 50% for adults and 10% for eggs, rates which are about average; table 32 shows what would happen. Using these figures, of course, any population in which the individuals produce more than ten eggs per pair will increase while any that

Table 32. Survival of adults and young and population change. Figures are based on a 50% adult survival and a 10% juvenile survival for one year to the next. For explanation see text.

No. of pairs	Average clutch	Total (adult & young)	Total next year	% change
10	11	20+110=130	10+11= 21	+ 5%
80	8	160+640=800	80+64=144	—10%

produce fewer will decrease. It follows that variations in clutch-size will have a stabilizing effect on the population without any other differential survival rates. Variation in the number of broods in relation to density, as found on the Continent, increases still further the effect of breeding density on the reproductive rate and so will cause an even sharper compensation.

A further reason for believing that these changes in clutch-size could not affect the size of the breeding population the following year was that there was no marked correlation between the numbers of young produced and the change in breeding numbers. However, large density-independent changes would mask small density-dependent changes. Hence, even though over long periods the latter might regulate the level around which the population fluctuated, their effects would be very difficult to demonstrate. In one German study, the number of pairs of Blue Tits (though not Great Tits) breeding was related to the number of young raised per pair in the previous year[424].

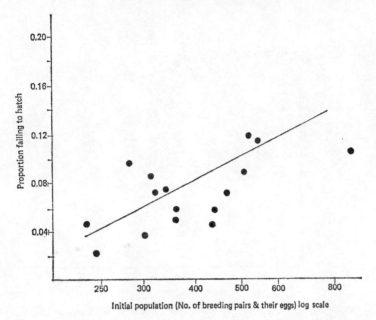

FIG. 86. Hatching success in relation to population density in the Great Tit (from Krebs 1970c).

The proportion of the eggs which hatch is also affected by the breeding density (fig. 86). This does not appear to have anything directly to do with the behaviour of the tits which is no less efficient when there are more competitors. The reason is that the weasels take proportionately more nests when there is a high breeding density; presumably the more they find the more they are encouraged to keep hunting for the tit nests (p. 264).

The combination of these two density-dependent effects of reduced breeding output and increased predation are sufficient to have a marked regulatory effect. The regulation would be even more marked if the survival of the juveniles were affected by density, but the evidence for this from Wytham is unconvincing (fig. 87). The statistical significance of these data depends on the single point in the lower left-hand corner of the figure. Similarly the survival of the young Belgian Great Tits may be worse at high than at low densities, but again the evidence is not very strong[81].

Kluijver has produced much more convincing evidence for the influence of density on the young birds. He noticed in one year (1955) that very cold weather during the early part of the nestling period greatly affected the survival of young from first broods; later in the season, the weather improved and the fledging success of young from second broods was about normal. However, by autumn, a marked change from normal years was apparent.

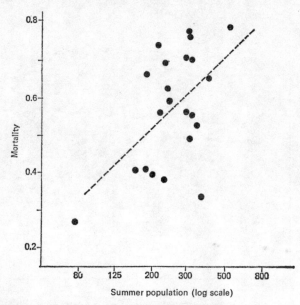

FIG. 87. Post-fledging mortality of Great Tits in relation to numbers at the end of the breeding season (from Krebs 1970c).

Usually by then, young from first broods predominate and few of the young from second broods are to be found around their natal area. This was not the case in 1955; few young had survived from the first broods, but there were many young from the second broods. Reasoning that the presence of the young from the early broods must affect the young from the second broods, Kluijver conducted an important experiment; in two years he removed about 90% of the young from the first broods, just as they were about to fledge[196]. The results confirmed his idea in that following these two years 16% and 18% of the late young were subsequently found breeding in the study area as opposed to an average of 6% in normal years.

In another experiment, with the small, isolated population on the island of Vlieland, Kluijver again showed that some form of competition between the birds must affect not only the survival of the young but also that of the adults. The Great Tits on Vlieland have many second broods, suffer negligible predation and raise about 11 young per pair. This is a very high number of young even for Continental populations (in Britain the number fledged per pair is usually around 7–8 even excluding predation). Under these conditions on Vlieland only some 27% of the adult Great Tits survived from one year to the next and only about 6% of the young were later found breeding there (some may have emigrated). For four years Kluijver removed about 60% of the young so that each pair only raised an average of about four young. As a result, the average survival rate of the adults rose to about 56% and that of the remaining young to about 22%.

Two important points emerge from this study. First, some form of competition between the birds clearly affects the survival of both the adults and the young; with many fewer competitors, an individual's chance of surviving increases markedly. Second, in spite of the removal of over half of the young from the population, the population continued to fluctuate about the level at which it was prior to the experiments (fig. 88). Hence the improved survival of the remaining birds was sufficient to compensate for the losses of the other young: 'cropping' did not affect the population as a whole. We do not know what gave rise to these changes; it may have been changes in aggression or an improved food supply (per individual) or something else again.

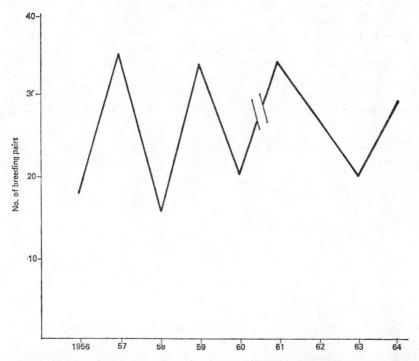

FIG. 88. The numbers of breeding Great Tits on the island of Vlieland, Holland. From 1960 onwards about 60% of the nestlings were removed just prior to fledging. Note that this marked loss of young birds did not affect the numbers breeding. Breeding numbers remained stable as a result of an increase in the survival rates of both adult and juvenile birds; immigration was negligible (after Kluijver 1966).

One might expect that mid-winter would be the time when competition for food was greatest and that therefore this would be a time when survival rates were dependent on density. However, such measurements are extremely difficult to make, especially since widely fluctuating food supplies will affect the situation. The most detailed study of winter food supply and survival of tits is that made by Gibb on the Coal Tits in the Breckland pine plantations. There, as discussed above (p. 133), the Coal Tits made heavy inroads on the winter food supplies, especially in those winters when food was less abundant. The level of this food supply affected the survival rates of the Coal Tits over the winter period and if the Coal Tits themselves affected their food supply their winter survival was probably density-dependent. However, this study was continued for four years only and a longer period would be needed for a completely convincing answer to some of these points.

To summarize, in addition to any effects of territorial behaviour, during at least five stages in the tits' year their numbers may be affected by their density; the clutch-size, the proportion of second broods, the number of eggs taken by weasels, the post-fledging survival and the winter survival may all depend on the number of birds present. In addition it seems likely that the rate of immigration may be affected by density[404]. It does not of course follow that all these potential restraints are equally effective in every year or in all the species of tits. In particular, winter survival of Great and Blue Tits in years with a rich beech crop might well not be dependent on density.

DIFFERENCES BETWEEN CONTINENTAL AND BRITISH GREAT TITS

The Continental Great Tit is a different subspecies from the British one; it is some 1–2 grams lighter. The two races also show marked behavioural differences. The British birds have fewer second broods and are more sedentary than the Continental birds. The first of these (which may be the result of different food supplies in the two areas – p. 186) may be the cause of the other fundamental differences in the lives of the Great Tits from the two areas. As a result of having more second broods during the season, the Continental Great Tits raise many more young than do their British counterparts. The average of 11 young raised per pair per year on Vlieland is about 50% more than the number usually raised by a pair in some parts of Holland, and double the number raised in Wytham.

Since in stable populations the numbers of births must on the average equal the number of deaths, there must be many more deaths each year in the Dutch populations than in the British ones. Since the survival rates of the adults in mainland Holland and Britain are similar it follows that, on the Continent compared with Britain, many more of the fledged young must perish before the following breeding season. Presumably this means that competition between individuals must be more marked on the Continent than in Britain, though whether this is competition for food soon after leaving the nest or competition for the most suitable habitats is not known.

The larger population in late summer may in part explain why far more movement of young tits is observed on the Continent than in Britain. Though much of this appears to be relatively short-scale migration and may be followed by return movements in spring, Continental birds also undertake more long-distance movements associated with irruptions (p. 141).

THE ABUNDANCE OF BIRDS

We have seen that a number of factors may affect the numbers of breeding tits. The carrying capacity of different areas may vary, though the actual number occurring in any one year may be markedly different from that of the year before; thus the carrying capacity appears to change.

Several factors can regulate the numbers in a density-dependent way; in the Coal, Great and Blue Tits the number of eggs laid, and in the Great Tit the number of second broods and the survival of the young in the summer have all been shown to be affected by density while in the Coal Tit winter mortality may be related to numbers.

By far the most important annual variation is that which affects the number of young birds that settle to breed[286]; this variation is already apparent by early autumn and seems to result from summer mortality. The same seems to hold true in Belgium[81]. It would be exceedingly interesting to know what causes the death of so many young tits in the summer. Kluijver's experiments (p. 250) show conclusively that the death and/or emigration of the young birds is affected by the presence of others probably long before territorial behaviour – but not before other aggressive behaviour – comes into play. Further the observations on Vlieland are of interest here since the survival of the adults also seems to be affected by the numbers of juveniles present, yet adults are normally dominant over juveniles in territorial disputes.

One can understand how many of these factors – such as the food supply – affect the tits in ways over which the tits themselves have no control, but the mechanisms which result in the birds laying smaller clutches and having fewer second broods under conditions of high density are not understood. In some ways the tits must be responding to their own numbers, but no one knows how they do this. There are a few occasions with high density when the parents have obvious difficulty in raising their young and I have suggested that the smaller clutch under these conditions may be an adaptation to the difficulties of raising young at such times. However, this needs to be substantiated.

Any given habitat has a different carrying capacity for the different species, for example, the Great and Blue Tit are much commoner in oak-woods than in pine whereas the reverse is true for Coal Tits. It is perhaps easy to understand how birds may be competing for resources when they are as numerous as a pair per acre and especially under conditions where every tree in the pine plantations is being visited on average once a day and the Coal Tits are removing 50% or more of some insect prey[127, 128]. However, it is harder to understand how the individuals of Willow Tits or Crested Tits, with much lower densities, can seriously be competing with one another. Nevertheless there is no reason why they should not be. Both species are dependent for nesting on hollow trees and both feed in more specialized situations within the wood. They will therefore have to range far more widely in order to obtain their food; but they may remove just as much of their food stocks as the commoner tits and so their numbers may be regulated in a similar manner.

In conclusion, the numbers of the tits in any habitat are probably regulated by a variety of density-dependent factors while the large irregular yearly changes are the result of highly variable survival of the young birds in late summer; the variations in survival may be due to changes in food supply or to changes in the birds' tolerance of one another. What causes the latter changes is not understood; however, since the large changes are synchronous in several habitats and in several countries they are likely to be induced by widespread changes such as might be associated with peculiarities in the weather. These changes, it must be stressed, are not ones that themselves regulate populations, but they may nonetheless influence the intensity of density-dependent mortality factors, for example by accentuating or alleviating food shortages. Territorial behaviour would modify these changes, but the level of its importance as a regulatory factor will have to be established by further research.

CHAPTER 18

OF PREY AND PREDATORS

THIS chapter is a *pot-pourri* of different ingredients; all are related to the all-important subject of food, though sometimes the tits are the prey and at other times the predators. In several sections I shall be concerned with the ways that natural selection may influence the behaviour of an organism either to enable it to get food or to help it avoid becoming someone else's food. A wide variety of factors affect the food and the predators of the tits and they justify a chapter to themselves.

EFFECT OF TITS ON THEIR FOOD SUPPLIES

By eating the leaves, caterpillars can impair the growth of trees and, on occasions when there is severe defoliation, even kill them. This does not normally happen in oakwoods where the caterpillars disappear shortly after the trees have been defoliated and the trees put out a second (Lammas) series of leaves; however, in some coniferous woods the larvae may so damage the trees that they never recover. Obviously foresters are anxious to reduce the caterpillar populations.

One possible way to do this would be to encourage the birds to come into the woods in larger numbers in the hopes that they would then remove more caterpillars. Many studies have been done on this subject, particularly in Germany. Tits are the main species that have been studied, since simply by providing nest-boxes they can be encouraged to nest in the plantations.

In oak woodlands, the tits take an almost negligible proportion of the total prey (p. 93). In a good year there may be about a quarter of a million winter moths alone on a large oak in Wytham, yet a pair of tits takes only some 10,000 larvae during the whole of the nestling period. In a quantitative study of the food of the tits in the Forest of Dean during the breeding season, the tits took 1·4% and 0·9% of the caterpillars in two different areas in 1950 and 4·8% and 2·6% in the same areas in 1951, a year of low caterpillar numbers[28]. The birds took slightly smaller proportions of the winter moth alone, the four comparable figures being 0·5% and 0·3% in 1950 and 2·6% and 1·7% in 1951.

Other people have made similar calculations and have shown that the birds took only a very small proportion of the total prey present. However, many of these calculations have been made at the time when the prey was present in plague proportions. Morris pointed out that while birds did not seem to be able to affect an outbreak in prey once the latter had started to increase rapidly, the birds might take significant proportions of the prey in years of lower numbers and it was possible that, during such periods, they took not only relatively larger numbers of their prey, but also sufficient to affect the prey population[252]. Morris argued that if this was so the birds might be performing an important function by keeping the numbers low and so extending the periods between outbreaks.

It is certainly true that the tits may take relatively large proportions of their prey when the prey is not exceptionally abundant. Tinbergen studied the effect of tits and other birds on the pine beauty moth *Panolis flammea* in conifer plantations in Holland; he showed that the tits sometimes took as many as 37% of the caterpillars and all species of predators combined took up to 49% of the pine beauty[377, 379]. At the same time, the tits took quite high proportions of several other prey species. Though they could have no effect on the numbers of the prey when the latter were abundant, if they took more than 25% of the prey they might damp the oscillations in the numbers of prey and so delay the next outbreak[380]. In the Breck, Coal Tits removed at least 20% of the larvae of the species of the genus *Evetria*[129] and it will be remembered that the tits took up to 54–60% of the pupae of the moth *Ernarmonia conicolana* (p. 134).

The effect of predation is likely to depend on the stage at which the insects are taken by the tits. Since huge numbers of eggs or small larvae fail to become adults, predation of these early stages is less important than predation on large larvae or pupae; predation on newly emerged adults is the most serious of all. Betts in her studies of winter moth predation suggested that predation on the adult females in winter might be more important than on the larvae in summer and thought that as many as 20% of the female moths might be taken[28]. However, this may not be as important as was thought at the time, for in order to affect the insect population, the birds must take the adult moths before they have had time to lay their eggs. The winter moth is beautifully adapted to avoid effective predation by the tits. The female winter moth is wingless; she emerges from the ground just after dusk and immediately starts the long ascent up the tree to lay her eggs. During the ascent she is found by the winged male who sits on her and mates with her while she continues to climb the tree. The female reaches the branches where she is to lay her eggs after mating has been completed and commences laying almost immediately; she may have laid the majority of her eggs before dawn. Hence, even if she is taken by a tit in the early hours of daylight, her job is largely done and the next generation of moths is already assured. Under these circumstances, even if the tits took 100% of the adult female winter moths, they would make little difference to the population of their prey.

Relatively little quantitative work has been done on the effect of tits on insect populations. The main work has been done in Germany where attempts have been made to see whether the presence of extra birds has any effect on the outbreak of the larvae. In particular, work by Bruns and his co-workers has concentrated on trying to raise the level of the breeding populations in state forests by the erection of large numbers of nesting boxes.

PLATE 15. Predation
II. *Left*, weasels can
enter tit nests without
difficulty. This weasel
is backing out of a box
with a young Great
Tit; it removed all
the young in a short
space of time. (The
photograph was taken
automatically; see
plate 8.)
Below, incubating birds
hiss vigorously at
intruders and may
succeed in frightening
them away or at least
in escaping as the
predator jumps back.

PLATE 16. Predators and parasites. *Above*, the Sparrowhawk is an important predator of fledgling tits. This pair brought 274 birds to the nest in 24 days, 213 of which were tits. Here the prey is a ringed Blue Tit. *Below*, parasites: the commonest parasite in tits' nests is the flea, *Ceratophyllus gallinae*. The fleas develop in the nest during the summer and, as shown, cluster round the entrance the following spring, waiting for birds to enter. Large numbers may cause serious discomfort and even lead the birds to desert the nest.

Bruns argues that if populations of birds at relatively low densities – such as those studied by Tinbergen *et al* (1960) – could take almost 40% of the total prey, then how much more could be taken by higher populations of birds[45]. By increasing the density of nesting boxes, he has shown that it is possible to increase the density of broods of birds in pinewoods to about one pair per acre (2·5 pairs per hectare) – there were only 0·2 pairs of tits per hectare in Tinbergen's study area. However, most of the increases in breeding populations reported by Bruns have been in species that are semi-colonial such as Starling, Tree Sparrow and Pied Flycatcher, and the increases in densities of breeding pairs of tits is much less marked. Moreover it is possible to get apparently high populations of tits in nesting boxes if relatively small areas are provided with nest-boxes amidst large areas of plantations where there are few if any nest-sites. As a result of this the birds may crowd into the boxes provided; the actual area that they should be considered as covering, in order to measure their true density, depends largely on one's opinions; obviously, however, it is larger than the area in which the boxes are provided.

Other German workers have claimed that the provision of nesting sites may have a marked effect on the population of insects. One wood containing nesting boxes remained green during an outbreak of caterpillars that defoliated an adjacent wood without nest-boxes[24]. This could have been due to a variety of reasons, but Appel and Schwartz, using the same woods, changed the area where nest-boxes were available to the birds and yet, in a later outbreak, the area where the trees retained their leaves again matched the area where there were nest-boxes; only the trees within about 50 metres of the areas with nest-boxes stayed green[9]. Freiberger also claimed that the numbers of caterpillars decreased in an area where nest-boxes were provided compared with other areas where they were not[112]. The provision of nest-boxes at densities of only two per acre (lower than that which Bruns used) was supposed to be sufficient to reduce the population density of caterpillars to only 50 per tree as opposed to 5000 per tree in adjacent woodland without nest-boxes[235], though the differences seem surprisingly large.

In another study nest-boxes were erected in an area where there were regular outbreaks of the pine looper *Bupalus piniarius*[151]. Although in later years there were further outbreaks of the moth in adjacent areas without nest-boxes, the areas containing nest-boxes did not suffer from an outbreak. In this area, such a situation has existed for at least 33 years since the boxes were first provided[161].

In Marley there was an extremely low density of tits in 1947 – the first year in which boxes were provided. There was a high density of caterpillars in that year, followed by a huge population in 1948 when the oak trees were defoliated. Since then there has not been another population as high as this. As mentioned earlier (p. 23), the winter moth has been studied intensively by the Hope Department in another part of Wytham some 1·5 kilometres from Marley. Nest-boxes were not erected in this area until the winter of

1957–58. In the 8 years prior to this date the winter moth larvae averaged 117 per square metre, but in eleven years since they have averaged 75 per square metre. The difference is not significant. Here, however, there is a major difference from the studies in Germany. In a pine plantation without nesting boxes, the breeding density of tits may well be very low as a result of insufficient nest-sites. However, in Wytham there may have been insufficient nest-sites for the total number of breeding pairs now present, but there were at least some natural holes so that the breeding population of tits would have been higher than in a conifer plantation (see also p. 231).

More work is plainly needed but the evidence tends to support Morris's suggestion that the combined action of the predators – including the tits – on some of these insects may be an important factor in reducing the frequency of outbreaks of defoliating insects. However, at least in Britain, it seems that such predation is much more likely to be effective in pinewoods than in oakwoods. The densities of insects are much lower in the former habitat and the recorded predation levels seem much higher there than in oakwoods, though this is not in accord with the observations, cited above, for German oakwoods.

While Tinbergen and Klomp showed that summer predation would at times be high enough to affect the populations of their insect prey it seems likely that the predation by tits on the winter prey populations is often more important. In particular some of the predation rates quoted by Gibb (p. 134) show that the tits can take high proportions of a variety of prey. At this time many of the prey are available for a long period; in addition, those that are over-wintering as large larvae or as pupae are, as discussed, more 'valuable' to the insect population than the earlier stages since they have survived more of the dangers of their lives and are more likely to produce breeding adults. Predation by tits at this time may therefore have a greater effect on the insect populations than predation on small larvae in summer.

Bruns suggested that it might be highly undesirable to put out food for the tits in winter if one wants them to help control the insect populations[45]. Food is short at this time and if they are to make the greatest impact on their prey populations they should not be given other sources of food. Any attempt to feed them will reduce their impact on the prey so allowing larger populations of the prey to survive. Only in periods of thick snow, when the birds cannot get their prey, should they be fed. There are several difficulties with this view, but it is one that would be worth examining.

INTERACTIONS BETWEEN INSECTS AND BIRDS

Two other factors could influence the effect that birds have on the populations of prey; they may change the balance of diseased or parasitized larvae in the population and they may carry diseases from one insect to other areas and so spread the disease.

Many larvae in insect populations are parasitized by other insects – often ichneumonids or other hymenopterans – which lay their eggs in or on their host. Eventually the developing parasite kills the host larva and emerges into another adult parasite which will parasitize future generations of larvae. During the later stages of being parasitized the host often shows acute signs of discomfort and is unusually active. In addition, it frequently shows a colour change, often becoming much darker than the normal larva.

Both these changes make parasitized larvae more liable to predation, since they increase their conspicuousness; under certain conditions the tits take disproportionately high numbers of parasitized larvae supporting the suggestion that they are more conspicuous than normal ones[129]. However, birds tend to ignore parasitized gypsy moth *Lymantria dispar* in favour of healthy ones[197].

When the predator removes disproportionately high numbers of parasitized larvae, calculations of what effect they are having on their prey becomes even more difficult. It is possible that by doing this the birds could actually be having a beneficial effect on the insect population; unless they are also taking many healthy larvae they may, by taking parasites, actually cause an increase in the population of their prey.

Birds may also affect their prey by transmitting viruses or other infections[111]. Again they may take disproportionate numbers of sickly, diseased prey and they could spread the disease around the wood to the detriment of the insect prey populations. Coal Tits eat the larvae of the Spruce Sawfly *Gilpinia herceniae*, and the virus which kills the sawfly can pass unharmed through the Coal Tit's digestive system[99]. It may then be spread around the wood in the tit's faeces. Hence it is at least possible that the Coal Tits may greatly accelerate the spread of the virus.

DEFENCES OF THE OAK TREES AND THEIR EFFECT ON THE TITS

I have been discussing the interactions between the tits and their prey. However, the oak trees are the 'prey' of the caterpillars. Natural selection acts on them also and will favour any that have developed ways of avoiding being eaten or reducing the damage of defoliating insects. The tits have timed their breeding season in an attempt to have their young in the nest at the best time for raising them – namely when the caterpillars are most abundant. However, the caterpillars are also attempting to time their season so that their food is most readily available, hence their emergence at different times in different years; they are trying to emerge when the leaves are young and tender.

The caterpillars hatch from their eggs very early in relation to the time of leaf opening, usually just when the leaves are beginning to break out of their buds. Many larvae hatch too early and perish, since the buds have not yet opened. Why do they do this? One can only infer that there must be great pressure on them to hatch early in order to survive, otherwise natural selection would have favoured larvae which hatched later, when they could be 'sure' that the leaves would have unfurled. Feeny has provided a partial answer to this question[102]. In the early stages of growth the leaves are soft and easily eaten, in addition they are more easily digested; later when the leaf is fully open the trees deposit a series of phenolic compounds including plant tannins in the leaves; these make the leaves harder to digest. As a result the caterpillars which eat the leaves earliest get the best diet and grow faster, become larger and survive better than those larvae which emerge later.

In recent years much work has been done on the phenolic compounds of plants[221]. It is clear that these are used by the plants to defend themselves against the actions of herbivores. It has also been shown that these compounds affect the growth of domestic chickens. The caterpillars collected by the tits contain large quantities of leaf in their gut and so the young tits must also consume fairly large quantities of oak-leaf tannins, especially in late broods which are feeding on the later larvae, since the oak leaves contain far more tannin at this time.

I tried to see whether these substances affected the growth of the tits as well as of the caterpillars[429]. Two broods, each of eight Blue Tits, were hand-raised on diets of mealworms in the laboratory; one brood received only mealworms and water, the other one received the same except that their water included small amounts of an extract of oak-leaf tannins, calculated to be about equivalent to what they would receive in the wild. Table 33 shows the results from these experiments. By the time the young Blue Tits were returned to their nests, the birds with a tannin-free diet had put on significantly more weight than those with tannin in their diet. Hence tits as well as domestic hens grow less well with tannin in their diet.

Table 33. Weight increments of young Blue Tits hand-raised on a diet of mealworms with or without the addition of oak leaf tannins. The weights show the increase in weight over a three-day period. The differences are significant (from Perrins 1976).

Young	No tannins in diet	Young	Tannins added to diet
1	2·7	1	2·6
2	2·8	2	2·5
3	3·4	3	2·4
4	2·4	4	2·3
5	3·0	5	2·2
6	2·7	6	2·2
7	2·9	7	2·1
8	3·0	8	3·3
Average	2·86		2·45

The oak tree has obviously evolved the use of tannins to try to reduce the effect of the caterpillars feeding on its leaves, and so the effect that these tannins have on the tits is, in a sense, accidental. Nevertheless the tits with tannins in their diet grow more slowly and the effect of this presumably contributes to the low weight of late nestlings. Certainly food is also scarcer at this time and the parent birds feed the young more slowly. However, the growth rates of the later broods in oakwoods may also be slower than those of early broods, because in part the food that they receive is less easily digested.

These findings may make one modify one's views about the reason for the low success of the later broods; these may be weakly because the young are short of food or short of food which is nutritious. The tits seem to find the winter moth larvae a less desirable food in the last few days before pupation. This is possibly for the same reason – that the larvae are no longer as nutritious as before; at this stage they contain very high levels of fat which they lay down as food reserves for the pupal stage.

The quality of food taken by the tits has not been examined to any great extent. Nevertheless, the tits select some species of insects and disregard others and one may infer that these actions are being made in response to the taste or some other quality of the food. Nestling Great Tits in pinewoods grow more slowly than those in oakwoods, even when receiving the same weight of food per day; hence presumably the caterpillars in pinewoods are less nutritious than those in oak[18]. Even within the pinewoods the quality of the food varies in relation to the season, the food for first broods contains a higher proportion of roughage than that brought to second broods[189]. This may partly account for the observation that food for first broods had a lower calorific value than that brought to second broods (5·53 kcals/g compared with 6·13 kcals/g)[129].

BEECHMAST

The importance of the beechmast and other seed crops as winter foods has already been discussed (chapter 12). These crops are so important that the populations of the tits fluctuate in relation to them – the birds survive better with a heavy crop than with a light one.

The beech does not have an annual crop because it does not produce fruiting buds in the same autumn as it produces the mast; it puts all its energy into one or the other (over and above the essential leaf buds for the next year). The beech therefore is clearly incapable of producing a rich seed crop in two successive years. Yet why this should be so is not clear since many other trees produce an annual crop of seeds.

One suggestion is that this is an adaptation by the beech trees to reduce the predation on their seeds[95, 287, 403]. If the beech produced a crop of seeds each year there would probably be a higher density of tits in woodland; possibly they would increase until they reached a level where they would be able to eat almost all the seed every year. If, however, many die in one winter for lack of food, then there will be relatively fewer the following year and these might not be able to consume the whole crop. Hence, if the beech was able to store material for its seeds and produce twice as many seeds every other year instead of a normal number every year, the seed would have a better chance of germinating. Even if the beech only produced a normal crop of seed every second year and in the alternate year used the energy for growth it still seems likely that the overall survival of the seed would be better than if it had an annual crop.

In spite of the large numbers of different species of birds and small mammals[385] that feed on the beech mast, when there is a good crop there is a high germination of seed suggesting that there is more than enough for the seed-eaters and good germination can still follow. Nonetheless, if there is a poor crop it may be followed by little or no germination suggesting that the animals are able to eliminate the seed unless it is there in great quantity. Presumably if there were still larger numbers of birds, even rich crops of seed might be eliminated.

While such suggestions are not easily open to experimental proof, it seems plausible that those tree species which have irregular crops may have evolved this habit in order to reduce the predation on their seeds. Nevertheless, this in itself would not be effective unless all the trees tended to be synchronized with one another, for it is essential that there be no crops of the seeds in years between crops so that the numbers of seed-eating animals should be held low. Since the beech tend to be synchronized by the weather over wide areas, this is not a problem. During the evolution of the habit, clearly those trees which tended to crop in the 'wrong' years would have been less successful than those that were synchronized with most other trees, and would have been selected against in the course of time. Presumably therefore the trees have taken the weather as their cue in order to synchronize their fruiting years. As noted earlier, the different tree species also tend to crop most heavily in the same years and even some of those which have a crop annually, such as the Silver Birch *Betula pubescens*, tend to have much heavier crops in the years when the beeches have crops.

PREDATORS OF TITS

Predators of animals are usually hard to study; they are scarce and may consume the individual prey so that no evidence remains. Nevertheless a number of different birds and mammals are known to be predators of tits and there is sufficient quantitative data to describe some of the hazards faced by tits. Clearly a predatory animal will take a wide variety of prey if it can catch it and a wide variety of different animals, including domestic cats, may take tits at various stages of the year. I am concerned here only with those natural predators which commonly take tits in woodland. In recent years two important studies have added greatly to our knowledge of the two main predators of tits in Wytham, Weasels and Sparrowhawks. Many of the findings presented here are based on the work of Geer[416, 417] for the Sparrowhawk and Dunn[91] for the Weasels. I am very grateful to these two workers for permission to quote their work.

Mammalian predators

The Weasel, *Mustela nivalis*, is by far the most serious mammalian predator of young tits; in some years as many as two-thirds of the broods have been lost in Marley largely as a result of its depredations, though over the whole of Wytham the losses are not usually as high as this. Most people tend to think of the Weasel as a ground-dwelling animal and seem surprised that it climbs trees. In view of this it seems worth outlining the evidence for its being the most common predator of the tits. Most nests are merely found to have been raided by predators, without any evidence as to the actual culprit, so it remains possible that another animal is also responsible for some of the losses.

In Wytham, apart from one record of a Stoat, *Mustela erminea*, entering a nest-box and taking the eggs of a Great Tit, no other species of mammal, apart from the Weasel, has ever been caught in the act of raiding a nest-box. Stoats have been very rare in Wytham for many years (see p. 271) and so seem much less likely than Weasels to be serious predators. Weasels are found in nest-boxes almost every year during our routine visits to the nests. In addition, when they take large young, they sometimes seem to remain in the nest-box for some considerable time, possibly because when they have eaten most of a large brood of Great Tits they find it difficult to get out through the hole again; I have once seen a large Weasel try to get out through the hole when I lifted the lid, but it failed, withdrew and leaped out through the open top. When they remain in the box for a long time, they leave a pile of faeces with a very characteristic mustelid odour as further evidence of their work.

The only likely sort of predator that we would not meet would be one that was strictly nocturnal, but if there were such a species one might expect that a larger proportion of the female tits would also be taken – unless possibly the predator was a small species such as a mouse that was not strong enough to kill the parent birds. Only one other mammal, the Grey Squirrel, *Sciurus carolinensis* is a predator of tits in Wytham. Occasionally squirrels enlarge the holes and remove young, but this habit is not common. Other mammals such as mice have been thought to be responsible for occasional nesting losses of tits, but there is no good evidence for this. Long-tailed Field Mice, *Apodemus sylvaticus*, and Bank Voles, *Clethrionomys glareolus*, are found in nest-boxes in Wytham, as is occasionally the Long-eared Bat, *Plecotus auritus*. In other areas the Dormouse, *Muscardinus avellanarius*, and the Edible Dormouse, *Glis glis*, have been recorded. These species may be more concerned with obtaining a hole for their own roosting or nesting habits than with preying on the tits. In Wytham, at least, these animals tend to occupy empty nest-boxes rather than those occupied by tits. Some of these animals may take the eggs or young of tits from time to time, but they cannot be important predators. All the available evidence, therefore, suggests that most of the predation is caused by weasels.

The Weasel (and the Stoat) climb much better than most people realize and can easily go up a tree with smooth bark such as a young ash. In addition the Weasel is a very slender animal that has no difficulty in getting through the hole of a normal nest-box. The female is markedly smaller than the male and can probably get through any hole that a Great Tit can enter and most of those that a Blue Tit can. The Weasel probably finds nests more easily in nest-boxes than in more concealed natural sites. At times individuals appear to go round almost all the boxes in a given area and remove all the clutches; this happens mainly in the early part of the spring before the ground vegetation grows up; doubtless at that time the Weasel can see a nesting box from a distance. Nevertheless much of the predation cannot be very dissimilar from the natural situation, since later in the season, when the young are in the nest, the ground herbage is well grown and it is unlikely that the Weasels find their prey by seeing the nest-boxes – at least until they are very close to the nest. For example, the average predation rate during incubation is about 8·3% for Blue Tits and 9·8% for Great Tits while during the nestling period the predation rates are only 4·4% for Blue Tits and 7·6% for Great Tits despite the fact that the nestling period is about 50% longer than the incubation period and that the nests are therefore at risk for a longer period. However, there are other possible reasons for this pattern and they are described below.

Individual Weasels seem to vary in their behaviour. Some obviously spend a long time in the nest box apparently eating their way through the whole brood and leaving just a small, sad pile of wings and legs. Others remove everything so that there is no trace of the brood. The Weasel photographed 'in the act' (plate 15) fell into the latter category. Before it knocked the watch off (plate 8) it removed three young at intervals of about 15 seconds; plainly it could not have been taking them very far. In one year what was presumably a single individual raided a number of nest boxes in one area of the wood and killed and ate the incubating females but never seemed to realise that the eggs were edible; these were always left untouched!

A number of different factors affect the pattern of predation by Weasels. One of the most important is the density of the small mammal population. Nestling tits are only available for a short period of the year and for the rest of the year small mammals, such as voles and mice, are the Weasel's staple diet. Indeed it appears that the weasels 'prefer' them to nestling tits and only switch to taking the latter when there are insufficient small mammals for them to prey on. In Wytham there is a clear tendency for the tits to be preyed upon most heavily when the small mammal populations are low and to be relatively immune from predation when the small mammals are abundant (fig. 89). We are particularly fortunate to have these data on small mammals; they were primarily collected by Dr H. N. Southern.

The Weasels appear to be looking into the nest-boxes from time to time even when there are only small numbers of birds in them or, possibly, none at all. As soon as they are rewarded by finding a nest, they are encouraged to

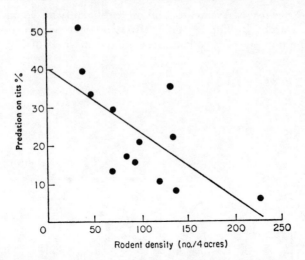

FIG. 89. Relationship between the percentage of tit nests (all species) preyed upon by weasels and the density of voles and field mice the same summer; the points are each for a separate year 1959 to 1970 inclusive and 1972 (from Dunn 1977).

start looking in more nest-boxes. One piece of evidence for this is that the chances of a Great Tit losing its nest to Weasels are increased if a neighbouring nest has been found and taken (fig. 90).

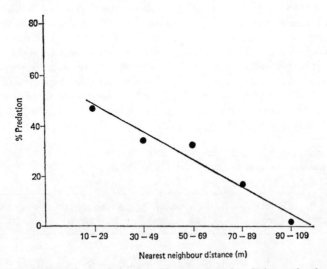

FIG. 90. The chances of a nest being found by a predator in relation to the closeness of the nearest nest. For explanation see text (from Krebs 1970a).

The tendency for the Weasel to hunt more diligently for young tits, once it has been rewarded by finding some, affects other aspects of the predation pattern. The number of broods taken is higher in years of high tit density (fig. 91).

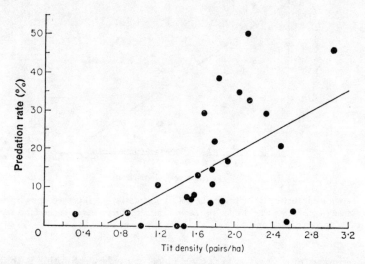

FIG. 91. Relationship between the percentage of tit nests (all species) in boxes preyed upon by weasels and nesting density; the points are each for a separate year 1947 to 1972 (from Dunn 1977).

Hence the Weasel's predation on tits' nests is influenced by both the numbers of tits and the numbers of small mammals. In fact the densities of these two groups explains almost two-thirds of the variation in predation rates[91]. Another obvious factor which might affect the predation rate is the numbers of the Weasels themselves; with higher numbers of Weasels, there would be fewer small mammals for each and the Weasels might be expected to turn to tits sooner. Unfortunately, we do not have long term records of the Weasel population. However, in 1969–70 when the Weasels were studied in Marley, there was a single pair of Weasels in one year while in the other, two pairs

Table 34. Predation (%) on tits' nests in Marley in 1969 and 1970 in relation to the number of pairs of Weasels present (from Dunn 1977).

Year	No. weasels (pairs)	Tit density (pairs/hectare)	Rodent density (no./4 acres)	Predation (%)
1969	1	2.7	83	22
1970	2	2.4	69	64

divided Marley between them. The densities of tits and small mammals in the two years was not very different, but predation on tits' nests was much higher in the year when the two pairs of Weasels were present (table 34). This is very scanty evidence, but does suggest the possibility that weasels may take more tits in years of high Weasel density.

The effect of increasing predation with increasing density of tits can even

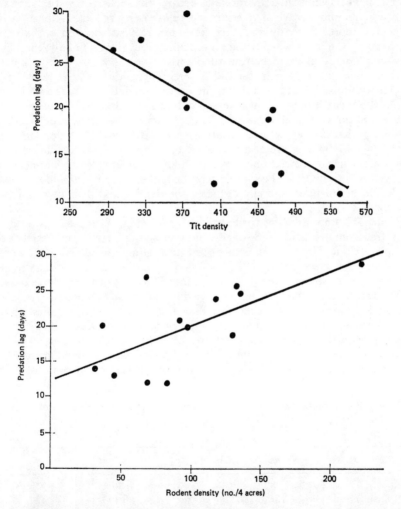

FIG. 92. Relationship between the extent to which predation on Blue and Great Tit nests lags behind laying ('predation lag') and (above) number of tit nests started in Wytham and (below) the density of voles and field mice in the same summer. The points are each for a separate year 1959 to 1972 inclusive, except that there are no data for small mammals for 1971 (from Dunn 1977).

be seen within a single year. We can measure the rapidity with which Weasels turn to preying on the tits by looking at the lag between the average date of laying of the tits and average date at which they are taken by the Weasels. This shows marked variation between years; we call it the 'predation lag'. In years when tits are abundant Weasels start taking the tits earlier than in years when tits are scarce. Similarly the predation lag is shorter in years when small mammals are scarce than when they are abundant (fig. 92). Presumably when voles are scarce Weasels are looking for alternative prey more diligently and therefore tend to visit the nest-boxes more frequently. Similarly, when tits are more abundant, the visit of a Weasel to a nest-box is more likely to be rewarded and hence early casual visits by the Weasels may more quickly turn into persistent raiding of the nest-boxes.

When the predation lag is short, the overall predation tends to be heavy (since the Weasels have a longer season of hunting). However, in years when predation starts late, early broods are at an advantage because much of their nesting period is over before predation gets under way. Therefore in such years the early nesters are at an advantage. However, in years when predation starts early, late nests may have the higher success rate. This appears to be because by the time the late nesters start, Weasels have already taken a high number of nests, thereby reducing the density and their own hunting pressure.

Hence it is impossible for tits to predict which time of the season would be most free from predation and, since almost all broods overlap, no nest can be completely safe. However, there are some interesting interspecific differences which appear to result from the fact that predation does not usually get underway immediately the birds start laying. The main difference is that, as I showed earlier, the different species have different mean laying dates (p. 169). Coal and Marsh Tits lay earlier than Blue and Great Tits; the earliest of all, Coal Tits, lay, on average, about six days before Great Tits. As a result, both Coal and Marsh Tits lay when there are very few other tits in the nest-boxes. Both species seem to benefit from this early period of very low density since they have lower losses to Weasels than the other species as shown in table 35.

Table 35. Predation (%) on the different tit species in relation to their dates of laying (from Dunn 1977).

Species	No. nests	Mean laying	No. lost	%
Coal Tit	163	23.4	17	10.4
Marsh Tit	90	24.4	16	17.8
Blue Tit	4988	25.7	953	19.1
Great Tit	4131	29.2	961	23.3

Almost certainly, the situation is not quite as simple as that. Where possible Coal Tits choose nest-boxes on coniferous trees (p. 31) and these nests suffer only an 8·6% predation rate compared with 13·8% for the nests in boxes on other trees. Hence there would appear to be some sort of habitat effect as well which may affect the Weasels hunting.

As mentioned above, Weasels and other predators might learn to find nests in nest-boxes more easily than those in nature. After all, nest-boxes are fairly conspicuous and it would be quite easy for an animal to learn to hunt for them. This could be true since, especially early in the season when the ground vegetation is very low, a Weasel should be able to see a nest-box from some distance. In addition, there is some evidence that nests are raided in groups at this time, as if a Weasel were hunting by sight. However, this is certainly not the only way in which Weasels always hunt. They show a strong tendency to take larger broods in preference to smaller ones (table 36).

Table 36. Predation by weasels on Great Tit broods in Wytham 1960–2. Broods have been divided into three groups for two parts of the season. For explanation see text (from Perrins 1965).

1960		*Up to 15 May*				*After 15 May*	
Brood-size	*No. nests*	*No. lost*	%		*No. nests*	*No. lost*	%
2– 5	13	1	7·7		20	3	15·0
6– 8	24	2	8·3		34	5	14·7
9–14	28	5	17·8		21	6	28·6
1961		*Up to 10 May*				*After 10 May*	
Brood-size	*No. nests*	*No. lost*	%		*No. nests*	*No. lost*	%
2– 5	22	2	9·1		33	7	21·2
6– 8	43	0	0		43	9	20·9
9–13	35	6	17·1		26	6	23·1
1962		*Up to 23 May*				*After 23 May*	
Brood-size	*No. nests*	*No. lost*	%		*No. nests*	*No. lost*	%
2– 7	31	1	3·3		42	5	11·9
8–10	30	3	10·0		26	4	15·4
11–14	20	3	15·0		19	4	21·1

As we have seen (p. 194), larger broods tend to have lighter, hungrier young and, because hungry young call more persistently for food, large broods are noisier. Certainly we hear large broods more frequently than we hear smaller ones and there seems little doubt that the Weasels locate them by sound also. This is presumably one of their main ways of hunting for broods in the wild. For obvious reasons there is rather little information on predation rates on broods of tits in natural sites but one study suggests that it is fairly high; out of 19 nests of Marsh Tits seven were taken by predators [268].

In the years in which I made the measurements in table 36, Weasels tended to take many more late broods than early ones. I attributed this to the fact that the Weasels themselves might need more food at this time since they were feeding their own young then. However, Dunn's more extensive study has shown that predation does not always result in the later broods being attacked more frequently than earlier ones.

The annual predation rate on tits' nests in Wytham is shown in fig. 93.

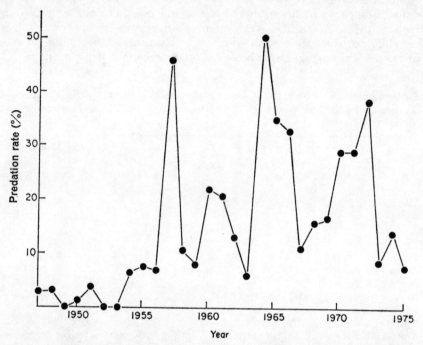

FIG. 93. Annual variation in predation rate (%) on tit nests (all species) by weasels in Wytham from 1947 to 1975 (from Dunn 1977).

During the first ten years of study, predation was relatively insignificant; it never reached 10% of the nests. This situation changed suddenly after 1956 and in the ensuing 19 years predation was usually much higher than 10%. Although we cannot quantify the details, there is a plausible reason for this marked and sudden change. In the early years, rabbits were abundant in Wytham as were stoats as well as Weasels. In late 1954 myxomatosis reached Oxfordshire and, over the next few months rabbits became very rare. In 1955 there was widespread evidence that many predators such as foxes were having difficulty in finding sufficient prey. Dr H. N. Southern later stated that 'it is tempting to believe that myxomatosis caused the big upheaval, lasting over several years, before the situation settled down again'[430]. By the time this happened stoats and rabbits had virtually disappeared from Wytham and although rabbits have made a slight recovery the stoat remained a very rare animal for many years. This situation may have had two quite different indirect effects on the tits. Firstly, Weasels were deprived of one of their main sources of food. Possibly up until that time they had always found sufficient prey either from rabbits or mice and voles so that they very rarely searched for tits. Secondly, Weasels may have been less common in the presence of of stoats than in their absence as a result of competition from a larger relative. The Weasel rarely seems to be a serious predator of tits in nest-boxes on the Continent. There, they are usually present in company with both stoats and martens and although the latter may be serious predators of tits, the weasels do not seem to be.

Although I have so far been talking about loss of broods, Weasels may also take the female if they find her at her nest. During Dunn's study about 15% of the female tits were recorded as killed in the nest when their brood was taken. In addition, we find a lower proportion of females whose nest was lost to Weasels in one year (but where there was no sign that the female had herself been taken) breeding in the following year than is the case for females with successful nests. We presume that this means that the missing females were carried off by the weasel without leaving any trace. Of the recorded losses of females, about 12% occur during the laying period, 55% during incubation and 33% during the nestling period. Even allowing for the different lengths of these periods, predation is much higher during incubation which is what one could expect since the females spend more time in the nest at this stage than at any other.

Avian predators

Apart from the sparrowhawks, *Accipiter nisus* (see p. 273), no birds are known to be serious predators of adult tits. Since they roost in holes for much of the year few are taken by owls. Only a small number have been recorded in the diet of the Tawny Owls in Wytham[348]; presumably these are often birds with poor roosting sites or ones going to roost late. Even so, birds form less than 5% of the diet of the Tawny Owls in Wytham and out of 213 identified birds in their diet only 24 were tits.

Other avian predators, however, take young tits regularly. It is not widely realized that the Great Spotted Woodpecker, *Dendrocopus major*, is a serious predator of small hole-nesting birds. There are a number of references to their depredations on the young of hole-nesting species, mostly but not all from nest-boxes[61, 109, 140, 163, 169, 181, 184, 217, 254, 255, 328, 331, 355]. In many cases the young tits are fed directly to the woodpeckers' own young; where the young birds have been identified, they were usually tits, often Blue Tits.

In Wytham, individual woodpeckers have sometimes caused considerable losses, though not so high as those noted by Mountfort[254]. In Germany, Great Spotted Woodpeckers take a number of broods of Marsh and Willow Tits; the latter species seems particularly vulnerable since its nests – in small rotten stumps – are so easily opened[232].

There are three main ways in which these tits are taken. Some woodpeckers, especially those described by Mountfort, learn that nest-boxes contain eggs and may go round systematically enlarging the holes and pulling out the nests and eggs. It seems that they may look into the holes before they open them, since more damage is done to nesting boxes containing nests than to those without. Normally the bird opens the hole just sufficiently to enable it to reach in and pull out the contents.

However, in Wytham losses due to Great Spotted Woodpeckers usually occur during the nestling period. At this stage the method of opening the nest is quite different since the bird no longer enlarges the entrance. The woodpecker appears to be attracted by the sound of the calling young since it makes a completely new hole at the level of the young. As soon as this is large enough, it puts its beak through and pulls out the young tits. By opening the nest in this way, the woodpeckers often need to make only a hole large enough for their head, since their long neck and beak enable them to reach most young in the nest; if they are large the young may be crushed as they are pulled out through the small hole. Obviously in nature, it is worth the woodpecker's while to try and open the tree as close to the young as possible since the nest entrance may be some way from the young birds; if they can be located by call, this makes it easy for the woodpecker.

When the young are large, the woodpecker may not have to open the nest at all. By landing outside it may be able to catch a large chick as it jumps up to the hole, thinking the woodpecker is one of its parents arriving with food. When this happens, the woodpecker removes the young bird, flies with it up to a branch where it kills it with a few powerful blows on the head and then flies off to feed it to its young. This last type of predation leaves no mark on the nest by which the predator may be identified but is probably more common than realized. Broods where a few large young disappear just prior to fledging may well have been attacked by the Great Spotted Woodpecker.

The Great Spotted Woodpecker normally feeds on animals which it obtains by opening dead wood; doubtless, to the woodpecker, the taking of small tits is little different from the opening of wood to get large beetle grubs. The species appears to specialize on removing young of hole-nesting species, not those in open nests[328], although one would think that the latter were easier to obtain. Parent tits and Pied Flycatchers evidently recognize the woodpecker as a potential predator since they will mob it furiously when it is near their nest, although they will ignore other birds of a similar size such as Blackbirds. The film records at one of our camera boxes, placed at a Great Tit nest close to a nest of a Great Spotted Woodpecker, show a number of attempts by the woodpeckers to reach the young tits. The birds came down and tugged at the trigger mechanism in an attempt to get through the hole. A slightly surprising feature was how quickly the Great Tits started feeding again after the woodpecker had left; the intervals were usually very short.

Some of the Corvidae, especially the Jay, *Garrulus glandarius*, may also be important predators of young tits, though they do not take them until after they have fledged. It is not uncommon to find a Jay near by to a party of newly fledged young tits. The Jay's method of hunting is to rush in beating its wings and trying to knock the young tits down; if it can unbalance them and knock them to the ground, then it may be able to catch them. It is possible that the Jay takes a number of newly fledged tits in this way.

The Sparrowhawk is the only serious predator of adult tits in woodland. This species is a woodland bird which specializes in hunting for small birds such as tits. Relatively few quantitative data are available but in May, in Holland, Sparrowhawks took 5·7% of the Great Tits, 2·3% of the Coal Tits, 3·2% of the Blue Tits and 1·5% of the Crested Tits[376]; these represented 44% of the total losses of the Great Tit and 15% of those of the Coal Tit (the two most intensively studied species). It is not known how these figures compare with the losses at other times of the year.

The Sparrowhawk also times its breeding so that its young are in the nest when the young tits have just fledged – thus assuring itself of a maximum number of young (and incompetent) birds for it to feed to its young. At this time it takes a large number of young tits and a smaller proportion of adults. Recent studies in Wytham, where there are as many as eight pairs of Sparrowhawks, show that these birds are very serious predators of young tits just after they have left the nest.

While more information is badly needed about the effects of Sparrowhawks on tits, we do now know a little more about the effect they have on the tits in Wytham during the nesting period. Sparrowhawks take up nesting territories early in the year and, from about March onwards, spend a considerable time in the vicinity of the nest. They lay their eggs in early May and the young hatch about the 10th of June just as the young tits are leaving the nest in large numbers. The nesting period can be broken up into four periods, pre-nesting, laying and incubation, the nestling and the post-fledging periods. The latter three of these periods last for about one month each. During the post-fledging period, young Sparrowhawks remain in the vicinity of the nest and are still dependent on their parents for food. The significance of making such a division of the nesting season is that the female does little hunting during the incubation period and during the first half of the nestling period. At this stage the male does virtually all the hunting for the family.

This is important from the tits' point of view since the two sexes take different prey. The male, who weighs only about 140 grams tends to take much smaller prey than his mate who weighs about 225 grams. In general, the male takes birds such as tits, warblers, sparrows and finches while the female, although she also takes these birds, is more likely to take larger prey such as thrushes, blackbirds and starlings. Hence, a lower proportion of tits are taken when both members of the pair are hunting, than when the male is the sole provider for his family. As a result, adult tits are at greatest risk during the period when they are raising their young. At this stage they are very busy flying backwards and forwards to their nest and hence perhaps not as wary as usual. In the Breckland pine plantations many parent tits were taken at this stage, apparently because the Sparrowhawks learned the routes the tits were using in their search for food and lay in wait for them[127]. The young tits also leave the nest when the male is the main hunter. They are particularly vulnerable at this stage since they are not experienced at looking after themselves.

Apart from the Dutch studies little is known about the effect that Sparrowhawk predation has on the adult population. However, they have two noticeable effects on the breeding tits in Wytham. Firstly, there are very few tits nesting within about 60 metres of the Sparrowhawks' nests; their density here is significantly lower than that in the rest of the wood (table 37). We cannot be certain whether this is because few tits risk nesting near to a Sparrowhawk or whether those that do are caught and eaten by Sparrowhawks before they nest. It seems more likely that the latter is the case since every winter the wood fills up with young tits looking for a territory. The proportion of boxes occupied is only low when the Sparrowhawk's nest is successful; when the Sparrowhawk's nest fails, the rate of occupancy of the

Table 37. Nesting success of tits in relation to their distance from Sparrowhawk nests (from Geer in press.).

Distance from Sparrowhawk nest (metres)	No. nest boxes	No. used	%	No. raising young	%
Successful Sparrowhawk nests					
0–60	30	5	16.7	1	20.0
60–120	108	47	43.5	43	91.5
120–180	133	59	44.4	47	79.7
180–240	161	76	47.2	56	73.7
Unsuccessful Sparrowhawk nests					
0–60	10	8	80.0	6	75.0
60–120	26	19	73.1	16	84.2
120–180	48	35	72.9	26	74.3
180–240	34	22	64.7	18	81.8

boxes is normal. Further support for the view that the Sparrowhawks are taking the tits comes from a second point; those tits that do nest within 60 metres of a Sparrowhawk nest have extremely low nesting success (table 37). Almost certainly this is because the Sparrowhawks succeed in catching one or both of the parents before the young are raised. A female may exceptionally rear a brood by herself, but since the male neither incubates the eggs nor broods the young, a male will not raise a brood without the female, so the loss of one parent may be sufficient to cause the brood to fail. There is a lot of 'lore' that predators do not disturb individuals of their prey which nest near to their own nests or lairs. Plainly the Sparrowhawk data do not support such views.

It is difficult to calculate precisely the proportion of tits which are taken during the nesting period since several factors affect the number taken. In particular, whether or not the Sparrowhawks succeed in raising their chicks is a vital factor. However, table 38 shows the proportion of adult and juvenile Blue and Great Tits which are thought to have been taken during the two seasons 1976 and 1977 in Wytham. The slightly lower proportion of juveniles

Table 38 Estimated predation (%) on adult and young Blue and Great Tits by Sparrowhawks in Wytham during the three months of the nesting cycle (from Geer in press.).

	Percent of birds taken			
	Adult		*Juvenile*	
	1976	1977	1976	1977
Blue Tit	16.8	12.8	34.1	18.3
Great Tit	18.4	10.5	35.8	28.3

taken in 1977 compared with 1976 would fit with the much higher tit populations in the second year.

As mentioned above, these calculations do not in any way take into consideration the amount of predation which is happening during the other nine months of the year. Plainly this is considerable, but equally plainly the figures given in table 38 cannot simply be multiplied by four! Sparrowhawks are present in the wood throughout the year and regularly attack tit flocks during the winter[53]. Although there are a number of immigrant finches and thrushes in the general area of Wytham, many small birds, especially warblers, have left the area for the winter. Hence for the smaller males at least, tits are likely to be a very important part of the winter diet.

Long-term records shed some light on the overall effect of Sparrowhawks on tit populations. In general there have been some marked changes in the numbers of Sparrowhawks over the last fifty years [428]. Pre-war, heavy and effective keepering probably reduced the number of birds below the natural level. During the war years, keepering was greatly reduced and the number of Sparrowhawks increased considerably. There was probably a slight reduction after the war as keepering became more effective. However, numbers probably did not reach the low levels of the pre-war period. The next major change resulted from the introduction of toxic chemicals for use as pesticides. These, as is usually the case, had marked effects on the animals at the top of the food chain, in this case Sparrowhawks. These chemicals, especially dieldrin, were becoming particularly widespread by the late fifties. Matching the spread of use of these substances, the Sparrowhawk declined in southern Britain. It disappeared as a breeding species from Wytham after about 1959. Voluntary bans on dieldrin and related chemicals from 1962 onwards were followed by a steady increase in the Sparrowhawk until today it is once more quite a common bird. In Wytham, Sparrowhawks were seen again in the mid-sixties, after a lapse of several years, but no nests were found until 1968 and the bird was certainly not breeding widely until after that date. Hence, Sparrowhawks were unusually abundant during the war years and unusually scarce during the early mid-sixties.

This recent increase in the numbers of Sparrowhawks is reflected in the nesting success of the tits. Relatively few nests of the tits fail without any apparent cause at all. During the years 1964–67 when there were no Sparrowhawks in Wytham only about 1·9% of the tits nests failed without apparent cause. In the years 1973–77 when Sparrowhawks became common again, this figure rose to 6·6%, a significant difference. We are fairly certain that much of this change is due to adult tits being taken by Sparrowhawks.

It is interesting to compare the changes in Sparrowhawk numbers with the breeding numbers of tits. Unfortunately, we do not have British figures for breeding populations of tits during the war years. The only ones that exist are those recorded by Kluijver in Holland (fig. 78 p. 233). If we assume, as seems likely, that the same situation prevailed in Holland as in Britain, namely that the Sparrowhawk was more abundant during the war than before, there is little evidence for much effect on the tits. The numbers in some of the war years were slightly lower than the trend for Dutch populations, but at the same time, there were several cold winters at that stage and rather few beech crops. Certainly, there is no striking change. The most striking change might be expected to be associated with the disappearance and return of the Sparrowhawk during the decade or so from 1960 onwards. The changes in numbers of the Sparrowhawks were very marked and, at the same time, there are good figures for the tit populations in the same place (fig. 80, pp. 234–5). Rather surprisingly, it is again difficult to see any very striking effect of the Sparrowhawks on the tit numbers. It is true that some of the years in the early 1960s had higher breeding numbers than before or since these years. However, the striking increase in tit numbers during the period from 1960 to 1961 was clearly the result of a very good breeding season in 1961, and a mild winter with a very rich beech crop. There were other good beech crops during the early 1960s and these seem as likely to account for the high numbers of tits at this time as is the absence of Sparrowhawks. Further, the numbers of tits do not seem to have declined markedly during the 1970s when many Sparrowhawks are taking them.

Hence the evidence does not support the likelihood that the Sparrowhawks have major effects on the breeding numbers of the tits in Wytham, despite the large numbers that they take. There is some slight evidence that the proportion of immigrants in the breeding population has increased during the 1970s, suggesting perhaps that the balance between woodland areas and gardens may have changed. However, on the whole the evidence supports the view that populations of small animals limited in a density-dependent manner are highly resilient.

POSTSCRIPT

I HOPE that I have managed to describe the lives of these small birds in a reasonably coherent way; but the huge amount of literature has not always made this easy; in some ways we know a great deal, in others very little.

We might perhaps consider that this knowledge should be divided into three sections, 'What', 'Why' and 'How'. To take but one example, we know *what* clutch-size may be laid under a number of conditions and I have tried to guess *why* the birds should lay clutches of such sizes, but we have really no idea of *how* the birds 'know' how many eggs to lay. The more we learn about them, the more involved their lives are seen to be. For example, we realize that in their search for food they are not just dashing hither and thither through the trees, but are searching in a complex and highly non-random manner; further, each species has its own way of working. Whether we are 'scientific' and regard them as having a 'large number of adaptive responses', or are anthropomorphic and look on them as 'clever', their lives are quite extraordinarily intricate. As with most aspects of biology the further we delve the more there is to know. However, in ecological matters we also – albeit slowly – begin to understand why there are so many ways in which we, quite unwittingly, can upset the delicate balance and how cautious we should be. Who, for example, would have predicted that the introduction of myxomatosis would have led to an increase in the predation on nests of tits?

In view of their popularity and abundant studies, it is perhaps surprising that no one has attempted to write a book like this before; perhaps, wisely, they were daunted. Certainly we know how much there is we do not know. In trying to give reasons for the tits' behaviour I have sometimes overstepped the bounds of certain knowledge. However, if this book stimulates a greater interest and sparks off further studies, both my efforts and those of the many people on whose information the book is based will have been worthwhile.

BIBLIOGRAPHY

1 ADAMS, J. K. (1947). Courtship feeding of Willow Tit. *Brit. Birds 40:* 51.
2 ALEXANDER, H. G. (1927). The Birds of Latium, Italy. *Ibis (12)3:* 245–83.
3 ALEXANDER, W. B., & LACK, D. (1944). Changes in status among British breeding birds. *Brit. Birds 38:* 62–9.
4 ALLDERIDGE, M. G. (1950). Plumage variation in Coal Tit. *Brit. Birds 43:* 295.
5 ALMOND, W. E. (1959). Great Tit stung to death by bees. *Brit. Birds 52:* 314.
6 ALTEVOGT, R. (1953). Über das 'Schöpfen' einiger Vogelarten. *Behaviour 6:* 147–52.
7 AMANN, F. (1949). Junge Kohlmeisen (*Parus major*) und Blaumeisen (*Parus caeruleus*) im gleichen Nest. *Orn. Beob. 46:* 187–90.
8 ANTOINE, N. J. (1959). Blue Tit feeding young Treecreepers. *Brit. Birds 52:* 432–3.
9 APPEL, O., & SCHWARTZ, M. (1921). Die Bedeutung des Vogelschutzes für den Pflanzenschutz. *Nachr. Pflanzenschutzdienst, Berl. 1:* 49–50.
10 ARN, H. (1955). Mischbruten von Kohlmeisen, Blaumeisen und Kleiber. *Orn. Beob. 52:* 129.
11 ARNOLD, G. A., & ARNOLD, M. A. (1952). The nesting of a pair of Blue Tits. *Brit. Birds 45:* 175–80.
12 ASH, J. S. (1950). Robin rearing young Great Tits. *Brit. Birds 43:* 300.
13 ASH, J. S. (1951a). Colour variation in tits. *Brit. Birds 44:* 93.
14 ASH, J. S. (1951b). The effect of a snow-storm on breeding birds. *Brit. Birds 44:* 57–9.
15 AUSTIN, O. L. (1961). *Birds of the World.* Hamlyn, London.

16 BALEN, J. H. VAN (1967). The significance of variations in body weight and wing length in the Great Tit, *Parus major*. *Ardea 55:* 1–59.
17 BALEN, J. H. VAN, & CAVÉ, A. J. (1970). Survival and weight loss of nestling Great Tits, *Parus major*, in relation to brood-size and air temperature. *Neth. J. Zool. 20:* 464–74.
18 BALEN, J. H. VAN (1973). A comparative study of the breeding ecology of the Great Tit *Parus major* in different habitats. *Ardea 61:* 1–93.
19 BALDWIN, S. P., & KENDEIGH, S. C. (1938). Variation in the weight of birds. *Auk 55:* 416–67.
20 BAKER, J. R. (1938). The relation between latitude and breeding season in birds. *Proc. Zool. Soc. Lond. Series A. Vol. 108:* 557–82.
21 BARRINGTON, R. M. (1911). Introduction of the Marsh Tit and Nuthatch into Ireland. *Irish Nat. 20:* 220.
22 BENZ, E. (1950). Notizen über eine Kohlmeisenbrut. *Orn. Beob. 47:* 186–7.
23 BERGMAN, S. (1935). *Zur Kenntnis Nordost-asiatischer Vögel.* Albert Bonniers, Stockholm.
24 BERLEPSCH, H. VON (1929). *Der Gesamte Vogelschutz.* 12th ed. Neumann, Neudman.
25 BERNDT, R. (1938). Über die Anzahl der Jahresbruten bei Meisen und ihre

Abhängigkeit vom Lebensraum, mit Angaben über Gelegestärke und Brutzeit. *Dtsch. Vogelwelt 63:* 140–51, 174–81.

26 BERNDT, R., & WINKEL, W. (1972). Über das Nächtigen weiblicher Meisen (*Parus*) während der Jungenaufzucht. *J. Orn. 113:* 357–65.

27 BETTS, M. M. (1954). Experiments with an artificial nestling. *Brit. Birds 47:* 229–31.

28 BETTS, M. M. (1955a). The food of titmice in oak woodland. *J. Anim. Ecol. 24:* 282–323.

29 BETTS, M. M. (1955b). The behaviour of a pair of Great Tits at the nest. *Brit. Birds 48:* 77–82.

30 BETTS, M. M. (1958). The behaviour of adult tits towards other birds and mammals near the nest. *Brit. Birds 51:* 426–9.

31 BILBY, L. W., & WIDDOWSON, E. M. (1971). Chemical composition of growth in nestling blackbirds and thrushes. *Brit. J. Nutr. 25:* 127–34.

32 BIRD, C. R. (1949). Plumage variation in Coal Tit. *Brit. Birds 42:* 215.

33 BJÖRN, L. (1960). On the sex ratio, the wing length and the total length of the Great Tit. *Vår Fågelvärld. 19:* 146–57.

34 BLURTON JONES, N. G. (1968). Observations and experiments on causation of threat displays of the Great Tit (*Parus major*). *Anim. Behav. Monog. 1:* 75–158.

35 BOGDANOWICZ, H. (1937). Von Sommer- und vom Herbstzuge 1936 in Lettland. *Vogelzug 8:* 64–6.

36 BOYLE, G. L. (1961). Coal Tit plucking fur from remains of Field Vole. *Brit. Birds 54:* 288–9.

37 BRANDER, T. (1949). Om blåmesens, *Parus caeruleus* L., expansion mot norr i Finland. *Ornis Fenn. 26:* 80–2.

38 BROOKS-KING, M. (1941). Intelligence tests with tits. *Brit. Birds 35:* 29–32.

39 BROOKS-KING, M. (1956). Experiments in bird psychology. *Devon Birds 9:* 19–21.

40 BROOKS-KING, M., & HURRELL, H. G. (1958). Intelligence tests with tits. *Brit. Birds 51:* 514–24.

41 BROUWER, G. A., & VERWEY, J. (1919). Waarnemingen van het 'Trekstation Noordwijk aan Zee'. *Ardea 8:* 1–92.

42 BROUWER, G. A., & VERWEY, J. (1920). Waarnemingen over 1919. *Ardea 9:* 21–34.

43 BROWN, J. L. (1969). The buffer effect and productivity in tit populations. *Am. Nat. 103:* 347–54.

44 BROWNETT, A. (1965). Willow Tit survey 1964. *Banbury Orn. Soc. Newsletter 118.*

45 BRUNS, H. (1960). The economic importance of birds in forests. *Bird Study 7:* 193–208.

46 BULMER, M. G. (1973). Inbreeding in the Great Tit. *Heredity 30:* 313–25.

47 BULMER, M. G., & PERRINS, C. M. (1973). Mortality in the Great Tit, *Parus major. Ibis 115:* 277–81.

48 BUXTON, E. J. M. (1948). Tits and peanuts. *Brit. Birds 41:* 229–32.

49 BUXTON, P. A. (1921). Notes on birds from northern and western Persia. *J. Bombay Nat. Hist. Soc. 27:* 844–82.

50 CAMPBELL, B. (1953). *Finding nests.* Collins, London.

51 CAMPBELL, B. (1968). The Dean nestbox study 1942–1964. *Forestry 41:* 26–46.

52 CAMPBELL, B. (1971). *The Crested Tit.* Forestry Commission Leaflet 41. H.M.S.O., London.

53 CARIS, J. L. (1958) Great Tit killing and carrying Goldcrest. *Brit. Birds 51:* 355
54 CASEMENT, M. B. (1951). Three Long-tailed Tits at one nest. *Brit. Birds 44:* 388–9
55 CHANDLER, K. R. (1943). Nest of Blue Tit in fork of tree. *Brit. Birds 37:* 55.
56 CHAPLIN, S. B. (1974). Daily energetics of the Black-capped Chickadee, *Parus atricapillus*, in winter. *J. Comp. Physiol. 89:* 321–30.
57 CHENG TSO-HSIN & CHIEN YEN-WEN (1959). Studies on the breeding behaviour of some insect-eating birds in the fruit-producing district of Chang-le, Hopei Province. (1) *Paris major atratus* Thayer & Bangs. *Acta Zool. Sin. 11:* 101–15.
58 CHITTY, D. (1967). What regulates bird populations? *Ecology 48:* 698–701.
59 CHOW, F. H. L. (1973). *Experimental studies in mimicry*. D. Phil. thesis, Oxford University.
60 CLEMENS, J. H. (1956). Blackbird feeding brood of tits. *Brit. Birds 49:* 503–4.
61 COHEN, E. (1947). Great Spotted Woodpecker taking young Blue Tits from nesting box. *Brit. Birds 40:* 88.
62 COHEN, E. (1955). Wing-measurements of Blue Tits. *Brit. Birds 48:* 371–2.
63 COLQUHOUN, M. K. (1941). Visual and auditory conspicuousness in a woodland bird community: a quantitative analysis. *Proc. Zool. Soc. Lond. (A) 110:* 129–48 (1940).
64 COLQUHOUN, M. K. (1942). Notes on the social behaviour of Blue Tits. *Brit. Birds 35:* 234–40.
65 COLQUHOUN, M. K., & Morley, A. (1943). Vertical zonation in woodland bird communities. *J. Anim. Ecol. 12:* 75–118.
66 CORNWALLIS, R. K., & TOWNSEND, A. D. (1968). Waxwings in Britain and Europe (1965/66). *Brit. Birds 61:* 97–81.
67 CRAMP, S., PETTET, R., & SHARROCK, J. T. R. (1960). The irruption of tits in autumn 1957. *Brit. Birds 53:* 49–77, 99–117, 176–92.
68 CRAMP, S. (1963). Movements of tits in Europe in 1959 and after. *Brit. Birds 56:* 237–63.
69 CREUTZ, G. (1949). Verfrachtungen mit Kohl- und Blaumeisen (*Parus m. major* und *Parus c. caeruleus* L.). *Vogelwarte 15:* 78–93.
70 CROWE, R. W. (1951). Colour-variations in tits. *Brit. Birds 44:* 388.
71 CURIO, E. (1959). Verhaltensstudien am Trauerschnäpper. Beiträge zur Ethologie und Oekologie von *Muscicapa h. hypoleuca* Pallas. *Z. Tierpsychol.*, Beih. 3.
72 CURRIER, N., HOWORTH, M., & HAZELWOOD, A. (1957). An unusual tit's nest, probably of Blue Tit. *Brit. Birds 50:* 393–5.
73 CURRY-LINDAHL, K. (1961). Great Tits collecting fur from moulting European Bisons. *Brit. Birds 54:* 404.

74 DAVIS, J. W. F. (1973). *Aspects of the breeding ecology and feeding of certain gulls*. D. Phil. thesis, Oxford University.
75 DAVIS, S., DAVIS, B. S., & DAVIS, J. (1973). Some factors affecting foraging behaviour of Plain Titmice. *Condor 75:* 481–2.
76 DAWSON, D. G. (1972). *The breeding biology of House Sparrows*. D. Phil. thesis, Oxford University.
77 DEADMAN, A. J. (1973). *A population study of the Coal Tit* (Parus ater) *and the Crested Tit* (Parus cristatus) *in a Scottish Pine plantation*. Ph.D. thesis, Aberdeen University.
78 DELMÉE, E. (1940). Dix Années d'observations sur les moeurs de la Mésange charbonnière et de la Mésange bleue, *Parus major major* L. et *Parus caeruleus*

caeruleus L. par les nichoirs et le baguage. *Gerfaut 30:* 97–129, 169–87.

79 DHONDT, A. A., & HUBLÉ, J. (1968). Fledging-date and sex in relation to dispersal in young Great Tits. *Bird Study 15:* 127–34.

80 DHONDT, A. A. (1970). The sex ratio of nestling Great Tits. *Bird Study 17:* 282–6.

81 DHONDT, A. A. (1971a). The regulation of numbers in Belgian populations of Great Tits. *Proc. Adv. Study Inst. Dynamics Numbers Popul. (Oosterbeek 1970):* 532–47.

82 DHONDT, A. A. (1971b). Some factors influencing territory in the Great Tit, *Parus major. Gerfaut 61:* 125–35.

83 DHONDT, A. A. (1973). Postjuvenile and postnuptial moult in a Belgian population of Great Tits, *Parus major*, with some data on captive birds. *Gerfaut 63:* 187–209.

84 DIXON, K. L. (1949). Behaviour of the Plain Titmouse. *Condor 51:* 110–36.

85 DIXON, K. L. (1962). Notes on the molt schedule of the Plain Titmouse. *Condor 64:* 134–9.

86 DRENT, R. (1972). Adaptive aspects of the physiology of incubation. *Proc. 15th Int. Orn. Congr. The Hague, 1970:* 255–80.

87 DROST, R. (1932). Wanderungen deutscher Kohlmeisen und Blaumeisen (*Parus m. major* L. und *Parus c. caeruleus* L.). *Vogelzug 3:* 169–73.

88 DROST, R. (1951). Kennzeichen für Alter und Geschlecht bei Sperlingsvögeln. *Orn. Merkbl. Nr. 1.*

89 DROST, R., & SCHÜZ, E. (1933). Weitere Fernfunde der Kohlmeise und Blaumeise (*Parus major* und *caeruleus*). *Vogelzug 4:* 84–5.

90 DUNN, E. K. (1976). Laying dates of four species of tits in Wytham Wood, Oxfordshire. *Brit. Birds 69:* 45–50.

91 DUNN, E. K. (1977). Predation by Weasels (*Mustela nivalis*) on breeding tits (*Parus* spp.) in relation to the density of tits and rodents. *J. Anim. Ecol. 46:* 633–652.

92 DUNNET, G. E., & HINDE, R. A. (1953). The winter roosting and awakening behaviour of captive Great Tits. *Brit. J. Anim. Behav. 1:* 91–5.

93 DURANGO, S. S. (1945). Till kännedomen om tofsmesens, *Parus cristatus cristatus* L., utbredning och biologi i Sverige. *Svensk. Faun. Revy 7:* 6–21.

94 DURANGO, S. (1946). Om svartmesens (*Parus ater ater* L.) bioptop- och boplatsval. *Vår Fågelvärld 5:* 1–9.

95 ELTON, C. S. (1924). Periodic fluctuations in the numbers of animals; their causes and effects. *Brit. J. Exp. Biol. 2:* 119–63.

96 ENEMAR, A., NYHOLM, E. and PERSSON, B. (1972). Om inverkan av holkuppsättning på Fågelsångsdalens småfågelsamhälle. *Vår Fågelvärld 31:* 263–8.

97 ENNION, E. A. R. (1962). Food of tits. *Brit. Birds 55:* 187–8.

98 ERRINGTON, F. P. (1961). Blue Tits roosting in street lamps. *Brit. Birds 54:* 287–8.

99 ENTWHISTLE, P., ADAMS, P. H. W. & EVANS, H. F. (1977). Epi-zootiology of a nuclear polyhedrosis virus in European Spruce Sawfly (*Gilpinia hercyniae*): The status of birds during the breeding season. *J. Invert. Path. 29:* 354–60.

100 EVANS, P. R. (1969). Ecological aspects of migration and pre-migratory fat deposition in the Lesser Redpoll, *Carduelis flammea cabaret. Condor 71:* 316–30.

101 EYKMAN, C., *et al.* (1936–49). *De nederlandsche vogels.* Waginingen.

102 FEENY, P. P. (1970). Oak tannins and caterpillars. *Ecology 51*: 565–81.

103 FELIX, J. (1958). Zur Kenntnis der Tagesaktivität von Meisen der Gattungen *Parus* und *Aegithalos*. *Sylvia 15*: 5–21.

104 FISHER, J., & PETERSON, R. T. (1964). *The World of Birds*. Rathbone Press, London.

105 FISHER, J., & HINDE, R. A. (1949). The opening of milk bottles by birds. *Brit. Birds 42*: 347–57.

106 FLEGG, J. J. M., & COX, C. J. (1969). The moult of British Blue Tit and Great Tit populations. *Bird Study 16*: 147–57.

107 FOGDEN, M. P. L., & FOGDEN, P. (in prep.) The role of fat and protein reserves in the annual cycle of the Grey-backed Camaroptera in Uganda.

108 FOSTER, J., & GODFREY, C. (1950). A study of the British Willow Tit. *Brit. Birds 43*: 351–61.

109 FRANZ, J. (1940). Der Grosse Buntspecht (*Dryobates major pinetorum* Brehm) als Nesträuber bei Höhlenbrütern. *Anz. Schädlingsk. 16*: 6–8.

110 FRANZ, J. (1943). Über Ernährung und Tagesrhythmus einiger Vögel im arktischen Winter. *J. Orn. 91*: 154–65.

111 FRANZ, J., KRIEG. A. & LANGENBUCH, R. (1955). Untersuchungen über den Einfluss der Passage durch dem Darm von Raubinsekten und Vögeln auf die Infectiosität insektenpathogener Viren. *Z. Pflanzenkr. 62*: 721–6.

112 FREIBERGER, W. (1926–27). Zur vogelschutzfrage, inbesondere zur wissenschaftlichen Begrundung des wirtschaftlichen Vogelschutzes. *Allg. Forst- u Jagdzg. 102*: 425–30; *103*: 19–30, 49–63, 92–115.

113 FROCHOT, B. (1971). *Écologie des oiseaux forestiers de Bourgogne et du Jura*. Doctoral thesis, Dijon University.

114 FRYER, J. C. F. (1939). The destruction of buds of trees and shrubs by birds. *Brit. Birds 33*: 90–4.

115 GARNETT, M. C. (1976). *Some aspects of body size in the Great Tit*. D. Phil. thesis, Oxford.

116 GASTON, A. J. (1973). The ecology and behaviour of the Long-tailed Tit. *Ibis 115*: 330–51.

117 GAUSE, G. F. (1934). *The struggle for existence*. Williams & Wilkins, Baltimore.

118 GIBB, J. A. (1950). The breeding biology of Great and Blue Titmice. *Ibis 92*: 507–39.

119 GIBB, J. A. (1954a). The feeding ecology of tits, with notes on the Treecreeper and Goldcrest. *Ibis 96*: 513–43.

120 GIBB, J. A. (1954b). Population changes of titmice 1947–51. *Bird Study 1*: 40–8.

121 GIBB, J. A. (1955). Feeding rates of Great Tits. *Brit. Birds 48*: 49–58.

122 GIBB, J. A. (1956). Territory in the genus *Parus*. *Ibis 98*: 420–9.

123 GIBB, J. A. (1957). Food requirements and other observations on captive tits. *Bird Study 4*: 207–15.

124 GIBB, J. A., & HARTLEY, P. H. T. (1957). Bird foods and feeding habits as subjects for amateur research. *Brit. Birds 50*: 278–91.

125 GIBB, J. A. (1958). Predation by tits and squirrels on the eucosmid *Ernarmonia conicolana* (Heyl.). *J. Anim. Ecol. 27*: 375–96.

126 GIBB, J. A. (1959). Feeding methods of Long-tailed Tits with large food. *Brit. Birds 52*: 200–1.

127 GIBB, J. A. (1960). Populations of tits and goldcrests and their food supply in pine plantations. *Ibis 102*: 163–208.

128 GIBB, J. A. (1962). L. Tinbergen's hypothesis of the role of specific search images. *Ibis 104:* 106–11.

129 GIBB, J. A., & BETTS, M. M. (1963). Food and food supply of nestling tits (Paridae) in Breckland Pine. *J. Anim. Ecol. 32:* 489–533.

130 GIBB, J. A. (1970). The turning down of marked eggs by Great Tits. *Bird-Banding 41:* 40–1.

131 GILBERT, H. A., & WALKER, C. W. (1954). *Herefordshire Birds.* Woolhope Naturalists' Field Club, Hereford.

132 GILLIARD, E. T. (1958). *Living birds of the World.* Hamish Hamilton, London.

133 GLASE, J. C. (1973). Ecology of social organization in the Black-capped Chickadee. *Living Bird 12:* 235–67.

134 GLUTZ VON BLOTZHEIM, U. N. (1962). *Die Brutvögel der Schweiz.* Schweizerischen Vogelwarte, Sempach.

135 GOMPERTZ, T. (1961). The vocabulary of the Great Tit (*Parus major*) and some other related species. *Brit. Birds 54:* 369–94, 409–17.

136 GOMPERTZ, T. (1967). The hiss-display of the Great Tit (*Parus major*). *Vogelwelt 88:* 165–9.

137 GOODBODY, I. M. (1952). The post-fledging dispersal of juvenile titmice. *Brit. Birds 45:* 279–85.

138 GROTE, H. (1937). Zur Kenntnis der Tannenmeisenzüge. *Vogelzug 8:* 11–14.

139 GRUBB, B. (1944). Roosting behaviour of Long-tailed Tits. *Brit. Birds 38:* 54.

140 GURNEY, J. H. (1890). Greater Spotted Woodpecker eating young Titmice. *Zoologist (3rd Ser.) 14:* 435–6.

141 GURR, L. (1955). A pneumatic nest-recording device. *Ibis 97:* 584–6.

142 HAARTMAN, L. VON (1973). Talgmespopulationen Lemsjöholm. *Lintumies 8 (1):* 7–9.

143 HAFTORN, S. (1951). En undersøkelse over vekt-variasjoner i vinterhalvåret hos Kjøttmeis. *Fauna, Oslo 4:* 83–91.

144 HAFTORN, S. (1953a). Contribution to the food biology of tits, especially about storing of surplus food. Part. I. The Crested Tit (*Parus c. cristatus* L.). *K. Norske Vidensk. Selsk. Skr. 1953 nr. 4.*

145 HAFTORN, S. (1953b). Contribution to the food biology of tits, especially about storing of surplus food. Part II. The Coal Tit (*Parus a. ater* L.). *K. Norske Vidensk. Selsk. Skr. 1953 nr. 2.*

146 HAFTORN, S. (1953c). Observasjoner over hamstring av naering også hos lappmeis (*Parus c. cinctus* Bodd). *K. Norske Vidensk. Selsk. Forh. 26:* 76–82.

147 HAFTORN, S. (1956a). Contribution to the food biology of tits, especially about storing of surplus food. Part III. The Willow Tit (*Parus atricapillus* L.). *K. Norske Vidensk. Selsk. Skr. 1956 nr. 3.*

148 HAFTORN, S. (1956b). Contribution to the food biology of tits, especially about storing of surplus food. Part IV. A comparative analysis of *Parus atricapillus* L., *P. cristatus* L. and *P. ater* L. *K. Norske Vidensk. Selsk. Skr. 1956 nr. 4.*

149 HAFTORN, S. (1960). The proportion of spruce seeds removed by the tits in a Norwegian spruce forest in 1954–55. *K. Norske Vidensk. Selsk. Forh. 32:* 121–5.

150 HAFTORN, S. (1972). Hypothermia of tits in the Arctic Winter. *Ornis Scand. 3:* 153–66.

151 HÄHNLE, H. (1940). *Das Schutzgebeit Behr – Steckby (Anhalt) des Reichsbundes für Vogelschutz.* Bundes für Vogelschutz e.V., Stuttgart.

152 HALL-CRAGGS, J. (1959). Feeding methods of Long-tailed Tits with artificial food. *Brit. Birds 52:* 21–2.

153 HARDIN, G. (1960). The competitive exclusion principle. *Science 13:* 1292–7.

154 HARRISON, J. M. (1946). Continental Great Tit in Kent. *Brit. Birds 39:* 153.

155 HARRISON, J. M. (1948). Autumn migration of Great Tit, Blue Tit and Coal Tit in Thanet, Kent. *Brit. Birds 41:* 182–3.

156 HART, D. (1958a). Hoarding of food by Willow Tit. *Brit. Birds 51:* 122.

157 HART, D. (1958b). Hoarding of food by Willow and Coal Tits. *Brit. Birds 51:* 527.

158 HARTLEY, P. H. T. (1953). An ecological study of the feeding habits of the English titmice. *J. Anim. Ecol. 22:* 261–88.

159 HEIM DE BALSAC, H. (1952). Rhythm sexuel et fécondité chez les oiseaux du Nord-ouest de l'Afrique. *Alauda 20:* 213–42.

160 HELLE, T., & MIKKOLA, H. (1969). Hömötiaisen (*Parus montanus*) vaelluksista Keski-Suomessa 1965–68. *Ornis Fenn. 46:* 136–9.

161 HERBERG, M. (1959). *Erfahrungen bei der biologischen Bekampfung waldschädlicher Insekten durch Ansiedlung von Hohlenbrütern in Vogelschutzgebiet Steckby.* Vortrag auf der Zentralen Tagung für Ornithologie in Erfurt.

162 HERTER, W-R. (1940). Über das 'Putten' einiger Meisen-Arten. *Orn. Monatsver. 48:* 104–9.

163 HICKLING, R. A. O., & FERGUSON-LEES, I. J. (1959). Predation by Great Spotted Woodpeckers on nestlings in nest-boxes. *Brit. Birds 52:* 126–9.

164 HILDÉN, O. (1968). Die Invasion der Lapplandmeise *Parus cinctus* in Finland 1963/64. *Vogelwarte 24:* 189–98.

165 HINDE, R. A. (1952). The behaviour of the Great Tit (*Parus major*) and some related species. *Behaviour, Suppl. II:* 1–201.

166 HINDE, R. A., & FISHER, J. (1952). Further observations on the opening of milk bottles by birds. *Brit. Birds 44:* 393–6.

167 HINDE, R. A. (1953). A possible explanation of paper tearing behaviour in birds. *Brit. Birds 46:* 21–3.

168 HINDE, R. A., & TINBERGEN, N. (1958). The comparative study of species, specific behaviour. In *Behavior and Evolution* (eds. A. Roe & G. G. Simpson) ch. 12: 251–68. Yale University Press, New Haven.

169 HODGETTS, J. W. (1943). Young Great Spotted Woodpecker fed on nesting bird. *Brit. Birds 37:* 97.

170 HOLLOM, P. A. D. (1952). *The Popular Handbook of British Birds.* Witherby, London.

171 HOPE JONES, P. (1966). Effects of consecutive, contrasting winters on the bird population of an Anglesey pine plantation. *Bird Study 13:* 77–83.

172 HOPKINS, A. D. (1938). Bioclimatics, a science of life and climate relations. *U.S. Dept. Agr., Misc. Publ. 280.*

173 HOWARD, L. (1952). *Birds as individuals.* Collins, London.

174 HUDSON, R. (1965). Summary of foreign-ringed birds in Britain and Ireland during 1906–63. *Brit. Birds 58:* 87–97.

175 IMMELMANN, K. (1971). Ecological aspects of periodic reproduction. In *Avian Biology* (eds. D. S. Farner & J. R. King), ch. 8: 341–89. Academic Press, London.

176 JELLICOE, M. R. (1950). Nest of a Blue Tit on a bough. *Brit. Birds 43:* 117.

177 JESPERSEN, P. (1944). Topmejsen, *Parus cristatus* L., i Danmark. *Dansk Orn. Foren. Tidsskr. 38:* 1–13.

178 JOHNSTON, T. L. (1936). Nesting habits of the Willow Tit in Cumberland. *Brit. Birds 29:* 378–80.

179 JONES, P. J. (1973). Some aspects of the feeding ecology of the Great Tit *Parus major* L. D. Phil. thesis, Oxford.

180 JONES, P. J. (1976). The utilisation of calcareous grit by laying *Quelea quelea*. *Ibis 118:* 575–6.

181 JOURDAIN, F. C. R. (1929). Spanish Great Spotted Woodpecker eating young Blue Titmice. *Brit. Birds 23:* 131.

182 KÄLLANDER, H. (1974). Advancement of laying of Great Tits by the provision of food. *Ibis 116:* 365–7.

183 KENWARD, R. E. (1976). *The effect on Woodpigeon populations of predation by Goshawks.* D. Phil. thesis, Oxford.

184 KIERSKI, W. (1932). Nesträubereien des Grossen Buntspechts. *Beitr. Fortpflanzen-biol. Vögel 8:* 160.

185 KIRKMAN, F. B., & JOURDAIN, F. C. R. (1930). *British Birds.* T. C. & E. C. Jack, London.

186 KLEINSCHMIDT, O. (1898). Weitere Notizen über Sumpfmeisen. *Orn. Monatsber. 6:* 33–6.

187 KLUIJVER, H. N. (1933). Bijdrage tot de biologie en de ecologie van den Spreeuw (*Sturnus v. vulgaris* L.) gedurende zijn voortplantingstijd. *Versl. Meded Planten-ziektenk. Dienst Wageningen 69:* 1–145.

188 KLUIJVER, H. N. (1939). Ueber die Variabilität der Flügellänge in einer beringten *Parus major* Population. *Limosa 12:* 80–6.

189 KLUIJVER, H. N. (1950). Daily routines of the Great Tit, *Parus m. major* L. *Ardea 38:* 99–135.

190 KLUIJVER, H. N. (1951). The population ecology of the Great Tit, *Parus m. major* L. *Ardea 39:* 1–135.

191 KLUIJVER, H. N. (1952). Notes on body weight and time of breeding in the Great Tit, *Parus m. major* L. *Ardea 40:* 123–41.

192 KLUIJVER, H. N., & TINBERGEN, L. (1953). Territory and the regulation of density in titmice. *Arch. Néerl. Zool. 10:* 265–89.

193 KLUYVER, H. N. (1961) Food consumption in relation to habitat in breeding chickadees. *Auk 78:* 532–50.

194 KLUYVER, H. N. (1963). The determination of reproductive rates in Paridae. *Proc. 13th Int. Orn. Congr. Ithaca 1962:* 706–16.

195 KLUYVER, H. N. (1966) Regulation of a bird population. *Ostrich suppl. 6:* 389–396.

196 KLUYVER, H. N. (1971). Regulation of numbers in populations of Great Tit 19 (*Parus m. major*). *Proc. Adv. Study Inst. Dynamics Numbers Popul. (Oosterbeek 1970):* 507–23.

197 KOROLKOVA, G. E. 1963 [The effects of birds on the number of insect pests]. *Acad Nauk. Moscow.*

198 KRÄTZIG, H. (1939). Untersuchungen zur Siedlungsbiologie waldbewohnender Höhlenbrüter. *Dtsch. Vogelwelt 1:* 1–96.

199 KREBS, J. R. (1970a). *A study of territorial behaviour in the Great Tit,* Parus major L. D. Phil. thesis, Oxford University.

200 KREBS, J. R. (1970b). The efficiency of courtship feeding in the Blue Tit, *Parus caeruleus*. *Ibis 112:* 108–10.

201 KREBS, J. R. (1970c). Regulation of numbers in the Great Tit (Aves: Passeriformes). *J. Zool. Lond. 162:* 317–33.

202 KREBS, J. R. (1971). Territory and breeding density in the Great Tit, *Parus major* L. *Ecology 52:* 2–22.

203 KREBS, J. R., MACROBERTS, M. H., & CULLEN, J. M. (1972). Flocking and feeding in the Great Tit *Parus major* – an experimental study. *Ibis 114:* 507–30.

204 KREBS, J. R. (1973). Social learning and the significance of mixed-species flocks of chickadees (*Parus* spp.). *Can. J. Zool. 51:* 1275–88.

205 LACK, D. & VENABLES, L. S. V. (1939). The habitat distribution of British woodland birds. *J. Anim. Ecol. 8:* 39–71.

206 LACK, D., & SOUTHERN, H. N. (1949). Birds of Tenerife. *Ibis 91:* 607–26.

207 LACK, D. (1954a). The evolution of reproductive rates. In *Evolution as a Process,* ed. J. S. Huxley. Allen & Unwin, London. Pp. 143–56.

208 LACK, D. (1954b). *The natural regulation of animal numbers*. Clarendon Press, Oxford.

209 LACK, D. (1955). British Tits (*Parus* spp.) in nesting boxes. *Ardea 43:* 50–84.

210 LACK, D. (1956.) *Swifts in a tower*. Methuen, London.

211 LACK, D. (1958). The significance of the colour of turdine eggs. *Ibis 100:* 145–66.

212 LACK, D., & LACK, E. (1958). The nesting of the Long-tailed Tit. *Bird Study 5:* 1–19.

213 LACK, D., & MOREAU, R. E. (1965). Clutch-size in tropical passerine birds of forest and savanna. *Oiseau Rev. Fr. Orn. 35* (no. spécial): 76–89.

214 LACK, D. (1966). *Population studies of birds*. Clarendon Press, Oxford.

215 LACK, D. (1968). *Ecological adaptations for breeding in birds*. Methuen, London.

216 LACK, D. (1971). *Ecological isolation in birds*. Blackwell, Oxford.

217 LARSEN, V. H. (1974). An analysis of breeding results in tits *Paridae* in Denmark. *Dansk. Orn. Foren. Tidsskr. 68:* 49–62.

218 LAWSON, D. F. (1950). Blue Tit feeding nestling Blackbirds. *Brit. Birds 43:* 186.

219 LEHTONEN, H. (1954). Die Gesangesrhythmik und die Lautausserungen der Kohlmeise in den verschieden Zeiten des Jahres. *Ornis Fenn. 31:* 99–115.

220 LE LOUARN, H., & FROISSART, Y. (1973). Statut de la Mesange alpestre dans le région de Briançon. *Nos Oiseaux 32:* 73–82.

221 LEVIN, D. A. (1971). Phenolic compounds in plants. *Am. Nat. 105:* 157–81.

222 LOGAN-HOME, W. M. (1953). Paper-tearing by birds. *Brit. Birds 46:* 16–21.

223 LÖHRL, H. (1950). Beobachtungen zur Soziologie und Verhaltensweise von Sumpfmeisen (*Parus palustris communis*) im Winter. *Z. Tierpsychol. 7:* 417–24.

224 LÖHRL, H. (1957). Populationsökologische Untersuchungen beim Halsbandschnäpper (*Ficedula albicollis*). *Bonn. Zool. Beitr. 8:* 130–77.

225 LÖHRL, H. (1966a). Experiments on the nesting ecology and ethology of the Great Tit, *Parus major*, and related species. *Abstract, 14th Int. Orn. Congr. Oxford:* 81–2.

226 LÖHRL, H. (1966b). Eizahl und Bruterfolg der Haubenmeise (*Parus cristatus*) und der Sumpfmeise (*Parus palustris*). *Vogelwelt 87:* 15–21.

227 LÖHRL, H. (1966c). Zur Biologie der Trauermeise (*Parus lugubris*). *J. Orn. 107:* 167–86.

228 LÖHRL, H. (1968) Das Nesthäckchen als biologisches Problem. *J. Orn. 109:* 383–95.

229 LÖHRL, H. (1973). Einfluss der Brutraumfläche auf die Gelegegrösse der Kohlmeise (Parus major). J. Orn. 114: 339–47.

230 LÖHRL, H. (1974). Die Tannenmeise. Die Neue Brehm-Bücherei, No. 472. Wittenberg Lutherstadt, Germany.

231 LORENZ, K. (1937). Über die Bildung das Instinktbegriffs. Naturwissenschaften 45: 289, 307, 324.

232 LUDESCHER, F.-B. (1973). Sumpfmeise (Parus p. palustris L.) und Weidenmeise (P. montanus salicarius Br.) als sympatrische Zwillingsarten. J. Orn. 114: 3–56.

233 MACKENZIE, J. M. D. (1950). Competition for nest-sites among hole-nesting species. Brit. Birds 43: 184–5.

234 MACGILLIVRAY, W. (1837–40). A History of British Birds. London.

235 MANSFELD, K. (1956). Zur Vertilgung behaarter Raupen durch Singvögel. Waldhyg. 1: 160–4.

236 MARLER, P. (1955). Characteristics of some animal calls. Nature 176: 6–8.

237 MARPLES, G. (1935). Observations on times of feeding. Brit. Birds 29: 45–9.

238 MARSHALL, A. J. (1949). Weather factors and spermatogenesis in birds. Proc. Zool. Soc. Lond. 119: 711–16.

239 MARSHALL, A. J. (1954). Bower-birds. Clarendon Press, Oxford.

240 MAYNARD-SMITH, J. (1965). The evolution of alarm calls. Am. Nat. 99: 59–63.

241 MAYNARD-SMITH, J., & PRICE, G. R. (1973). The logic of animal conflict. Nature 246: 15–18.

242 MAYR, E., & AMADON, D. (1951). A classification of recent birds. Am. Mus. Novit. No. 1496.

243 MERTENS, J. A. L. (1969). The influence of brood-size on the energy metabolism and water loss of nestling Great Tits Parus major major. Ibis 111: 11–16.

244 MONTAGU, G. (1802). Ornithological dictionary or alphabetical synopsis of British Birds. London.

245 MOOK, J. H., MOOK, L. J., & HEIKENS, H. S. (1960). Further evidence for the role of 'searching images' in the hunting behaviour of titmice. Arch. Néerl. Zool. 13: 448–65.

246 MORBACH, J. (1951). Von der Kohlmeise, Parus major major L. Bull. Ligue. Luxemb. Prot. Ois. 31: 394–400.

247 MOREAU, R. E. (1947). Relations between number in brood, feeding rate and nestling period in nine species of birds in Tanganyika Territory. J. Anim. Ecol. 16: 205–9.

248 MORLEY, A. (1949). Observations on courtship-feeding and coition by the Marsh Tit. Brit. Birds 42: 233–9.

249 MORLEY, A. (1950). The formation and persistence of pairs in the Marsh Tit. Brit. Birds 43: 387–93.

250 MORLEY, A. (1953). Field observations on the biology of the Marsh Tit. Brit. Birds 46: 233–8, 273–87, 332–46.

251 MORRIS, F. O. (1870). A History of British Birds. 2nd edition. Groombridge, London.

252 MORRIS, R. F., et al. (1958). The numerical response of avian and mammalian predators during a gradation of the spruce bud-worm. Ecology 39: 487–94.

253 MORSE, D. H. (1973). Interactions between tit flocks and Sparrowhawks Accipiter nisus. Ibis 115: 591–3.

254 MOUNTFORT, G. R. (1959). Great Spotted Woodpeckers killing nestling tits. *Brit. Birds 52:* 270–1.

255 MOUNTFORT, G. R. (1962). Further notes on Great Spotted Woodpeckers attacking nest-boxes. *Brit. Birds 55:* 43–4.

256 MYLNE, C. K. (1959). Birds drinking the sap of a birch tree. *Brit. Birds 52:* 426–7.

257 NAKAMURA, T. (1962). Observations on the breeding biology of the Long-tailed Tits *Aegithalos caudatus trivirgatus. Misc. Rep. Yamashina Inst. Orn. 3:* 155–73.

258 NAKAMURA, T. (1967). Studies on the fluctuations in numbers of Long-tailed Tits *(Aegithalos caudatus)* along the slopes of the River Tenryu, Nagano. III. Seasonal changes in mode of life. *Jap. J. Ecol. 16:* 17–22.

259 NAKAMURA, T. (1969). Structure of flock range in the Long-tailed Tit. I. Winter flock, its home range and territory. *Misc. Rep. Yamashina Inst. Orn. 5:* 1–29.

260 NAKAMURA, T. (1972). Home range structure of a population of *Aegithalos caudatus.* 2. Home range and territorialism in the breeding season. *Misc. Rep. Yamashina Inst. Orn. 6:* 424–88.

261 NETHERSOLE-THOMPSON, C. & D. (1941). The Crested Tits of Strathspey. *The Field* 24 May, p. 655.

262 NETHERSOLE-THOMPSON, D. (1942). Passerines laying twice on same day. *Brit. Birds 36:* 95.

263 NETHERSOLE-THOMPSON, C. & D. (1943). Nest-site selection by birds. *Brit. Birds 88:* 94.

264 NETHERSOLE-THOMPSON, D., & WATSON, A. (1974). *The Cairngorms.* Collins, London.

265 NEWTON, I. (1966). The moult of the Bullfinch *Pyrrhula pyrrhula. Ibis 108:* 41–67.

266 NEWTON, I. (1972). *Finches.* New Naturalist Series. Collins, London.

267 NICHOLSON, E. M., & KOCH, L. (1936). *Songs of Wild Birds.* Witherby, London.

268 NILSSON, S. G. (1975) Kullstorlek och häckningsframgång i holkar och naturliga hål. *Vår Fågelvärld 34:* 207–11.

269 NISBET, I. C. T. (1973). Courtship feeding, egg size and breeding success in Common Terns. *Nature 241:* 141–2.

270 O'CONNOR, R. J. (1973). *Growth and metabolism in some insectivorous birds compared with a granivorous species.* D. Phil. thesis, Oxford.

271 ODUM, E. P. (1941–42). Annual cycle of the Black-capped Chickadee. *Auk 58:* 314–33, 518–35, and *59:* 499–531.

272 ODUM, E. P. (1942). A comparison of the chickadee seasons. *Bird-Banding 13:* 154–9.

273 OGASAWARA, K. (1970). Analysis of mixed flocks of tits in the Botanical Garden in Tohoku University, Sendai. 2. Foraging layers by species and their inter-relations within the mixed flock. *Misc. Rep. Yamashina Inst. Orn. 6:* 170–8.

274 ONIONS, C. T. (ed. 1968). *The Shorter Oxford English Dictionary.* Clarendon Press, Oxford.

275 OWEN, D. F. (1954). The winter weights of Titmice. *Ibis 96:* 299–309.

276 OWEN, J. H. (1945a). Unusual feeding behaviour of Tits. *Brit. Birds 38:* 173.

277 OWEN, J. H. (1945b). The nesting of the Long-tailed Tit. *Brit. Birds 38:* 271–3.

278 PARSLOW, J. L. F. (1973). *Breeding birds of Britain and Ireland.* Poyser, Berkhampstead.

279 PARSONS, J. (1971). *The breeding biology of the Herring Gull* (Larus argentatus). Ph.D. thesis, Durham.

280 PARTRIDGE, L. (1974). *Behavioural aspects of the ecology of some Paridae.* D. Phil. thesis, Oxford University.

281 PAULUSSEN, W. (1949). Mezen in kasjes. *De Wielwaal 15:* 152

282 PAYNE, R. B. (1973). Mechanisms and control of moult. In *Avian Biology,* vol. 2, ch. 3, pp. 103–55 (eds. D. S. Farner & J. R. King). Academic Press, New York & London..

283 PENNIE, I. D. (1962). A century of bird-watching in Sutherland. *Scott. Birds 2:* 167–92.

284 PERRINS, C. M., & OWEN, D. F. (1958). Mésange noire au large de Dieppe en septembre. *Alauda 26:* 69.

285 PERRINS, C. M. (1963). *Some factors influencing brood-size and populations in tits.* D. Phil. thesis, Oxford.

286 PERRINS, C. M. (1965). Population fluctuations and clutch-size in the Great Tit, Parus major L. *J. Anim. Ecol. 34:* 601–47.

287 PERRINS, C. M. (1966). The effect of beech crops on Great Tit populations and movements. *Brit. Birds 59:* 419–32.

288 PERRINS, C. M. (1968). The purpose of the high-intensity alarm call in small passerines. *Ibis 110:* 200–1.

289 PERRINS, C. M. (1970). The timing of birds' breeding seasons. *Ibis 112:* 242–55.

290 PERRINS, C. M. (1973). Some effects of temperature on breeding in the Great Tit and Manx Shearwater. *J. Reprod. Fert., Suppl. 19:* 163–73.

291 PERRINS, C. M. (1974). *Birds.* Collins, London.

292 PERRINS, C. M., & JONES, P. J. (1974). The inheritance of clutch-size in the Great Tit (Parus major L.). *Condor 76:* 225–9.

293 PERRINS, C. M., & MOSS, D. (1974). Survival of young Great Tits in relation to age of female parent. *Ibis 116:* 220–4.

294 PERRINS, C. M., & MOSS, D. (1975). Reproductive rates in the Great Tit. *J. Anim. Ecol. 44:* 695–706.

295 PFEIFER, S. (1938). Die Schwanzmeise als Erdbrüter. *Beitr. Fortpflanzenbiol. Vögel 14:* 146–7.

296 PFEIFER, S., & KEIL, W. (1958). Versuche zur Steigerung die Siedlungsdichte hohlen und freibrutender Vogelarten und ernahrungsbiologische Untersuchungen an Nestlingen einiger Singvogelarten in einem Schadgebiet des Eichenwicklers (*Tortrix viridana* L.) im Osten von Frankfurt am Main. *Biologische Abhandlungen 15–16:* 1–52.

297 PLESKE, T. (1912). Zur Lösung der Frage, ob *Cyanistes pleskei* Cab. eine selbstandige Art darstellt, oder für einen Bastard von *Cyanistes caeruleus* (Linn) und *Cyanistes cyanus* (Pall.) angesprochen werden muss. *J. Orn. 60:* 96–109.

298 POULSEN, C. M. (1947). Fuglene i Vestjyllands plantager Syd for Limfjorden. *Dansk. Orn. Foren. Tidsskr. 41:* 237–66.

300 PULLEN, N. D. (1945). Feeding of Blue Tit nestlings. *Brit. Birds 38:* 205–10.

301 PULLEN, N. D. (1946). Further notes on the breeding of Blue Tits. *Brit. Birds 39:* 162–7.

302 RÄBER, H. (1949). Das Verhalten gefangener Waldohreulen (*Asio otus otus*) und Waldkauze zur Beute. *Behaviour 2:* 1–95.

303 RADFORD, M. C. (1952). Blue Tits usurping a Great Tit's nest. *Brit. Birds 45:* 30.

304 RANKIN, W. T. C. (1950). Blue Tit robbing nest material. *Brit. Birds 43:* 186.

305 RICHARDS, T. J. (1949). Concealment of food by Nuthatch, Coal Tit and Marsh Tit. *Brit. Birds 42:* 360–1.

306 RICHARDS, T. J. (1958). Concealment and recovery of food by birds, with some relevant observations on squirrels. *Brit. Birds 51:* 497–508.

307 RIDPATH, M. G. (1951). Blue Tit excavating nest hole. *Brit. Birds 44:* 278–9.

308 RIEHM, H. (1970) Ökologie und Verhalten der Schwanzmeise (*Aegithalos caudatus*). *Zool. Jahrb. Syst. 97:* 338–400.

309 ROBERTSON, A. W. P., & PORTER, S. C. (1952). Long-tailed Tits' unorthodox nesting arrangements. *Brit. Birds 45:* 257–8.

310 ROEBUCK, A. (1944). Marsh Tits attacking cypress cones. *Brit. Birds 37:* 180.

311 ROMANOFF, A. L., & ROMANOFF, A. J. (1949). *The avian egg.* John Wiley, New York.

312 ROMER, M. L. R. (1949). Autumn immigration of Great Tit, Blue Tit and Coal Tit at Dungeness, Kent. *Brit. Birds 42:* 386–7.

313 ROSS, W. M. (1933). Notes on incubation and fledging of Crested Tit. *Brit. Birds 27:* 49.

314 ROTHSCHILD, W. (1907). The British Willow Tit (*Parus atricapillus kleinschmidti* Hellm.). *Brit. Birds 1:* 44–7.

315 ROTHSCHILD, M. (1964). An extension of Dr Lincoln Brower's theory on bird predation and food specificity, together with some observation on bird memory in relation to aposematic colour patterns. *The Entomologist 97:* 73–8.

316 ROWAN, W. (1926). On photoperiodism, reproductive periodicity and the annual migrations of birds and certain fishes. *Proc. Boston Soc. Nat. Hist. 38:* 147–89.

317 ROYAMA, T. (1962). *A study of the breeding behaviour and ecology of the Great Tit,* Parus major L. Unpub. thesis. Tokyo University.

318 ROYAMA, T. (1966a). A re-interpretation of courtship feeding. *Bird Study 13:* 116–29.

319 ROYAMA, T. (1966b). Factors governing feeding rate, food requirement and brood size of nestling Great Tits Parus major. *Ibis 108:* 313–47.

320 ROYAMA, T. (1970). Factors governing the hunting behaviour and selection of food by the Great Tit (*Parus major* L.). *J. Anim. Ecol. 39:* 619–68.

321 ROYAMA, T. (1971). Evolutionary significance of predators' response to local differences in prey density, a theoretical study. *Proc. Adv. Study Inst. Dynamics Numbers Popul. (Oosterbeek 1970):* 344–57.

322 RÜPPELL, W. (1934). Sind wandernde Meisen ortstreu? *Vogelzug 5:* 60–6.

323 RYDER, W. D. (1955). Great Tit hopping up and down vertical tree trunk. *Brit. Birds 48:* 234.

324 RYVES, B. H., & QUICK, H. M. (1946). A survey of the status of birds breeding in Cornwall and Scilly since 1906. *Brit. Birds 39:* 3–11.

325 SCHERRER, B. (1972). Migration et autres types de déplacements de la Mésange Noire Parus ater en transit au Col de la Golèze. *Terre Vie 26:* 54–97, 257–313.

326 SCHIERMANN, G. (1934). Studien über Siedlungsdichte in Brutgebeit. II. Der Brandenburgische Kiefernwald. *J. Orn. 82:* 455–86.

327 SCHIFFERLI, L. (1973). The effect of egg weight on the subsequent growth of nestling Great Tits Parus major. *Ibis 115:* 549–58.

328 Schnurre, O. (1936). Zum Vogelfang des Grossen Buntspechtes. *Beitr. Fortpflanzenbiol. Vögel 12:* 232–4.

329 Scott, C. (1976). Long-tailed Tit feeding young Great Tits. *Brit. Birds 69:* 34–5.

330 Sharrock, J. T. R. (1976). The Atlas of Breeding Birds in Britain and Ireland. British Trust for Ornithology, Tring, England.

331 Sirvonen, L. (1942). Större hackspetten, *Dryobates m. major* L. som fiende till småfåglarna och deras bon. *Fauna Flora. Upps., 37:* 32–8.

332 Simson, C. (1966). *A bird overhead.* Witherby, London.

333 Slagsvold, T. (1975). Breeding time of birds in relation to latitude. *Norw. J. Zool. 23:* 213–18.

334 Smith, J. M. N. & Sweatman, H. P. A. (1974). Food-searching behaviour of titmice in patchy environments. *Ecology 55:* 1216–32.

335 Smith, S. M. (1967). Seasonal changes in the survival of the Black-capped Chickadee. *Condor 69:* 344–59.

336 Smith, S. M. (1972a). Roosting aggregations of Bushtits in response to cold temperatures. *Condor 74:* 478–9.

337 Smith, S. M. (1972b). Communication and other social behavior in *Parus carolinensis. Publ. Nuttall Orn. Club.* No. 11, Cambridge, Mass.

338 Snow, D. W. (1949).Jämförande studier över våra mesarters näringssökande. *Vår Fågelvärld 8:* 156–69.

339 Snow, D. W. (1952). The winter avifauna of Arctic Lapland. *Ibis 94:* 133–43.

340 Snow, D. W. (1953). *Systematics and Comparative Ecology of the Genus* Parus *in the Palaearctic region.* D. Phil. thesis, Oxford.

341 Snow, D. W. (1954a). Trends in geographical variation in Palaearctic members of the genus *Parus. Evolution 8:* 19–28.

342 Snow, D. W. (1954b). The habitats of Eurasian tits (*Parus* spp.). *Ibis 96:* 565–85.

343 Snow, D. W. (1956). The annual mortality of the Blue Tit in different parts of its range. *Brit. Birds 49:* 174–7.

344 Snow, D. W. (1958a). The breeding of the Blackbird *Turdus merula* at Oxford. *Ibis 100:* 1–30.

345 Snow, D. W. (1958b). *A study of Blackbirds.* Methuen, London.

346 Snow, D. W. (1967). Family Paridae. pp. 10–24 in *Check-List of Birds of the World,* vol. *12* (ed. R. A. Paynter). Cambridge, Mass.

347 Southern, H. N., & Morley, A. (1950). Marsh Tit territories over six years. *Brit. Birds 43:* 33–47.

348 Southern, H. N. (1954). Tawny Owls and their prey. *Ibis 96:* 384–410.

349 Southern, J. B. (1946a). Unusual feeding behaviour of tits. *Brit. Birds 39:* 214.

350 Southern, J. B. (1946b). Display flight of Marsh Tit. *Brit. Birds 39:* 316–17.

351 Soper, E. A. (1969). Birds taking honey. *Brit. Birds 62:* 200–1.

352 Spitzer, G. (1972). Jahreszeitliche Aspekte der Biologie der Bartmeise (*Panurus biarmicus*). *J. Orn. 113:* 241–75.

353 Stadie, R. (1935). Schlesische Beringungsergebnisse bei Kohlmeisen, Blaumeisen, Grünfinken, Goldammern un Kernbeissern. *Ber. Ver. Schles. Ornithol. 20:* 58–73.

354 Steen, J. (1958). Climatic adaptation in some small northern birds. *Ecology 39:* 625–9.

355 Steinfatt, O. (1937). Aus dem Leben des Grossbuntspechtes. *Beitr. Fortpflanzenbiol. Vögel 13:* 45–54, 101–13, 144–7.

356 Steinfatt, O. (1938). Das Brutleben der Sumpfmeise und einige Vergleiche

mit dem Brutleben der anderen einheimischen Meisen. *Beitr. Fortpflanzen-biol. Vögel 14:* 84–9, 137–44.

357 STEPHENSON, F. E. (1963). Blue Tit lining and laying in nest of Blackbird. *Brit. Birds 56:* 461.

358 STEWART, I. F. (1963). Variation of wing length with age. *Bird Study 10:* 1–9.

359 STOKES, A. W. (1960). Nest-site selection and courtship behaviour of the Blue Tit *Parus caeruleus. Ibis 102:* 507–19.

360 STRESEMAN, E. (1919). Über die Formen der Gruppe *Aegithalos caudatus* und ihre Kreuzungen. *Beiträge zur Zoogeographie der paläarktischen Region 1:* 3–24.

361 STURKIE, P. D. (1965). *Avian Physiology* (2nd Ed.). Cornell University Press.

362 SULKAVA, S. (1969). On small birds spending the night in snow. *Aquilo, Ser. Zool. 7:* 33–7.

363 SUOMAILAINEN, H. (1937). The effect of temperature on the sexual activity of non-migratory birds stimulated by artificial lighting. *Ornis Fenn. 14:* 108–12.

364 SVÄRDSON, G. (1957). The 'invasion' type of bird migration. *Brit. Birds 50:* 314–43.

365 SVÄRDSON, G. (1967). Irruptions of Great Tits and other species. *Brit. Birds 60:* 173–4.

366 SVENSSON, L. (1970). *Identification guide to European Passerines.* Nat. Hist. Mus. Stockholm.

367 THIELEMANN, A. (1956). Schwanzmeise (*Aegithalos caudatus*) als Bodenbrüter. *Orn. Mitt. 8:* 76–7.

368 THIELCKE, G. (1968). Gemeinsames der Gattung *Parus.* Ein bioakustischer Beitrag zur Systematik. *Vogelwelt, Beih. 1:* 147–64.

369 THIELCKE, G. (1973). Uniformierung des Gesangs der Tannenmeise (*Parus ater*) durch Lernen. *J. Orn. 114:* 443–54.

370 THONEN, W. (1962). Stimmgeographische, Ökologische und verbreitungs-geschichtliche Studien über die Mönchsmeise (*Parus montanus* Conrad). *Orn. Beob. 59:* 101–72.

371 THORPE, W. H. (1943). A type of insight learning in birds. *Brit. Birds 37:* 29–31.

372 THORPE, W. H. (1951). The learning abilities of birds. *Ibis 93:* 1–52, 252–96.

373 THORPE, W. H. (1956a). Records of the development of original and unusual feeding methods by wild passerine birds. *Brit. Birds 49:* 389–95.

374 THORPE, W. H. (1956b). *Learning and instinct in animals.* Methuen, London.

375 TICEHURST, N. F. & HARTLEY, P. H. T. (1948). Report on the effect of the severe winter of 1946–47 on bird life. *Brit. Birds 41:* 322–34.

376 TINBERGEN, L. (1946). De Sperwer als roofvijand van zangvogels. *Ardea 34:* 1–213.

377 TINBERGEN, L. (1949). Bosvogels en insecten. *Ned. Boschb. Tijdschr. 4:* 91–105.

378 TINBERGEN, L., et al. (1960). The dynamics of insect and bird populations in pinewoods. *Arch. Néerl. Zool. 13:* 259–472.

379 TINBERGEN, L. (1960). The natural control of insects in pinewoods. (i) Factors influencing the intensity of predation by song-birds. *Arch. Néerl. Zool. 13:* 265–343.

380 TINBERGEN, L., & KLOMP, H. (1960). The natural control of insects in pine-woods. (ii) Conditions for damping of Nicholson oscillations in parasite-host systems. *Arch. Néerl. Zool. 13:* 344–79.

381 TINBERGEN, N. (1953). Specialists in nest-building. *Country Life* (30 Jan. 1953): 270–1.

382 TOLLENAAR, D. (1922). Legperioden en eierproductie bij eenige wilde vogels-oorten, vergeleken met die bij hoenderrassen. *Meded. Landb. Hoogesch. Wageningen 23 (2): 1–46.*

383 TUCKER, B. W. (1935). On differences in the microscopic characters of the crown feathers of tits of the genus *Parus*. With particular reference to the Marsh and Willow Tits. *Proc. Zool. Soc. Lond. 2: 431–41.*

384 TURČEK, F. J. (1952). Ecological analysis of the bird and mammalian population of a primeval forest on the Pol'ana mountain (Slovakia). *Bull. Int. Acad. Tchéque Sci. 53: 81–105.*

385 TURČEK, F. J. (1955). Doplnky k ekologickej analyze populacie vtakov a cicavcov prirodzeneho lasa na pol'ane (Slovensko). *Lesn. Sbor. 1: 23–44.*

386 TURNER, M. G. (1966). Blue Tit feeding mate with snail shell. *Brit. Birds 59: 78.*

387 ULFSTRAND, S. (1962). On the non-breeding ecology and migratory movements of the Great Tit (*Parus major*) and the Blue Tit (*Parus caeruleus*) in southern Sweden. *Vår Fågelvärld Suppl. 3.*

388 VAURIE, C. (1957). Systematic notes on Palaearctic birds. No. 26. Paridae: the *Parus caeruleus* complex. *Am. Mus. Novit. No. 1833.*

389 VAURIE, C. (1965). *The Birds of the Palaearctic Fauna*, Vol. 2. Witherby, London.

390 VILKS, E. K. (1966). (Migrations and territorial behaviour of Latvian tits and Nuthatches from ringing data.) *Trudy Inst. Biol., Riga 27: 69–88.*

391 VINCE, M. A. (1958). 'String-pulling' in birds. 2. Differences related to age in Greenfinches, Chaffinches and Canaries. *Anim. Behav. 6: 53–9.*

392 VINCE, M. A. (1960). Developmental changes in responsiveness in the Great Tit (*Parus major*). *Behaviour 15: 219–43.*

393 VINCE, M. A. (1964). Use of the feet in feeding by the Great Tit *Parus major*. *Ibis 106: 508–29.*

394 VOINSTVENSKI, M. A. (1954). In Dementiev G. P., *et al. Die Vogel der Sowjetunion.* Bd. 5. Moscow.

395 VOOUS, K. H. (1960). *Atlas of European Birds*. Nelson, London.

396 WALKER, J. E. S. (1972). Attempts at fledging of a runt Great Tit. *Bird Study 19: 250–1.*

397 WALLACE, G. J. (1941). Winter Studies of colour-banded chickadees. *Bird-Banding 12: 49–69.*

398 WALLIS, H. M. (1923). Recent changes in the birds of Scilly. *Brit. Birds 17: 55–8.*

399 WALPOLE-BOND, J. (1938). *A History of Sussex Birds*. Witherby, London.

400 WARD, P. (1965). Feeding ecology of the Black-faced Dioch *Quelea quelea* in Nigeria. *Ibis 107: 173–214.*

401 WARD, P., & ZAHAVI, A. (1973). The importance of certain assemblages of birds as 'information-centres' for food finding. *Ibis 115: 517–34.*

402 WARREN, R. P., & VINCE, M. A. (1963). Taste discrimination in the Great Tit (*Parus major*). *J. Comp. Physiol. Psychol. 56: 910–13.*

403 WATT, A. S. (1923). On the ecology of British beech woods with special reference to their regeneration. *J. Ecol. 11: 1–48.*

404 WEBBER, M. I. (1975). *Some aspects of the non-breeding population dynamics of the Great Tit* (Parus major). D. Phil. thesis, Oxford.

405 WHITELY, H. (1846). *Natural History of British Tits.*

406 WILSON, J. O. (1933). *The Birds of Westmorland and the Northern Pennines.* Hutchinson, London.

407 WINKEL, W. (1975). Studies in the comparative breeding biology of five tit species (*Parus* spp.) in an area of Japanese larch afforestation in lower Saxony. *Vogelwelt 96:* 41–63, 104–14.

408 WINKLER, R. (1974). Der Herbstdurchzug von Tannenmeise, Blaumeise und Kohlmeise (*Parus ater, caeruleus,* und *major*) auf dem Col de Bretolet (Wallis). *Orn. Beob. 71:* 135–52.

409 WITHERBY, *et al.* (1943). *The Handbook of British birds Vol. I.* Witherby, London.

410 YAPP, W. B. (1962). *Birds and Woods.* Oxford University Press.

411 YAPP, W. B. (1963). Colour variation and status of *Parus ater britannicus* and *P. a. hibernicus. Proc. 13th Int. Orn. Congr. Ithaca 1962:* 198–201.

412 YARRELL, W. (1843). *A History of British Birds.* John van Voorst, London.

413 YARRELL, W., & NEWTON, A. (1871–74). *A History of British Birds.* John van Voorst, London.

414 ZAHAVI, A. (1974). Communal nesting by the Arabian Babbler. *Ibis 116:* 84–7.

415 ZONOV, G. B. (1967). (On the winter roosting of Paridae in Cisbaikal.) *Ornitologiya 8:* 351–4.

ADDITIONAL REFERENCES

416 GEER, T. A. (in prep.). Sparrowhawk (*Accipiter nisus*) predation on tits (*Parus* spp.). D. Phil. thesis. University of Oxford.

417 GEER, T. A. (in press). Depression of nest use and breeding success in Great Tits and Blue Tits due to proximal nesting of Sparrowhawks. *Condor* Vol. 80.

418 GOCHFELD, M. 1977. Plumage variation in Black-capped Chickadees: is there sexual dimorphism? *Bird-Banding 48:* 62–6.

419 GREENWOOD, P. J., HARVEY, P. H. and PERRINS, C. M. 1978. Inbreeding and dispersal in the great tit. *Nature 271:* 52–4.

420 HERTZ, P. E., REMSEN, J. V. and ZONES, S. I. 1976. Ecological complementarity of three sympatic parids in a California oak woodland. *Condor 78:* 307–16.

421 HOGSTAD, O. 1975. Quantitative relations between hole-nesting and open-nesting species within a passerine breeding community. *Norw. J. Zool. 23:* 261–7.

422 KREBS, J. R., ASHCROFT, R. and WEBBER, M. 1978. Song repertoires and territory defence in the Great Tit. *Nature 271:* 539–42.

423 MAYER, G. 1963. Altersaufbau, Lebenserwartung und Mortalität einer Kohlmeisenpopulation. *Naturkundl. Jb. der Stadt Linz.* 1963: 331–44.

424 MAYER, G. 1965. Populationsbiologische untersuchungen an Blaumeisen. *Naturkundl. Jb. der Stadt Linz.* 1965: 319–33.

425 MAYER, G. 1966. Geschlecter-und Altersverhältnisse einiger oberösterreichischer Kohlmeisenpopulationen im Winter. *Naturkundl. Jb. der Stadt Linz.* 1966: 241–68.

426 MERTENS 1977. Temperatuurregulatie in de Nestholte van de Koolmees, *Parus major* L. Ph.D. thesis. University of Groningen.

427 MOSHER, J. I. and LANE, S. 1972. A method of determining the sex of captured Black-capped Chickadees. *Bird-Banding 43:* 139–40.

428 NEWTON, I. and BLEWITT, R. J. C. 1973. Studies of sparrowhawks. *Brit. Birds 66:* 271–8.

429 PERRINS, C. M. 1976. Possible effects of qualitative changes in the insect diet of avian predators. *Ibis 118:* 580–4.

430 SOUTHERN, H. N, 1970. The natural control of a population of Tawny Owls (*Strix aluco*). *J. Zool. Lond. 162:* 197–285.

INDEX

Plate references are in *italic* type; entries in **bold** type indicate major text references.